D1610720

Hydrography

Hydrography

C.D. de Jong
G. Lachapelle
S. Skone
I.A. Elema

DUP Blue Print

© VSSD
First edition 2002

DUP Blue Print is an imprint of:
Delft University Press
P.O. Box 98, 2600 MG Delft, The Netherlands
tel. +31 15 27 85678, telefax +31 15 27 85706, e-mail: info@library.tudelft.nl
internet: http://www.library.tudelft.nl/dup.

Published on behalf of:
Vereniging voor Studie- en Studentenbelangen te Delft
Poortlandplein 6, 2628 BM Delft, The Netherlands
tel. +31 15 27 82124, telefax +31 15 27 87585, e-mail: hlf@vssd.nl
internet: http://www.vssd.nl/hlf
URL on this and related books: http://www.vssd.nl/hlf/a030.htm

Printed in The Netherlands

ISBN 90-407-2359-1
NUGI 816

Keywords: hydrography, geodesy, positioning, law of the sea, estimation, propagation, sea floor mapping, acoustics

Preface

This book is based on the lecture notes for the graduate and undergraduate courses in hydrography as offered at the Department of Geomatics Engineering of the Universitiy of Calgary and the Department of Mathematical Geodesy and Positioning of Delft University of Technology. The purpose of the book is to present an introduction to and an overview of the broad field of hydrography. Since there is only a weak interdependence between the eleven chapters, each of them can be studied separately. When used for a course, it is therefore also possible to consider only a selected number of chapters.

Dr. Jan Krynski, Mr. Mark Petovello and Mr. Kyle O'Keefe are acknowledged for their assistance in adding explanatory text and correcting specific segments of the original lecture notes. The assistance of Ms. Ria Scholtes and Mr. Jacques Schievink in preparing the final version of the book is also gratefully acknowledged.

October 2002,

C.D. de Jong
Delft University of Technology
Delft, The Netherlands

G. Lachapelle
University of Calgary
Calgary, Canada

S. Skone
University of Calgary
Calgary, Canada

I.A. Elema
Netherlands Hydrographic Service
The Hague, The Netherlands

Table of contents

1	ELEMENTS OF OCEANOGRAPHY	1
1.1	Water	1
1.2	Ocean currents and general circulation	3
1.3	Waves	12
1.4	Major references	19
2	TIDES AND TIDAL CURRENTS	21
2.1	Introduction	21
2.2	Tide-generating forces	22
2.3	Tidal analysis and prediction	35
2.4	Major references	39
3	ESTIMATION AND QUALITY CONTROL	41
3.1	Least squares estimation	41
3.2	Quality control	48
3.3	Recursive estimation	55
3.4	Recursive quality control	65
3.5	Major references	70

4   COORDINATE SYSTEMS   71

4.1   Geodetic datums   71

4.2   Ellipsoidal computations   76

4.3   Map projections   80

4.4   Vertical datums   84

4.5   Major references   88

5   FUNDAMENTALS OF RADIO FREQUENCY PROPAGATION AND
        MEASUREMENTS   89

5.1   Radio Frequency definitions   89

5.2   Radiowave propagation   96

5.3   Time keeping   140

5.4   RF-wave measurements   150

5.5   Major references   160

6   UNDERWATER ACOUSTICS   163

6.1   Introduction   163

6.2   Wave equation   164

6.3   Sonar parameters   183

6.4   Sonar equations   191

6.5   Sound in water   193

6.6   Major references   198

7   LAW OF THE SEA   199

7.1   History   199

7.2   Baselines   201

7.3   Maritime zones   204

7.4   Boundaries between states   209

7.5   Third party settlement   215

7.6   Major references   217

8   CONCEPTS OF MARINE POSITIONING   219

8.1   Geometry of positioning   219

8.2   Classification of marine positioning systems   237

8.3   Marine positioning requirements and standards for hydrographic surveys 245

8.4   Major references   253

9   DESCRIPTION OF SELECTED POSITIONING SYSTEMS   255

9.1   Optical and laser systems   255

9.2   Omega   255

9.3   Loran-C   260

9.4   Satellite positioning systems   270

9.5   Speed determination   280

9.6   Major references   301

10   UNDERWATER ACOUSTIC POSITIONING   303

10.1   Introduction   303

10.2   Short baseline systems   305

10.3   Supershort baseline systems   309

10.4   Long baseline systems   311

10.5   Calibration and error sources   313

10.6   Major references   317

11   SOUNDING METHODS   319

11.1   Echo sounder operation   319

11.2   Transducer beam pattern   324

11.3   Single beam echosounders   327

11.4   Multibeam echosounders   327

11.5   Sidescan and oblique sonars   335

11.6   Echosounding measurement corrections   338

11.7   Airborne laser methods   340

11.8   Major references   344

INDEX   347

1 Elements of oceanography

1.1 Water

About 96.5% of the contents of the oceans is water, H_2O. The remaining 3.5% consists of dissolved salts. The two H^+ atoms of a water molecule are connected to the O^{2-} atom in such a way that the two valences of oxygen join the valences of the two hydrogen atoms at an angle of 105°, see Figure 1.1. A consequence of this asymmetric distribution of electric charges is a strong dipole moment. This strong dipole moment, in turn, results in a number of special properties of water:

*   Pure water has the highest dielectric constant ε of all liquids. This is of importance for the behaviour of dissolved substances: the larger ε, the smaller the attractive forces between positively charged cations and negatively charged anions.
*   There is a great associative power of water molecules, which leads to the formation of molecular groups. This process is called polymerisation. For example, at 0°C, the average group size is six H_2O molecules. These polymers determine to a great extent the physical properties of water, such as the strong surface tension and viscosity and high melting and boiling temperatures.

Water also has a very large heat capacity. This large capacity enables the oceans to

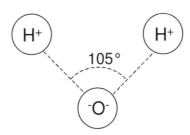

Figure 1.1: H_2O molecule.

Table 1.1: Composition of sea water with a salinity of 35 ppt.

Cations	gr/kg	Anions	gr/kg
Sodium	10.752	Chlorine	19.345
Potassium	0.39	Bromine	0.066
Magnesium	1.295	Fluorine	0.0013
Calcium	0.416	Sulphate	2.701
Strontium	0.013	Bicarbonate	0.145
		Boric acid	0.027

store great quantities of heat, which can be released at differrent places and times. Finally, one of the best known properties of water is the increase in volume while freezing. Pure water has its highest density at 4°C. At 0°C, the volume increases by about 9%. As a results, ice will float on water.

In the open ocean salinity varies between 3.4-3.8%, or, as it is more commonly expressed, 34-38 ppt (parts per thousand). For land-locked adjacent seas, the salinity may differ considerably. In humid zones with strong river run-offs from land it is much lower. For example, salinity in the Baltic Sea can be as low as 0.5-1 ppt. In arid regions, where evaporation exceeds precipitation, salinity is much higher, e.g., 43-45 ppt in the Red Sea. Despite the large variations in salinity, the relative proportions of its constituents are constant to within a few percent. The major constituents of sea water with a salinity of 35 ppt are shown in Table 1.1.

The density ρ of sea water depends on salinity S, temperature T and pressure p (relative to atmospheric pressure). Small differences in density may already result in significant sea level differences and currents. In practice, i.e., on board ships, density cannot be measured directly from the mass of a volume of water. Instead, it is derived from measurements of salinity, temperature and pressure. Since density does not change very much, the quantity σ is introduced, defined as

$$\sigma = (\rho - 1) \cdot 10^3 \qquad (1.1)$$

At sea level ($p=0$) and for a temperature of 0°C, σ_0 is given by the empirical relationship

$$\sigma_0 = -0.0093 + 0.8149 \cdot S - 0.000482 \cdot S^2 + 0.0000068 \cdot S^3 \qquad (1.2)$$

where S is expressed in ppt and σ_0 in 10^3 kg/m^3.

Pure water has its maximum density at 4°C. The temperature of maximum density decreases with increasing salinity according to

$$T_{\rho_{max}} = 3.95 - 0.266 \cdot \sigma_0 \qquad (1.3)$$

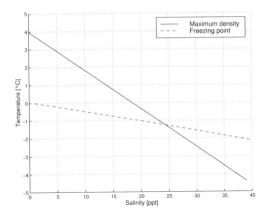

Figure 1.2: Temperature of maximum density and
freezing point for sea water of different salinities.

where the temperature is expressed in °C. Thus, for salinities above 18 ppt, the temperature of maximum density is below the freezing temperature of pure water. Due to its salt content, the freezing temperature of sea water is below that of pure water. This temperature T_g, in °C, as a function of salinity is given by the relationship

$$T_g = -0.0086 - 0.064633 \cdot \sigma_0 - 0.0001055 \cdot \sigma_0^2 \qquad (1.4)$$

As can be seen from Figure 1.2, the temperature of maximum density and the freezing temperature are the same (-1.33°C) for a salinity of 24.7 ppt. If the salinity is less than 24.7 ppt, the temperature of maximum density, with cooling of the water, is reached before the freezing temperature. At a given temperature above the freezing point, the water from the surface to the bottom has reached its maximum density. A little more cooling of the surface layers results in water at the surface that is lighter than the subsurface waters and therefore does not sink. Eventually, when the freezing point is reached, an ice sheet is formed. If the salinity is above 24.7 ppt, vertical convection continues with coooling until the entire water column has reached its freezing point. Thus, the cooling of water of a high salinity extends to a much greater depth and to much lower temperatures than in the case of low salinities.

In conclusion, it is not just the depression of the freezing point of the sea water that explains why the salty sea does not freeze as rapidly as, e.g., fresh water lakes or seas of low salinity, but rather the relationship between the temperature of density maximum and freezing temperature.

1.2   Ocean currents and general circulation

When the atmosphere and the ocean meet, the energy from the moving air is passed to the water through friction. It results in movement of the surface layer of water due to the drag exerted by winds blowing steadily across the ocean. The major horizontal

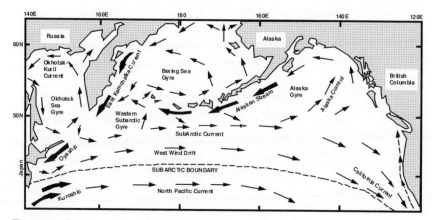

Figure 1.3: Surface currents in the North Pacific Ocean.

movements of the surface waters, the *surface circulations*, are closely related to the general circulation of the atmosphere, which is generated by the unequal heating of the Earth by the Sun. *Surface currents* are wind driven. They occur in the most upper layer of the ocean, i.e., the first 1000 m of water. The Gulf Stream in the Atlantic Ocean is an example of a surface current. *Thermohaline circulation* refers to the water movement which takes place when the density is changed by a change of temperature (thermocline) or of salinity (halocline). Heat combined with salinity causes vertical density variations which results in vertical circulation sometimes called *thermohaline currents*. Ocean currents are a result of surface circulations and thermohaline circulations. Surface currents in the North Pacific Ocean are shown in Figure 1.3. The winter and summer surface circulation in the Pacific Ocean off the coasts of British Columbia and Washington is shown in Figure 1.4 while the general ocean circulation is shown in Figure 1.5.

A number of major current types can be distinguished. *Sub-tropical gyres* span the entire east-west dimension of each ocean basin in both the northern and southern hemispheres (e.g. Gulf Stream). Due to the Coriolis effect as well as surface wind stress, the gyres are:

- Clockwise in the northern hemisphere, e.g., Gulf Stream/Canary/North Equatorial

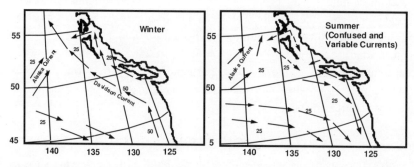

Figure 1.4: Winter (left) and summer circulation off British Columbia and Washington State coasts.

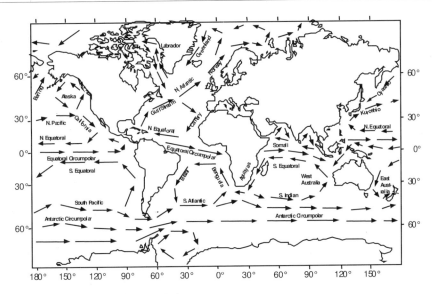

Figure 1.5: General ocean circulation.

Current.

- Counterclockwise in the southern hemisphere, e.g. South Equatorial/Brazil/South Atlantic/Benguela.

Equatorial currents cross the ocean in easterly direction along the equator. The *Antarctic Circumpolar current* flows eastward. The velocity and volume of major currents are given in Table 1.2.

The main factor generating the surface currents is the wind, which is related to the general circulation of the atmosphere. Atmospheric circulation in turn is generated by the unequal heating of the Earth by the Sun. The energy which is gained by the Earth is equal to that lost to space. There is a net gain of energy in the low latitudes and a net loss at higher latitudes. Since neither polar regions nor the tropics progressively change temperature, there must be a transfer of heat from areas of excess to areas of deficit. This transfer is done by means of winds (about 75% of heat transfer) and ocean currents (about 25% of heat transfer). Solar radiation accounts for more than

Table 1.2: Velocity and transport of major ocean currents.

Current	Maximum velocity (cm/s)	Transport (10^6 m³/s)
Gulf Stream	200-300	100
North Equatorial Pacific	20	45
Kuroshio	200	50
Equatorial Undercurrent	100-150	40
Brazil	-	10
Antarctic Circumplolar	-	100
Peru (or Humboldt)	-	20

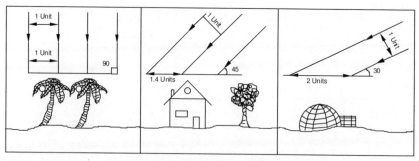

Figure 1.6: Variations in solar energy reaching the Earth's surface.

99% of the energy that heats the Earth.

The seasonal variations in the elevation of the Sun relative to the equator affect the amount of energy received at the Earth's surface in two ways:

• The lower the elevation angle, the more spread out and less intense is the solar radiation that reaches the surface (most important factor).

• The lower the elevation angle, the longer the path of the rays through the atmosphere, and the greater absorption, reflection and scattering by the atmosphere, which reduces the intensity at the surface (less important factor).

Changes in the Sun elevation angle cause variations in the amount of solar energy reaching the Earth's surface, as shown in Figure 1.6. At higher latitudes, the Sun rays strike the Earth at a lower angle and must traverse more of the atmosphere: this results in greater depletion by reflection and absorption, as shown in Figure 1.7.

Two models of global circulation will be considered: a model for a non-rotating Earth and a model for a rotating Earth. In the *non-rotating Earth model*, more intensely heated equatorial air rises and moves poleward. This upper level flow reaches the poles, where it sinks and spreads out at the surface and returns to the equator. Cold polar air moves towards the equator on the Earth's surface, becomes re-heated, and rises again, as shown in Figure 1.8. In the *rotating Earth model*, the effect of Coriolis forces on winds results in the general patterns shown in Figure 1.9.

The effects of Coriolis forces on currents follow from the equation of motion in oceanography, derived from Newton's second law, which states that the observed

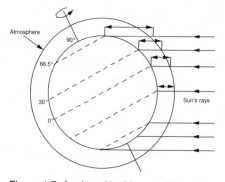

Figure 1.7: Angles of incidence of Sun rays.

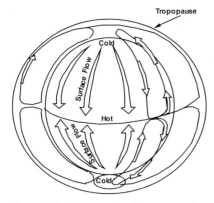

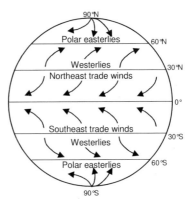

Figure 1.8: Pole-equator air movement. Figure 1.9: Effect of Coriolis force on winds.

acceleration is due to the resultant force acting per unit mass. This acceleration is the sum of the forces due to pressure, Coriolis effect, gravity, friction and tides, divided by a unit mass.

The *Coriolis force* f_C is defined as

$$f_C = -2\omega \times v \qquad (1.5)$$

where ω is a vector of angular velocity of the Earth rotation about its spin axis, parallel to the spin axis, and pointing towards the north pole and v is the vector of velocity of the unit mass, with respect to the Earth. The Coriolis force is thus present only if the particle is *in motion* on the *rotating* Earth. The surface velocity of the current causes an additional force, i.e., a Coriolis force, that is normal to both vectors ω and v. The horizontal component of the Coriolis force (the one which causes the water flow) varies from zero at the equator to a maximum at the poles.

If the velocity vector v points eastwards, then the Coriolis force f_C points outside the Earth; if it points westwards, the Coriolis force points inside the Earth. The horizontal component of the Coriolis force will therefore always be to the right of v in the northern hemisphere, and to the left of v in the southern hemisphere. Thus, in view of the effect of the predominant winds (which themselves are also affected by the Coriolis force), the subtropical gyres are, see also Figure 1.5, clockwise in the northern hemisphere and counterclockwise in the southern hemisphere.

The horizontal component $f_{C,h}$ of the Coriolis force per unit mass (or horizontal component of the Coriolis acceleration) is

$$f_{C,h} = 2 \cdot \|\omega\| \cdot v_h \cdot \sin\varphi \qquad (1.6)$$

where $\|\omega\| = 7.29 \cdot 10^{-5}$ rad/s, v_h is the horizontal component of the velocity vector v of the unit mass with respect to the Earth and φ is latitude.

Example 1.1
Consider a current speed of 1 m/s (2 knots – typical major current). Then

$f_{C,h} = 1.5 \cdot 10^{-4}$ m/s^2 at the pole ($\varphi = 90°$)

$f_{C,h} = 1.0 \cdot 10^{-4}$ m/s^2 at latitude $\varphi = 45°$

$f_{C,h} = 0$ m/s^2 at the equator ($\varphi = 0°$)

The concepts of geopotential surface and isobaric surface are now introduced in order to discuss the geostrophic method of calculating currents. A *geopotential surface* is the surface on which the gravity potential is constant (gravity potential is the same at all points on the geopotential surface). A geopotential surface is also called a *level surface*. An example of a geopotential surface is the smooth surface of a calm lake (with no currents and no waves).

An *isobaric surface* is a surface on which the pressure is constant (pressure is the same at all points on the isobaric surface). An example of an isobaric surface is the smooth surface of a calm lake, with no currents and no waves, and with the atmospheric pressure being constant. Such a surface is both a geopotential and an isobaric surface. Isobaric surfaces are level in the stationary state.

The currents resulting from the Coriolis forces are called *geostrophic* (Earth-turning) flows. In the absence of friction they move approximately along the surfaces of constant elevation (constant dynamic height). Consider the non-stationary case illustrated in Figure 1.10, where the isobaric surfaces do not coincide with level surfaces. An isobaric surface (dashed line) is inclined to the level surface (full line) by an angle *i*. A and B are particles of water of unit mass.

The pressure force on the particle A is $\alpha \cdot \partial p / \partial n$, where α is the reciprocal of the density and $\partial p / \partial n$ is the pressure gradient along the normal to the isobaric surface (isobar); it should be viewed in the plane of the paper. Besides the pressure, gravity also acts on the particle A. At A, the total pressure and gravity forces are not parallel. Thus these two forces do not balance. There is a resultant force component to the left. The horizontal and vertical components of the pressure force are shown for particle B:

- The horizontal component: $\alpha \cdot \partial p / \partial n \cdot \sin i$ which is unbalanced and causes accelerated motion to the left.
- The vertical component $\alpha \cdot \partial p / \partial n \cdot \cos i$ which balances with the gravity force g, i.e., $\alpha \cdot \partial p / \partial n \cdot \cos i = g \approx 9.81$ m/s^2.

The horizontal component to the left can be expressed as

$$\alpha \cdot \frac{\partial p}{\partial n} \cdot \sin i = \alpha \cdot \frac{\partial p}{\partial n} \cdot \cos i \cdot \frac{\sin i}{\cos i} = g \cdot \tan i$$

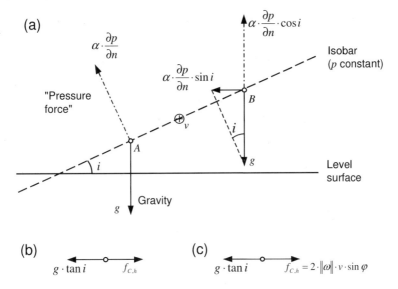

(a)

$\alpha \cdot \dfrac{\partial p}{\partial n} \cdot \cos i$

$\alpha \cdot \dfrac{\partial p}{\partial n}$

Isobar
(p constant)

$\alpha \cdot \dfrac{\partial p}{\partial n} \cdot \sin i$

"Pressure
force"

B

v

A

i

i

g

Level
surface

g

Gravity

(b)

$g \cdot \tan i$ $f_{C,h}$

(c)

$g \cdot \tan i$ $f_{C,h} = 2 \cdot \|\omega\| \cdot v \cdot \sin \varphi$

Pressure terms in relation to isobaric and level surfaces -
Northern hemisphere (v into paper).

Figure 1.10: Geostrophic equation.

To balance the acceleration to the left, it is necessary to apply the same acceleration to the right. Such acceleration is generated by the Coriolis force by having the water move into the paper (in the Northern hemisphere), or out of the paper (in the Southern hemisphere) at speed v. The requirement for such a balance generates ocean current. The horizontal component to the left is thus balanced by a Coriolis force component $2 \cdot \|\omega\| \cdot v \cdot \sin i$ such that

$$2 \cdot \|\omega\| \cdot v \cdot \sin \varphi = g \cdot \tan i \qquad (1.7)$$

The above equation is called the *geostrophic equation*. It expresses a balance between pressure and Coriolis forces in a current.

Example 1.2

Consider the current with speed $v=1$ m/s at latitude $\varphi = 45°$. The departure (sea slope i) of the sea level from the level or geopotential surface of the current follows from (1.7) as

$$i = \tan^{-1} \frac{2 \cdot \|\omega\| \cdot \sin 45°}{g} = 10^{-5} \ \text{rad}$$

i.e., 1 m in 100 km.

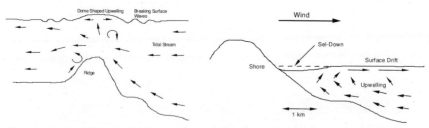

Figure 1.11: Upwelling caused by cold water.

Figure 1.12: Upwelling caused by leeward winds.

Satellite Altimetry has been used successfully to estimate the sea slope of major ocean currents. This data can then be used to determine the direction and velocity of currents. In case of the Gulf Stream, the sea slope $i = (1.2 \pm 0.3) \cdot 10^{-5}$ rad. This results in a sea surface elevation of 140 cm ± 35 cm, based on SEASAT radar altimetry data collected during the late 1970's.

Upwelling is a vertical movement of cold water from deeper layers to replace warmer surface water. It affects fisheries, weather and current patterns in many parts of the world. Shown in Figure 1.11 is cold water that forces its way upward and pushes the warmer water away. On a local scale, leeward winds push the water away from the shore, as shown in Figure 1.12. On a large scale, predominant winds, combined with Coriolis forces, push warm surface water away, and cold water rises to replace it, see Figure 1.13.

Measurements, using radioactive tracer techniques have shown that the ocean's vertical circulation brings its interior water into contact with the atmosphere every 600 years. In this "overturning" circulation, cold, dense water sinks near the poles and is replaced by warmer water flowing poleward from low latitudes. In northern

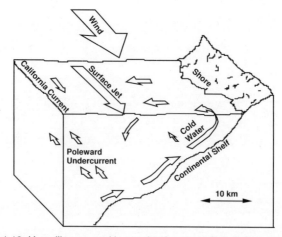

Figure 1.13: Upwelling caused by predominant winds and Coriolis forces.

(1)   (2)

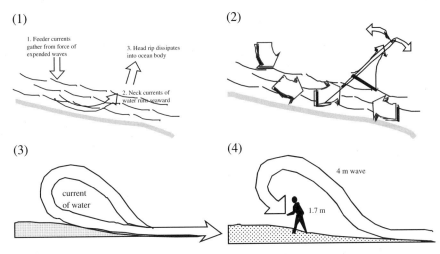

1. Feeder currents
gather from force of
expended waves

3. Head rip dissipates
into ocean body

2. Neck currents of
water runs seaward

(3)   (4)

4 m wave

current
of water

1.7 m

Figure 1.14: Rip currents.

and southern areas, the ocean gives up large amounts of heat to the atmosphere, namely on the order of 50 W/m^2, an amount equal to the solar energy reaching the surface in those areas. This in itself has a major impact on climate. By the time the water reaches the poles, it is cold and dense and sinks to the bottom. This overturning circulation has a major consequence on the Earth's carbon cycle and on the cycling of nutrients in the ocean. Much remains to be understood on the characteristics of these currents.

Rip currents occur when two opposing currents meet, setting up a swirling action which can carry swimmers away from the safety of shallow waters. The cycle is shown in Figure 1.14. The powerful current retreats and pulls the victim out to sea. Rip currents are the primary cause for 80% of ocean rescues. Look for (a) rough, choppy water and/or (b) deeper, darker water, (c) debris, kelp or sand.

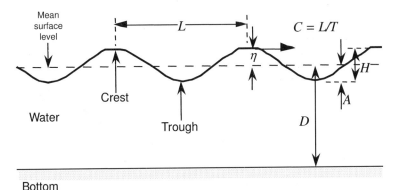

Mean surface level

L

$C = L/T$

η

Crest

H

Water

Trough

A

D

Bottom

Figure 1.15: Wave characteristics.

Table 1.3: Depth range of waves.

Feature	Range	Examples
Deep water	$D > 1/4L$	Sea and swell in open oceans.
Intermediate water	$1/4L > D > 1/20L$	Long swell over shelf, sea outside surf zone.
Shallow water	$D < 1/20L$	Tsunamis, tides, swell near shore.

1.3 Waves

The characteristics of a wave depend on the following three factors:

- The type of disturbance initially applied to the water and whether it is continuously applied to produce a forced wave or is quickly removed to allow the wave to propagate away as a free wave.
- The type of restoring mechanism that forces the water back to equilibrium.
- The properties of the wave itself.

These characteristics can be expressed in terms of the following parameters, shown in Figure 1.15:

- *Wavelength* (L) - distance from crest to crest or trough to trough.
- *Period* (T) - time between two successive crests or troughs passing a fixed point.
- *Amplitude* (A) - the maximum displacement of a wave.
- *Wave height* (H) - the vertical distance from trough to crest ($2 \times A$).
- *Depth of water* (D) - distance between mean surface level and sea bottom.
- *Speed* (celerity C) - speed at which a wave passes a fixed point.
- *Surface elevation* (η) - elevation of wave above mean sea level.

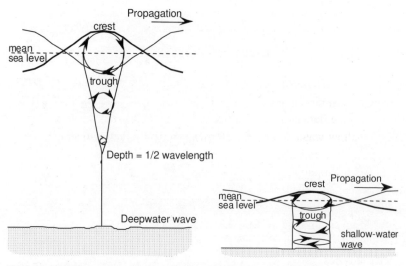

Figure 1.16: Water motion for deep (left) and shallow water waves.

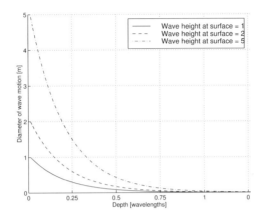

Figure 1.17: Short wave motion as a function of water depth.

The depth range valid for each type of wave is presented in Table 1.3. Deep water waves (short waves) are usually wind-generated and are unaffected by the sea bottom. Shallow waves (long waves) e.g., tide waves or tsunamis have wavelengths which exceed hundreds of kilometres whereas the ocean depth is less than 13 km.

Water does not move at the wave speed but according to a circular (deep water wave) or an elliptic motion (shallow water wave), as shown in Figure 1.16. For deep water waves, the motion is a combination of horizontal motion of the water (forth and back) with the vertical motion of the wave (up and down) which results in a nearly circular motion. Water motion decreases with depth. For short waves, the diameter of circular motion is described by

$$\text{Diam}(z) = H \cdot \exp(2\pi \cdot z / L) \tag{1.8}$$

where Diam is the diameter of motion, H the height of the wave at the surface ($z = 0$), z the depth relative to the mean water level ($z \leq 0$) and L the wavelength. Since z is negative, Diam decreases rapidly as depth increases, see Figure 1.17, and the water becomes calm very rapidly as depth increases. The diameter of the circle for a deep water wave is $1/23H$ at a depth of $1/2L$. At a depth of L, it is only $1/535H$. This is why water gets calmer quickly as the depth increases. For intermediate water waves the circles become flattened into ellipses as the bottom restricts the vertical motion of water. For shallow water waves, the ellipses practically flatten to straight lines. The motions are almost entirely in a horizontal plane. The horizontal motions decrease only slightly from top to bottom.

There is another useful classification of waves in terms of period (or frequency). Spectral analysis is a convenient tool to represent the *wave energy* against the wave period (or frequency). The surface elevation η (vertical displacement of the free surface from the mean sea level) observed over time can be expressed as a trigonometric series

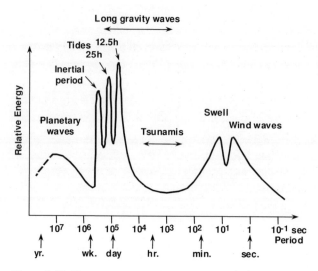

Figure 1.18: Wave energy spectrum versus period.

$$\eta = \sum_i A_i \{ \sin(\omega_i t + \phi_i) + \cos(\omega_i t + \phi_i) \} \tag{1.9}$$

where A_i is the amplitude, ϕ_i is the phase, t is time and ω_i is the angular frequency in radians per second. Spectral analysis provides the amplitude and phase coefficients A_i and ϕ_i determined as a function of frequency f. A_i^2 is not only proportional to the wave energy, it is also proportional to the square of surface elevation η^2 and as such has units of m^2. A_i^2 versus frequency or period gives the wave *energy spectrum*, as shown in Figure 1.18. The basic types of surface waves are given in Table 1.4. The theory of wave speed discussed below corresponds to waves of small

Table 1.4: Basic types of surface waves with approximate range of periods and wavelengths and primary generating and restoring mechanisms.

Name	Period	Wavelength	Generating mechanism	Restoring mechanism
Capillary waves (ripples, wavelets)	Less than 0.1 s	Less than 2 cm fluctuations	Wind, pressure, tension	Surface
Gravity waves (chop, sea, swell)	0.5 - 30 s	10 cm - 1000 m	Wind	Gravity
Infragravity waves	Minutes	100's of m - 100's of km	Storm systems (winds and atmospheric pressure gradients)	Gravity
Tsunamis	10's of minutes - 1 h	100's of km	Submarine earthquakes, shoreline slumping	Gravity
Tides	Mainly 12.5 and 25 h	1000's of km	Gravitational attraction of Sun and Moon	Gravity and Coriolis force

amplitudes. For a relative height or steepness, defined as H/L, less than 1/20, linear theory can be applied. For example, for a swell of length 200 m, the small amplitude theory would apply to a height of 10 m (which is very large for a given swell). The relative height in this case will be $10/200 = 1/20$, which is the limit of the linear theory.

One of the most useful measures of larger waves is the *significant wave height* H_s which is defined as mean height of the highest one-third of the waves. The use of the significant wave height as a sea state forecast tool was developed during World War II. It is used in offshore engineering to calculate possible destructive effects on ship and drilling platforms. Assume a wave travelling in the x-direction. The vertical displacement η of the free surface from the mean level is

$$\eta = A\cos\{2\pi(\frac{x}{L}-\frac{t}{T})\} \qquad (1.10)$$

where x is the actual displacement of the wave, t is time and T is the period. Using

$$k = \frac{2\pi}{L}, \text{ the radian wave number}$$

$$\omega = \frac{2\pi}{T}, \text{ the radian (angular) frequency}$$

the vertical displacement η can be expressed as

$$\eta = A\cos(kx - \omega t) \qquad (1.11)$$

where $kx - \omega t$ is the *phase of the wave* which varies from 0 to 2π as one goes from one crest to the next (distance L). The wave speed C, defined as

$$C = \frac{L}{T} \qquad (1.12)$$

is the speed at which a point of fixed phase travels. It is called a *phase speed*. The wave phase speed can be derived from the equation of motion for waves

$$C = \sqrt{\frac{gL}{2\pi}\tanh(\frac{2\pi h}{L})} = \sqrt{\frac{g}{k}\tanh(kh)} \qquad (1.13)$$

where h is the depth of water below mean sea level and g is gravity.

If $L < 2h$, the wave is a short wave (found in deep water) and the above formula (1.13) is approximated by

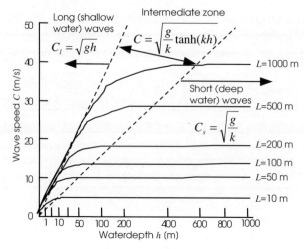

Figure 1.19: Wave speed versus water depth for various
wavelenghts from 10 m to 1,000 m.

$$C_s = \sqrt{\frac{gL}{2\pi}} = \sqrt{\frac{g}{k}} \qquad (1.14)$$

If $L > 2h$, the wave is a long wave (found in shallow water) and the formula is
approximated by

$$C_l = \sqrt{gh} \qquad (1.15)$$

The relationship between the radian frequency ω and radian wave number k, or
equivalently between the wavelength L and period T is called the dispersion relation
and is derived from the equation of motion. It has the following form

$$\omega^2 = gk \tanh(kh) \qquad (1.16)$$

The wave speed as a function of water depth for wavelengths of 10 m to 1,000 m is
shown in Figure 1.19.
The rate at which the energy of the wave is propagated is the group speed C_g; it can
be expressed as

$$C_g = \frac{C_p}{2}\{1 + \frac{2kh}{\sinh(2kh)}\} \qquad (1.17)$$

where C_p is the phase speed (C_s or C_l) and h is the depth of the wave. For long
waves, $kh \ll 1$, $\sinh 2kh$ can be approximated by $2kh$ and $C_g \approx C_l$. Similarly, for
short waves, $kh \gg 1$, $\sinh(2kh) \gg 2kh$ and $C_g \approx C_s/2$. Since modulations are

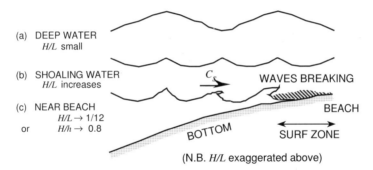

(a) DEEP WATER
    H/L small

(b) SHOALING WATER
    H/L increases

C_g WAVES BREAKING

(c) NEAR BEACH
    H/L → 1/12
or *H/h* → 0.8

BEACH

BOTTOM   SURF ZONE

(N.B. *H/L* exaggerated above)

Figure 1.20: Transition of waves from deep to shallow water.

simply modifications of energy and may contain information, it follows that information can be transmitted no faster than the group speed. When the wave moves from deep to shallow waters, the period T remains constant, but C and L decrease, as shown in Figure 1.20.

Waves form on the sea surface by the transfer of energy from the air to the water. Amongst the different mechanisms generating waves, winds contribute most to the ruffled veneer of the waters on Earth, see Figure 1.21. The longer and harder the wind blows, the greater the amount of energy transferred from the wind to the waves. Wave energy is proportional to wave height. Wind waves are initiated by the wind blowing for some hours over a sea surface many kilometres long. The length of the sea surface directly affected by the wind is called the fetch. The oscillations of the sea surface caused by the wind continue to run across the sea far beyond the direct influence of the wind. The wind waves transferred beyond the fetch are called swell. The swell consists of fairly uniform wave trains. It decays for a long distance while its wavelength increases and wave height H decreases. When the swell enters shallow water:

- The wave speed C decreases.

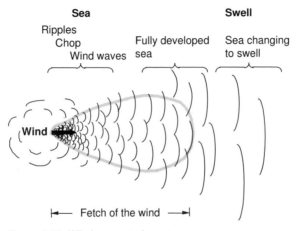

Sea   **Swell**

Ripples
Chop   Fully developed   Sea changing
Wind waves   sea   to swell

Wind

◄— Fetch of the wind —►

Figure 1.21: Wind generated waves.

Table 1.5: Minimum fetch and duration to produce fully developed seas at various wind speeds. Significant height is average height of highest 1/3 of observed waves, maximum probable wave height is 1.8 × significant height.

Wind speed [m/s]	Fetch [km]	Duration [h]	Average height [m]	Significant height [m]	Average highest 10% waves [m]	Period of greatest energy concentration [s]
5	19	2.4	0.3	0.4	0.6	4
8	63	6	0.8	1.1	1.5	6
11	139	10	1.5	2.4	3.1	8
13	296	16	2.7	4.3	5.5	10
16	518	23	4.3	6.7	8.4	12
22	1315	42	8.5	13.4	17.4	16
27	2630	69	14.6	23.8	30.2	20

- The wavelength L decreases.
- The wave height H increases.
- The period T remains constant.

The swell finally peaks up into waves, breaks, and is dissipated as surf. Wind can saturate the sea with energy, and waves begin to break and result to a fully developed sea. This process is a function of wind speed, fetch and duration. For a fully developed sea, the *duration, fetch* and *significant wave height H_s* are given in Table 1.5.

The *Beaufort Scale* of wind force, originally devised by Admiral Beaufort in the early 19th century, relates wind speed to the physical appearance of sea surface by considering an apparent wave height, the prominence of breakers, whitecaps, foam and spray, see Table 1.6. It has since been repeatedly modified to make it more relevant to modern navigation.

Information concerning the wave heights and periods can be obtained using a number of methods, namely

- Visual method - based on a visual estimate of the sea state.
- Vertical scale method - based on visual observation of the water surface against a vertical scale mounted on a pier or on a float equipped with a deep horizontal damper to limit vertical movement.
- Pressure sensor method - based on the measurement of the hydrostatic pressure below surface waves (the pressure varies as a function of water depth).
  - Pressure sensor mounted below depth of deepest trough; practical only for deep waters (short waves).
  - Bottom-mounted pressure sensors for long waves (shallow waters) such as tsunamis and tides.
  - On a ship, the pressure sensor is mounted on the lower part of the ship's hull; a one-axis (vertical) accelerometer is used to measure vertical motion. The differences in wave heights are determined.
- Electrical method - based on the electrical penetration of the sea surface. Many pairs of wires, with a small gap between the wires of each pair, are mounted horizontally on vertical rods. Immersed wires are short circuited and, by

Table 1.6: Beaufort wind scale.

Beaufort number	Wind	Sea state	Wind speed [km/hr]	Wave height [m]
0	Calm	Sea smooth as mirror	< 1	0
1	Light air	Small wavelet-like scales; no foam crests	2-5	0.15
2	Light breeze	Waves short; crests begin to break	6-11	0.3
3	Gentle breeze	Foam has glassy appearance; not yet white	12-20	0.6
4	Moderate breeze	Waves now longer; many white areas	21-29	1.6
5	Fresh breeze	Waves pronounced and long; white foam crests	30-39	3.1
6	Strong breeze	Larger waves form; white foam crests all over	40-50	4.7
7	Moderate gale	Sea heaps up; wind blows foam instreaks	51-61	6.2
8	Fresh gale	Height of waves and crests increasing	62-74	7.8
9	Strong gale	Foam is blown in dense streaks	75-87	9.3
10	Whole gale	High waves with long overhanging crests; large foam patches	88-101	10.8
11	Storm	High waves; ships in sight hidden in troughs	102-120	-
12	Hurricane	Sea covered with streaky foam; air filled with spray	> 120	-

recording continuously the number of pairs from the bottom which are short-circuited, a record of sea surface level is obtained. This method is used for analysis of detailed wave structures.

• Airborne and satellite-borne radar altimetry - based on measuring distance from the aircraft or the satellite to the sea surface. From the observations and known positions of the aircraft or satellite the surface elevation along the flight path can be derived.

Internal waves may occur in underwater surfaces when vertical density variations are present (sea consists of layers of different density). Density differences between the layers result in restoring forces (gravitational or hydrostatic pressure). They are caused by, e.g., current shear or surface disturbances. Internal waves are frequent in oceanic waters on the thermocline (layer at a depth of 50 - 100m with large temperature variations) and in coastal waters on the halocline (layer with large salinity variations).

1.4 Major references

Apel, J.R.: *Principles of ocean physics.* International Geophysics Series, Vol. 38, Academic Press, 1987.

Lutgens, F.K., E.J. Tarbuck: *The atmosphere - an introduction to meteorology.* Prentice Hall, 1989.

Neumann, G, W.J. Pierson, Jr.: *Principles of physical oceanography.* Prentice Hall, 1966.

Pond, S., G.L. Pickard: *Introductory dynamical oceanography.* Pergamon Press, 1983.

Thomson, R.E.: *Oceanography of the British Columbia coast.* Fisheries and Aquatic Sciences 56, Fisheries and Oceans, Canada, 1981.

Van Dorn, W. G.: *Oceanography and seamanship.* Cornell Maritime Press, 1993.

2 Tides and tidal currents

2.1 Introduction

An ocean tide is a periodic motion of water due to the differential gravitational forces of celestial bodies (mostly Moon and Sun) upon different parts of the rotating Earth. Due to greater distance the effect of the Sun is only 46% of that of the Moon. The tide is most commonly observed as the vertical rise and fall of the sea level and has an average period of 12.4 hours (24.8 hours in some places). The prime phenomenon is however the *horizontal tidal current*. A tidal current is a horizontal water movement that builds up in vertical rises and falls along the coastlines.

Tides and tidal currents are intimately related and parts of the same phenomenon, caused by tide-producing forces of Moon and Sun. The response of the oceans to tide producing forces are usually first estimated using tidal *equilibrium theory*, primarily developed by Newton in the 17th century.

The equilibrium theory ignores the size, depth and configuration of the basins or waterways, friction, landmasses, inertia of water masses, and Coriolis acceleration. In this theory the entire Earth is assumed to be covered with water of uniform depth and density, and infinite time is allowed for equilibrium to occur between the hydrostatic and tractive forces. The differences between this first approximation and observed tides can be considerable.

Four classes of tides can be distinguished:

- *Diurnal* (D): only one HW (High Water) and one LW (Low Water) each lunar day.
- *Semi-Diurnal* (SD): two nearly equal HW's and two nearly equal LW's approximately uniformly spaced over each lunar day.
- *Mixed, Mainly Diurnal* (MD): either two unequal HW's and LW's at irregular spacing over a lunar day, or only one HW and one LW in a day.
- *Mixed, Mainly Semi-Diurnal* (MSD): two HW's and two LW's each lunar day, with irregular height and time intervals.

2.2 Tide-generating forces

The orbital motion of celestial bodies as well as the tide generating forces which occur on these bodies can be derived from Newton's *universal law of gravitation* which is mathematically expressed as

$$F = G\frac{m_1 m_2}{r^2} \qquad\qquad (2.1)$$

and where F is the magnitude of the force of gravitational attraction between the two point masses m_1 and m_2, r is the distance between the two point masses (or concentric spheres of homogeneous densities) and G is the universal constant of gravitation, which in SI units is equal to $6.6725985 \cdot 10^{-11}$ $m^3 kg^{-1} s^{-2}$.

The centre of mass of two bodies is termed their *barycentre*. For the Earth-Moon pair, it is located approximately 0.74 times the Earth radius from the centre of mass of the Earth, as shown in Figure 2.1. The barycentre is also the point about which the Earth and Moon rotate in an elliptical fashion (resembling an asymmetric dumbbell).

The Earth-Moon barycentre also describes an orbit that is elliptical about the Sun-Earth-Moon barycentre, as shown in Figure 2.2. The elliptical motion of the Earth and Moon about their barycentre causes both bodies to experience a centripetal force directed at the other body. At the Earth's centre of mass, and only at that point, is the gravitational force exerted by the Moon (on the Earth) exactly equal to the centripetal force, this being the condition for orbital motion of the Earth about the Earth-Moon barycentre. According to Newton's law of gravitation, the gravitational force the Moon exerts on the Earth's centre of mass is

$$F = G\frac{M_E M_M}{d_D^2}$$

where M_E and M_M are the masses of Earth and Moon, respectively, and d_D is the distance between their centres of mass.

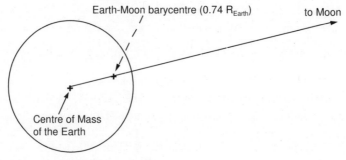

Figure 2.1: Earth-Moon barycentre.

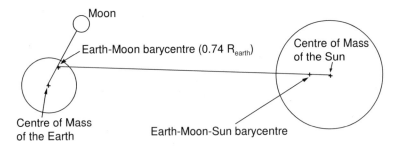

Figure 2.2: Earth-Moon and Earth-Moon-Sun barycentres.

Assume for the moment, that the Earth is not rotating about its own axis. Also assume that the Earth is orbiting about a point (point E in Figure 2.3) while maintaining the same orientation with respect to that point. Under these conditions, all points on the Earth will arc out a circle of similar radius, as shown in Figure 2.3. Consequently, *all* points of the Earth experience the same centripetal force in both magnitude and direction.

Combining Newton's universal law of gravitation with his second law of motion (force equals mass times acceleration), we obtain the following expression for the (centripetal/gravitational) acceleration a_c of the Earth's centre of mass about the Earth-Moon barycentre:

$$a_c = G \frac{M_M}{d_M^2} \qquad\qquad (2.2)$$

To determine the tide-generating forces of the Moon, it is simplest to first consider

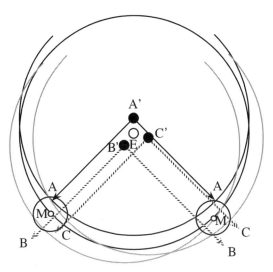

Figure 2.3: Centripetal force on Earth orbiting about point E.

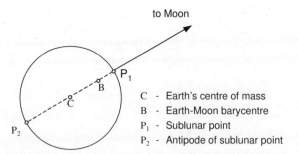

C - Earth's centre of mass
B - Earth-Moon barycentre
P_1 - Sublunar point
P_2 - Antipode of sublunar point

Figure 2.4: Sublunar point P_1 and antipode P_2.

the accelerations at the *sublunar* point and its antipode on the Earth as shown in Figure 2.4.

The accelerations a_1 and a_2 at the sublunar point P_1 and its antipode P_2, respectively, due to the gravitational attraction of the Moon are given by

$$a_1 = G\frac{M_M}{(d_M - R_E)^2}$$
$$a_2 = G\frac{M_M}{(d_M + R_E)^2}$$

(2.3)

where R_E is the radius of the Earth.

The differential acceleration at P_1 (relative acceleration of P_1 with respect to the centre of the Earth C) is

$$a_1 - a_C = G\frac{M_M}{(d_M - R_E)^2} - G\frac{M_M}{d_M^2}$$

(2.4)

Neglecting higher order terms, the above equation becomes

$$a_1 - a_C = 2G\frac{M_M R_E}{d_M^3}$$

(2.5)

Similarly, the differential acceleration at P_2 after simplifications is

$$a_2 - a_C = -2G\frac{M_M R_E}{d_M^3}$$

(2.6)

At P_2, the differential acceleration is negative and directed away from the Earth's centre of mass, as shown in Figure 2.5.

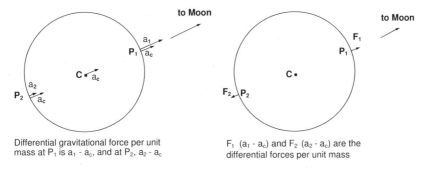

Differential gravitational force per unit
mass at P_1 is $a_1 - a_c$, and at P_2, $a_2 - a_c$

F_1 $(a_1 - a_c)$ and F_2 $(a_2 - a_c)$ are the
differential forces per unit mass

Figure 2.5: Differential gravitational forces per unit mass at sublunar point and its
antipode.

At points other than the sublunar point and its antipode, both the magnitude and the
direction of the Moon's gravitational forces differ from that at the Earth's centre of
mass. Therefore, to obtain the differential accelerations at such points, it is necessary
to use vector notation.

The differential acceleration (or differential force per unit mass) F_D at any point on
the Earth's surface is

$$F_D = a_M - a_C \tag{2.7}$$

where a_M is the vector of acceleration at the point under consideration due to the
Moon's gravitational force and a_C is the vector of acceleration of the Earth's centre
of mass due to the Moon's gravitational force. Both a_M and F_D are shown in Figure
2.6. The relative effects of accelerations a_M and a_C at various points along a great
circle through the sublunar point and its antipode, as well as at the Earth's centre of
mass, are shown in Figure 2.7. The corresponding differential forces F_D are shown
in Figure 2.8.

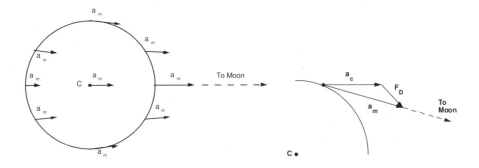

Figure 2.6: Differential acceleration in Earth-Moon system.

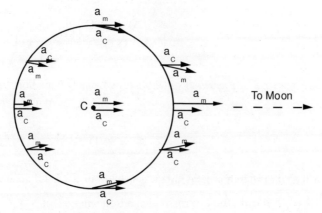

Figure 2.7: Relative effects of acceleration in Earth-Moon system.

With the assumption that the whole Earth is covered with a uniform layer of water, the differential forces can be represented by their vertical and horizontal components. The magnitudes of the horizontal and vertical components of F_D are given by

$$F_H = \frac{3}{2} G \frac{M_M R_E}{d_M^3} \sin 2\alpha$$

$$F_V = -\frac{1}{2} G \frac{M_M R_E}{d_M^3} (3\cos 2\alpha + 1)$$

(2.8)

where α is the angle at the Earth's centre between the direction to the Moon and the line from the centre of the Earth to the point under consideration, as shown in Figure 2.9.

The vertical components have the effect of changing the weight of the mass on which they are acting. They do not contribute to the tidal effect. The horizontal components have the effect of moving the water in horizontal direction toward the sublunar and

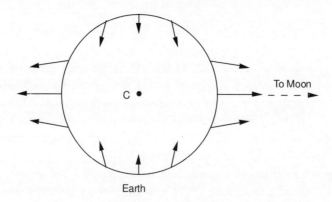

Figure 2.8: Differential forces in Earth-Moon system.

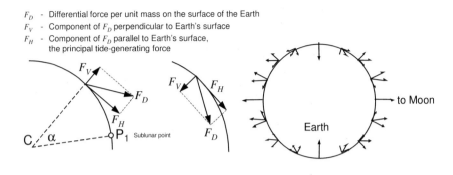

F_D - Differential force per unit mass on the surface of the Earth
F_V - Component of F_D perpendicular to Earth's surface
F_H - Component of F_D parallel to Earth's surface,
            the principal tide-generating force

(A)   (B)   (C)

Figure 2.9: Differential forces resolved into horizontal and vertical components: (A) - F_D directed out of surface, (B) - F_D directed into surface, (C) varying directions of F_D along a great circle through sublunar point.

antipodal points until an equilibrium is achieved. The horizontal components, also called *tractive forces*, are the principal tide-generating forces, as shown in Figure 2.10. F_H is zero at the sublunar point and antipode and maximum at $\alpha = 45°$.

The equilibrium is reached when a bulge of water has formed at the sublunar point and its antipode such that the tractive forces due to the Moon's differential gravitational forces are balanced by the Earth's gravitational attraction. The new water surface would be everywhere normal to the sum of gravity and tide-raising force.

So far, the effects of the Earth rotation were neglected. The bulges formed at the sublunar point and the antipode correspond to the *high tide*, which occurs at these points. At the same time, at the points with latitude differing by 90° from the sublunar point and the antipode and lying in the great circle formed by these two points, *low tide* will be experienced, as shown in Figure 2.11.

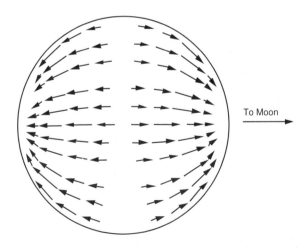

Figure 2.10: Tractive forces.

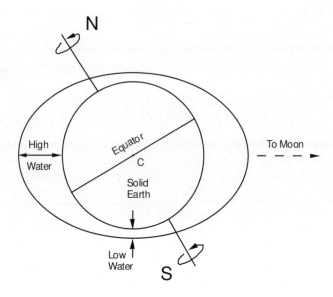

Figure 2.11: High and low tides in Earth-Moon system.

With a rotating Earth, the Moon transits every 24h50m. During that interval, two high tides and two low tides occur at any point on the Earth's surface. The range of this equilibrium tide is one metre at the equator.

When the Moon is in the plane of the equator, the forces are equal in magnitude at the two points on the same parallel of latitude and 180° apart in longitude. When the Moon declination is North or South, the forces are unequal at such points and tend to cause an inequity in the two high waters and the two low waters of a day. Observers at points X, Y and Z in Figure 2.12 experience one high tide when the Moon is on their meridian, then another high tide 12h25m later when at X', Y' and Z'. The high tides are the same at X and X' while the high tides at Y' and Z' are lower than those at Y and Z.

The tidal effect of the Sun can be expressed in a similar way to that of the Moon. The differential force at sublunar point is given by expression (2.5). Similarly, differential force at *subsolar* point is

$$a_1 - a_C = 2G \frac{M_S R_E}{d_S^3} \tag{2.9}$$

where S denotes the Sun. All formulae derived for the Moon apply also to the Sun. The relative effect of the Sun and Moon is given by the ratio, see also Table 2.1

$$\frac{F_{D,S}}{F_{D,M}} = \frac{M_S}{M_M} \cdot \frac{d_M^3}{d_S^3} = 0.46 \tag{2.10}$$

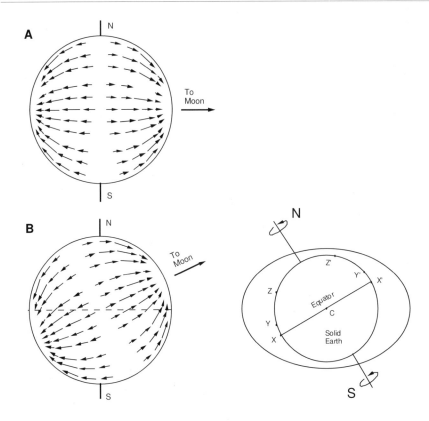

Figure 2.12: Effect of declination of the Moon.

The tidal effect of the Moon is more than twice that of the effect of the Sun, although the mass of the Moon is a very small fraction of the Sun's mass. This is due to the fact that the Moon is much closer to the Earth and the differential forces vary inversely as the cube of the distance.

The tides depend on the geometrical configuration of the Earth-Moon-Sun system. Two special cases occur when the Earth, Moon and Sun are approximately on the

Table 2.1: Some characteristic parameters for Earth, Moon and Sun.

Body	Radius	Mass
Earth	$6.38 \cdot 10^6$ m	$5.98 \cdot 10^{24}$ kg
Moon	$1.74 \cdot 10^6$ m	$7.35 \cdot 10^{22}$ kg
Sun	$6.96 \cdot 10^8$ m	$1.99 \cdot 10^{30}$ kg
Earth-Moon distance	$0.38 \cdot 10^9$ m	
Earth-Sun distance	$1.49 \cdot 10^{11}$ m	

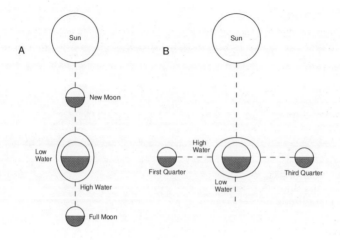

Figure 2.13: Spring (left) and neap tides.

same line, which correspond to new and full Moon (spring tide), and first and third quarters of the Moon (neap tide), shown in Figure 2.13.

Spring tide occurs at times of new and full Moon when the Sun, Moon and Earth are in line. The tractive forces are acting in the same direction, and the resulting tide is a higher tide.

Neap tide occurs at times of first and third quarter of the Moon when the tractive forces due to the Sun and the Moon are at right angles to each other, and the resulting tide is lower than average.

Priming and *lagging* the tides are the effects when the Moon is in positions between quadrature and new or full, as shown in Figure 2.14.

The tidal potential can be represented by a series of harmonic functions. The

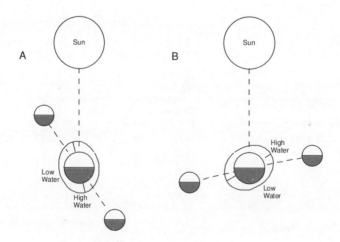

Figure 2.14: Priming (left) and lagging the tides.

Table 2.2: Principal tide-producing force constituents.

Species and name	Symbol	Period [solar hours]	Relative size
Semi-diurnal:			
Principal lunar	M_2	12.42	100
Principal solar	S_2	12.00	47
Larger lunar elliptic	N_2	12.66	19
Luni-solar semi-diurnal	K_2	11.97	13
Diurnal:			
Luni-solar diurnal	K_1	23.93	58
Principal lunar diurnal	O_1	25.82	42
Principal solar diurnal	P_1	24.07	19
Larger lunar elliptic	Q_1	26.87	8
Long period:			
Lunar fortnightly	M_f	327.9	17
Lunar monthly	M_m	661.3	9
Solar semi-annual	S_{sa}	4383	8

harmonic expansion of the luni-solar potential results in the decomposition of the various tidal effects of Sun and Moon in major components or constituents (the sum of many simple harmonics of different periods, phases and amplitudes). According to the periods, these harmonic constituents are classified into three groups

- *Semi-diurnal* type of tide - two high and two low waters each tidal day.
- *Diurnal* type of tide - single high and single low water each tidal day.
- *Long period* type of tide - fortnightly, monthly, semi-annual, 8.8 year period

Table 2.3: Magnitudes of four main constituents for selected sites along the west coast of North America.

Location (lat [°], lon [°])	Constituent [m]				Ratio
	O_1	K_1	M_2	S_2	$\dfrac{O_1 + K_1}{M_2 + S_2}$
Union Seamount (50,-133)	0.079	0.131	0.277	0.087	0.720
Tofino (49,-126)	0.246	0.389	0.991	0.280	0.500
Port Renfrew (49,-124)	0.287	0.458	0.712	0.210	0.809
Victoria (48,-123)	0.370	0.627	0.373	0.102	2.100
Port Townsend (48,-123)	0.437	0.616	0.680	0.190	1.210
Seattle (48,-122)	0.459	0.837	1.066	0.263	0.975
Sidney (49,-123)	0.445	0.766	0.555	0.132	1.763
Point Atkinson (49,-123)	0.477	0.858	0.917	0.233	1.161
Comox (50,-125)	0.489	0.885	1.002	0.253	1.095
Campbell River (50,-125)	0.485	0.846	0.826	0.203	1.293
Alert Bay (50,-127)	0.306	0.516	1.272	0.406	0.490
Queen Charlotte City (53,-132)	0.315	0.511	1.975	0.651	0.315
Prince Rupert (54,-130)	0.314	0.513	1.957	0.644	0.318

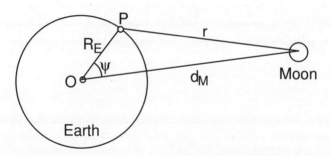

Figure 2.15: Geometry for the potential of point P in Earth-Moon system.

(alterations in the eccentricity of the Moon's orbit), 18.6 year period (revolution of the Moon's orbit with respect to the equator), 20.9 year period (revolution of the Earth's orbit about the Sun).

Characteristics of some of the principal tide-producing force constituents are given in Table 2.2 showing the symbol, period and relative size (with respect to the principal semi-diurnal lunar constituent M_2 taken as 100). The constituents M_2, S_2, K_1 and O_1 have the largest amplitude (the largest relative size) and they are considered as four main tide height constituents. The magnitude of these four constituents for selected sites along the west coast of North America is given in Table 2.3.

Harmonic functions are functions whose Laplacian is zero. The Laplace operator, denoted by Δ, has the form

$$\Delta = \frac{\partial^2}{\partial x^2} + \frac{\partial^2}{\partial y^2} + \frac{\partial^2}{\partial z^2} \qquad (2.11)$$

Therefore, a function V is harmonic only if the following expression holds

$$\Delta V = \frac{\partial^2 V}{\partial x^2} + \frac{\partial^2 V}{\partial y^2} + \frac{\partial^2 V}{\partial z^2} = 0 \qquad (2.12)$$

Every harmonic function is *analytic*, meaning the function and its derivatives of any order are continuous. The solution to Laplace's (differential) equation (i.e., $\Delta V = 0$) can be expressed in terms of spherical harmonics. In other words, if a function V is harmonic, the following statements can be made

• V is analytic.

• V satisfies Laplace's equation.

• V can be expressed in terms of spherical harmonics.

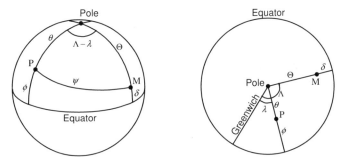

Figure 2.16: Coordinates of P and of the Moon on the unit sphere.

Assuming that the Moon attracts the Earth as a point mass, the potential of the gravitational attraction of the Moon at point P on the Earth's surface is

$$V = G\frac{M_M}{r} \tag{2.13}$$

with r being the distance between the Moon's mass centre and the point P, as shown in Figure 2.15. The reciprocal distance $1/r$ can be expanded into a series of Legendre polynomials $P_n(\cos\psi)$. The lunar gravitational attraction V at point P will be

$$V = GM_M \sum_{n=0}^{\infty} \frac{R_E^n}{r_M^{n+1}} P_n(\cos\psi) \tag{2.14}$$

where ψ is the spherical distance between the Moon and point P, as shown in Figure 2.16, and n is the degree of the polynomial. If we plot $R + \varepsilon \cdot P_n(\cos\psi)$, where $\varepsilon \ll R$, for the first three Legendre polynomials ($n=0,1,2$), we obtain the results shown in Figure 2.17.

The first two-degree ($n=0,1$) terms simply produce a scale and translation of the sphere, respectively. Only the terms of degree two or higher produce a true deformation. However, the terms of degree three or more are small compared to the second degree term and thus will be neglected. Consequently, the V_2 term is

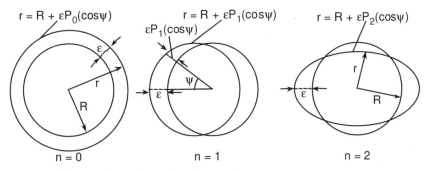

Figure 2.17: Lower-degree Legendre polynomials.

dominant and we can write

$$V \approx V_2 = G \frac{M_M R_E^2}{d_M^3} P_2(\cos \psi) = G \frac{M_M R_E^2}{d_M^3} (\frac{3}{2} \cos^2 \psi - \frac{1}{2}) \tag{2.15}$$

According to spherical trigonometry

$$\cos \psi = \cos \theta \cos \Theta + \sin \theta \sin \Theta \cos(\Lambda - \lambda) \tag{2.16}$$

where (θ, λ) are the coordinates of point P, at which the lunar gravitational potential is being calculated, see Figure 2.16, and (Θ, Λ) are the coordinates of the Moon. Using (2.16), V_2 can be decomposed into zonal V_{20}, tesseral V_{21}, and sectorial V_{22} components

$$V_2 = V_{20} + V_{21} + V_{22}$$

where

$$V_{20} = G \frac{M_M R_E^2}{d_M^3} (\frac{3}{2} \cos^2 \theta - \frac{1}{2})(\frac{3}{2} \cos^2 \Theta - \frac{1}{2})$$

$$V_{21} = G \frac{M_M R_E^2}{d_M^3} \frac{3}{4} \sin 2\theta \sin 2\Theta \cos(\Lambda - \lambda)$$

$$V_{22} = G \frac{M_M R_E^2}{d_M^3} \frac{3}{4} \sin^2 \theta \sin^2 \Theta \cos\{2(\Lambda - \lambda)\}$$

These components have different periods
- V_{20} - Long-periodical (up to 20 years)
- V_{21} - Diurnal
- V_{22} - Semi-diurnal

For the Sun similar expressions can be derived. In the early 20th century, Doodson decomposed the tidal potential into a sum of 396 harmonic oscillations, which are characterised by their frequencies, amplitudes and phases. The oscillations are functions of mean lunar time τ, the Moon's mean longitude s, the Sun's mean longitude h, the mean longitude of lunar perigee p, the negative mean longitude of the ascending lunar node N' and the mean longitude of solar perigee p_s. In later years the number of terms was increased to more than 1000. With this expansion it is possible to predict the astronomical tides. The actual tides, however, are much larger due to the dynamic response of the oceans to tidal forces. The frequencies and phases at which the actual tides have their maximum energy correspond to those of the astronomical tides. Thus, it is also possible to estimate the amplitude of each of the

Table 2.4: Tidal effects Δh due to wind for lakes Erié (L=390 km, D=17 m) and Ontario (L=275 km, D=170 m).

Wind speed [m/s]	Δh (Erié) [m]	Δh (Ontario) [m]
2	0.04	0.00
5	0.26	0.02
10	1.03	0.07
15	2.32	0.16
20	4.13	0.29
25	6.45	0.45

components from actual observations, provided the observation period is long enough.

A modern approach to tidal analysis is based on the assumption that although the tides are periodical, their periods do not depend on astronomical factors alone, but also on the characteristics of the oceans themselves, such as their depth and width.

Meteorological effects on tides are left as residuals by the harmonic analysis procedure and generally cannot be predicted. With no meteorological disturbances the tides can be predicted to about ±3 cm and ±5 minutes. Extreme meteorological effects, such as hurricanes, may cause differences of tens of centimetres and tens of minutes.

Wind-generated currents may upset the natural rhythm of tidal streams. Both the turn of the tide and the speed of the tidal current can be affected. A wind set-up is defined as the slope of the surface in the direction of the wind stress. A steady state is reached after a certain time, in which case the water is no longer accelerating and the pressure gradient force due to the surface slope on the one hand, and the surface and bottom stress on the water due to the wind and bottom drag on the other hand, are in equilibrium.

The height difference Δh, expressed in metres, over a surface of length L and depth D with a wind of speed W is

$$\Delta h = 4.5 \cdot 10^{-7} \cdot WL^2 / D$$

Table 2.4 shows the height difference Δh due to wind set-up observed for lakes Erié and Ontario under different wind speeds.

A *seiche* (pronounced *sigh-shh*) is a free oscillation, which can develop in a closed or semi-closed basin (bay or inlet). The period of this oscillation is the natural period of the basin.

2.3 Tidal analysis and prediction

At a given point $P(\theta, \lambda)$, the actual tide is the sum of its harmonic constituents of different periods, phases and amplitudes. If the tide is recorded at a fixed location for a suitable period of time, a harmonic analysis will yield the effect of the tide-

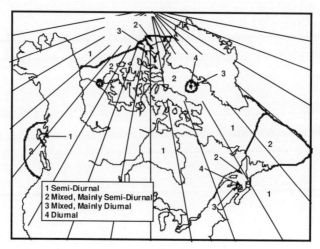

Figure 2.18: Types of tides in Canadian waters.

producing force constituents on the tide height of this location. These harmonic constituents can then be used to predict the tide into the future. The tidal theory does not yield tidal prediction to a satisfactory accuracy. It tells, however, what constituents to look for in the analysis of tide records.

The tidal constituents do not necessarily have the same proportion as the tide-producing force constituents for a given site. The shape of the basin around the point causes the water to respond in a unique manner to certain tide-producing force constituents. This is why continuous data at many tidal stations are required for an accurate tidal analysis and prediction over a large area.

The results of tidal analysis can be illustrated in the form of co-tidal charts showing
- the *co-phase* (degrees or time units) lines, and
- the *co-range* (tide amplitude or height) lines.

The number of constituents used for the prediction of tides depends on the accuracy required. Frequently, the first seven, i.e., M_2, S_2, N_2, K_2, K_1, O_1 and P_1, are sufficient to predict the tide to within about 10%. Generally 20 to 30 constituents are used for predicting two or three years ahead for ports close to the ocean, and 60 or more for river estuaries when the tide is strongly affected by bottom topography and non-linear effects. Figure 2.18 shows the type of tides in Canadian waters. Figures 2.19 to 2.21 show the M_2 global constituent and the M_2 and K_1 constituents in Canada's Hudson Bay.

Co-tidal or co-phase lines join points of equal phase at any instant. They usually rotate about a nodal point
- counterclockwise in the northern hemisphere, and
- clockwise in the southern hemisphere.

Such a node or *amphidrome* is a location of zero fall and rise with co-tidal lines rotating about it.

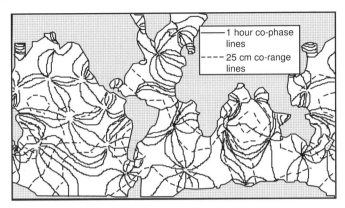

Figure 2.19: Global M_2 tidal constituent.

In a great number of countries national hydrographic offices provide a tide prediction service. In the case of Canada, this service is provided by the Canadian Hydrographic Service at www.lau.chs-shc.dfo-mpo.gc.ca/marees/produits/english/canada.htm. For the Netherlands it can be found at www.getij.nl.

In a local area, a co-tidal chart based on a few observation points can be constructed as shown in Figure 2.22. All co-tidal curves refer to the tide at the reference point A. Full lines (*time curves*) show time corrections which must be applied to the times of the tide at A to obtain the corresponding time at another point. The high or low water at B is 30 minutes earlier than that at A while at C it is 30 minutes later. Dotted lines (*range curves*) show range ratio at any point with respect to the tide at A. The tide at B is 0.74 times that at A. Most of the information used to generate the co-tidal charts comes from the observations obtained ashore. Therefore these observations should be performed with sufficient accuracy.

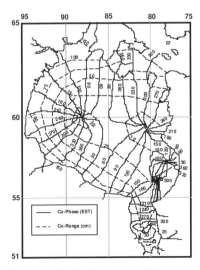

Figure 2.20: Co-tidal chart of M_2 constituent in Hudson Bay.

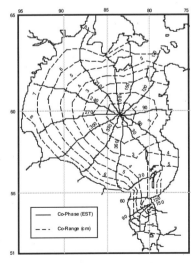

Figure 2.21: Co-tidal char of K_1 constituent in Hudson Bay.

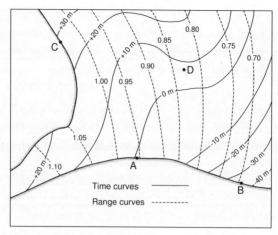

Figure 2.22: Local co-tidal chart.

In offshore regions when no tidal gauges are available and no actual tidal information
becomes available from ship observations, the existing co-tidal charts should be
used. Otherwise actual data from tidal gauges make it possible to construct local tidal
charts for offshore waters. The procedure for constructing a co-tidal chart is shown in
Figure 2.23 and can be summarised as follows:

- Known time differences and tidal ratios are needed at a minimum of three points.
- A reference tidal gauge for the chart datum is selected (station A in this case).
- Time differences are interpolated (in minutes in Figure 2.23) with reference to A.
  In this ideal case, there are six known tidal gauges, namely A, B, C, D, E and F.
- Amplitudes (tidal height differences) are interpolated with respect to A and are
  expressed as a ratio of amplitude at A.
- The proper tidal correction at a point within the survey area is obtained as:
  a) Obtain the time correction Δt from the time curve figure.
  b) Obtain the tidal height at A for $t + \Delta t$ using time series.
  c) Obtain the amplitude correction ratio (with respect to A) from the range curve
     figure.
  d) Multiply (b) by (c).

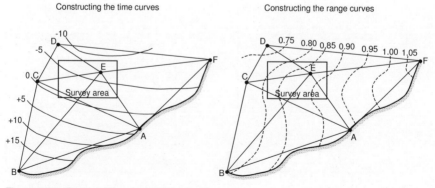

Figure 2.23: Construction of a co-tidal chart.

2.4 Major references

Apel, J.R.: *Principles of ocean physics.* International Geophysics Series, Vol. 38, Academic Press, 1987.

Bowditch, N.: *American practical navigator.* NIMA, 1995, available from http://pollux.nss.nima.mil/pubs or http://www.irbs.com/bowditch.

EMR/Surveys & Mapping Branch: *Surveying offshore Canada.* 3rd edition, 1982.

Forrester, W.D.: *Canadian tidal manual.* Fisheries and Oceans, Canada, 1983.

Godin, G.: *The analysis of tides.* University of Toronto Press, 1972.

Heiskanen, W., H. Moritz: *Physical geodesy.* W.H. Freeman and Company, San Francisco, 1967.

Moritz, H., I.I. Mueller: *Earth rotation - Theory and observation.* Ungar, New York, 1987.

Pond, S., G.L. Pickard: *Introductory dynamical oceanography.* Pergamon Press, 2nd edition, 1983.

Sideris, M.G.: *ENGO lecture notes on gravity field.* University of Calgary, 1997.

Thomson, R.E.: *Oceanography of the British Columbia coast.* Fisheries and Aquatic Sciences, 56, Fisheries and Oceans, Canada, 1981.

3 Estimation and quality control

3.1 Least squares estimation

Assume we want to determine n parameters, contained in the *parameter* or *state vector x* and that we have m observations available in the measurement vector y. If there is a known linear relationship between parameters and observations, we may set up the *measurement model* or *model of observation equations*

$$y = Ax \qquad\qquad (3.1)$$

where A is the *m×n design matrix*. Here we will assume that $m \geq n$ and that the rank (the number of linearly independent columns) of A is equal to n. A solution to this linear system exists if the vector y can be written as a linear combination of the columns of matrix A. In that case, y is an element of the *column space* (or *range space*) of A, denoted $R(A)$. If $y \in R(A)$, (3.1) is called a *consistent* system; if $y \notin R(A)$, the system is *inconsistent*. Figure 3.1 gives a geometric interpretation of consistent and inconsistent systems.

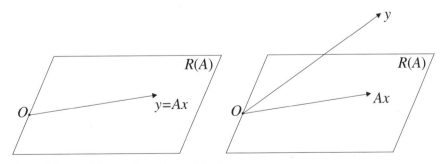

Figure 3.1: Consistent (left) and inconsistent system.

Inconsistent systems can be made consistent by introducing an m-vector e in the model (3.1)

$$y = Ax + e \qquad (3.2)$$

The *least squares* principle is based on minimizing the discrepancy between y and Ax. This leads to the minimization problem

$$\underset{x}{\text{minimize}} \|e\|^2 \Leftrightarrow \underset{x}{\text{minimize}} (y - Ax)^T (y - Ax) \qquad (3.3)$$

A solution to (3.3) exists if

$$\frac{\partial \|e\|^2}{\partial x} = 0 \qquad \text{and} \qquad \frac{\partial^2 \|e\|^2}{\partial x^2} > 0$$

Expanding the squared norm in (3.3) results in

$$\|e\|^2 = (y - Ax)^T (y - Ax) = y^T y - 2x^T A^T y + x^T A^T Ax \qquad (3.4)$$

Its first and second derivative with respect to x are

$$\frac{\partial \|e\|^2}{\partial x} = -2A^T y + 2A^T Ax \qquad (3.5)$$

$$\frac{\partial^2 \|e\|^2}{\partial x^2} = 2A^T A \qquad (3.6)$$

The matrix on the right-hand side of (3.6) is positive definite. This can be seen as follows: let z be an arbitry non-zero m-vector. The matrix $A^T A$ is positive definite if $z^T A^T Az > 0$. Since Az is a vector, $z^T A^T Az = \|Az\|^2 > 0$.

Expression (3.5) is zero if

$$A^T Ax = A^T y \qquad (3.7)$$

from which it follows that the estimator $\hat{x}$, the least squares solution to (3.2), is given by

$$\hat{x} = (A^T A)^{-1} A^T y \qquad (3.8)$$

The vector of adjusted observations $\hat{y}$ is defined as

$$\hat{y} = A\hat{x} = A(A^T A)^{-1} A^T y \tag{3.9}$$

This vector is an element of the range space of A. The vector of *least squares residuals* $\hat{e}$ is defined as

$$\hat{e} = y - \hat{y} = y - A\hat{x} \tag{3.10}$$

Note that $A^T \hat{e} = 0$: the vector $\hat{e}$ is orthogonal to the range space of A since the dot product of each of the columns of A with $\hat{e}$ is zero.
In the above derivations, it was assumed that all observations have equal weight. Introducing the positive definite matrix W allows us to assign different weights to the observations. The expression to be minimized becomes

$$\underset{x}{\text{minimize}}(y - Ax)^T W(y - Ax) \tag{3.11}$$

and its solution reads

$$\hat{x} = (A^T WA)^{-1} A^T Wy \tag{3.12}$$

For *weighted* least squares, $A^T W\hat{e} = 0$. The vector $\hat{e}$ is orthogonal to the range space of A in the metric W.

From now on we will assume that the vector y, which contains the numerical values of the observations, is actually a realisation of the *random* vector of observables $\underline{y}$. This vector of observables $\underline{y}$ will be written as the sum of a deterministic functional part Ax and a random residual part $\underline{e}$, which models the variability in the measurements

$$\underline{y} = Ax + \underline{e} \tag{3.13}$$

Here we will assume that the average variability in $\underline{e}$, or its *expectation*, is zero

$$E\{\underline{e}\} = 0 \tag{3.14}$$

where $E\{.\}$ denotes the *mathematical expectation* operator. The variability itself is characterised by the known *covariance matrix* Q_y

$$D\{\underline{e}\} = Q_y \tag{3.15}$$

where $D\{.\}$ is the *dispersion* operator, defined as $D\{.\} = E\{(.-E\{.\})(.-E\{.\})^T\}$. Using the propagation laws for means and covariances

$$E\{T\underline{u}+d\}=TE\{\underline{u}\}+d$$
$$D\{T\underline{u}+d\}=TD\{\underline{u}\}T^T$$

the measurement model can now be reformulated as

$$E\{\underline{y}\}=Ax \quad D\{\underline{y}\}=Q_y \tag{3.16}$$

It can be proved that choosing $W=Q_y^{-1}$ in (3.12) results in estimators for the parameters that have minimal variance. Substituting $W=Q_y^{-1}$ into (3.12) and taking into account the stochastic nature of the observations finally results in the least squares solution used throughout this chapter

$$\hat{\underline{x}}=(A^TQ_y^{-1}A)^{-1}A^TQ_y^{-1}\underline{y} \tag{3.17}$$

$$\hat{\underline{y}}=A\hat{\underline{x}}=A(A^TQ_y^{-1}A)^{-1}A^TQ_y^{-1}\underline{y}=P_A\underline{y} \tag{3.18}$$

$$\hat{\underline{e}}=\underline{y}-\hat{\underline{y}}=(I-P_A)\underline{y}=P_A^\perp\underline{y} \tag{3.19}$$

The covariance matrix of $\hat{\underline{x}}$ follows from applying the covariance law to (3.17) as

$$Q_{\hat{x}}=(A^TQ_y^{-1}A)^{-1} \tag{3.20}$$

For the adjusted observations $\hat{\underline{y}}$ we get in a similar way

$$Q_{\hat{y}}=AQ_{\hat{x}}A^T \tag{3.21}$$

and for the least squares residuals $\hat{\underline{e}}$ finally

$$Q_{\hat{e}}=P_A^\perp Q_y(P_A^\perp)^T=Q_y-Q_{\hat{y}}=P_A^\perp Q_y \tag{3.22}$$

So far we have assumed a linear relationship between observations and unknown parameters. If the relationship is non-linear, i.e., $y=F(x)$, we can make it linear by expanding the function F into a Taylor's series around some approximate value x^0 for x and truncating after the second (linear) term

$$y=F(x^0)+\left.\frac{\partial F}{\partial x}\right|_{x^0}\Delta x \tag{3.23}$$

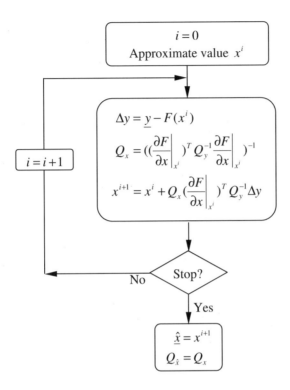

Figure 3.2: Least squares iteration.

where the n-vector Δx is defined as $\Delta x = x - x^0$ and $\partial F / \partial x$ constitutes an $m{\times}n$ matrix, comparable to the design matrix A of the linear model (3.16). Introducing $\Delta y = y - F(x^0)$ and denoting $\partial F / \partial x$ by A we can now write for the linearized measurement model

$$E\{\Delta \underline{y}\} = A\Delta x \quad D\{\Delta \underline{y}\} = Q_y \tag{3.24}$$

Example 3.1
The GPS pseudo-range *PR* can be considered as the sum of the geometric range *R* between receiver and satellite and the procduct of the speed of light *c* and the receiver clock bias $\delta_r t$. Expressed in receiver and satellite coordinates, denoted (X_r, Y_r, Z_r) and (X^s, Y^s, Z^s), respectively, the non-linear observation equation reads

$$PR = \sqrt{(X_r - X^s)^2 + (Y_r - Y^s)^2 + (Z_r - Z^s)^2} + c\delta_r t$$

The satellite coordinates can be assumed known from the navigation message transmitted by the satellites. Denoting the approximate value of the receiver coordinates by (X_r^0, Y_r^0, Z_r^0), the linearised observation equation becomes

$$\Delta PR = PR - (R^0 + c\delta_r t^0) = \frac{X_r - X^s}{R^0}\Delta X_r + \frac{Y_r - Y^s}{R^0}\Delta Y_r + \frac{Z_r - Z^s}{R^0}\Delta Z_r + c\Delta\delta_r t$$

where R^0 and $\delta_r t^0$ are the approximate values of the geometric distance and receiver clock bias.

The solution for Δx, $\Delta\hat{x}$, follows from (3.17) and $\hat{x}$ as $\hat{x} = x^0 + \Delta\hat{x}$. If x^0 is sufficiently close to x, then $\hat{x}$ will be the final solution. However, if this is not the case, an iteration process is required. After each iteration, the estimator $\hat{x}$ is used as the initial value for the next iteration. The procedure is repeated until the difference between subsequent solutions becomes negligible, i.e., if $\|\Delta\hat{x}\|$ becomes negligible. The iteration process is shown schematically in Figure 3.2.

For most practical applications nowadays, the model of observation equations is used to solve for the unknown parameters as it is easy to implement in software. The *model of condition equations* is a function of the observations only; the unknown parameters have been eliminated. If the number of observations m is greater than the number of unknown parameters n, there is a redundancy of m-n, since n observations in general would have been enough to solve for the m unknown parameters. The redundancy is equal to the number of conditions that can be imposed upon the observations. Geometrically this corresponds to a set of m-n m-vectors b_i that are orthogonal to the range space $R(A)$. In other words

$$b_i^T A = 0 \quad i = 1, \ldots, m-n \tag{3.25}$$

or, after introduction of the $m \times (m\text{-}n)$ matrix $B = (b_1 \ldots b_{m-n})$

$$B^T A = 0 \tag{3.26}$$

where the rank of B is m-n.
Premultiplication of (3.16) by B^T results in the model of condition equations

$$B^T E\{\underline{y}\} = 0 \quad D\{\underline{y}\} = Q_y \tag{3.27}$$

It can be shown that

$$P_A = A(A^T Q_y^{-1} A)^{-1} A^T Q_y^{-1} = I - Q_y B(B^T Q_y B)^{-1} B^T = P_{QB}^{\perp} \tag{3.28}$$

Together with (3.18), it follows that

$$\hat{\underline{y}} = P_{QB}^{\perp} \underline{y} \tag{3.29}$$

The covariance matrix $Q_{\hat{y}}$ is obtained from applying the covariance law to (3.29) as

$$Q_{\hat{y}} = P_{QB}^{\perp} Q_y (P_{QB}^{\perp})^T = P_{QB}^{\perp} Q_y \tag{3.30}$$

From (3.19), (3.22), (3.29) and (3.30) we may derive that

$$\hat{\underline{e}} = P_{QB} \underline{y} \tag{3.31}$$

and

$$Q_{\hat{e}} = P_{QB} Q_y P_{QB}^T = P_{QB} Q_y \tag{3.32}$$

Example 3.2
Assume the same position has been observed twice. The observation model reads

$$E\left\{\begin{pmatrix} \underline{X}_1 \\ \underline{Y}_1 \\ \underline{Z}_1 \\ \underline{X}_2 \\ \underline{Y}_2 \\ \underline{Z}_2 \end{pmatrix}\right\} = \begin{pmatrix} 1 & 0 & 0 \\ 0 & 1 & 0 \\ 0 & 0 & 1 \\ 1 & 0 & 0 \\ 0 & 1 & 0 \\ 0 & 0 & 1 \end{pmatrix} \begin{pmatrix} X \\ Y \\ Z \end{pmatrix}$$

The redundancy in this model is 6-3=3, so there are three conditions that can be set up. Since both measured positions should be the same, their difference should be zero. The condition equations therefore could read

$$\begin{pmatrix} 1 & 0 & 0 & -1 & 0 & 0 \\ 0 & 1 & 0 & 0 & -1 & 0 \\ 0 & 0 & 1 & 0 & 0 & -1 \end{pmatrix} E\left\{\begin{pmatrix} \underline{X}_1 \\ \underline{Y}_1 \\ \underline{Z}_1 \\ \underline{X}_2 \\ \underline{Y}_2 \\ \underline{Z}_2 \end{pmatrix}\right\} = \begin{pmatrix} 0 \\ 0 \\ 0 \end{pmatrix}$$

Note that this choice is not unique, linear combinations of the rows of the matrix on the left-hand side provide equally valid conditions.

The condition equations can also be set up for the non-linear case, i.e., for the case that

$$G^T(E\{\underline{y}\}) = 0 \qquad (3.33)$$

Substituting $E\{\underline{y}\} = F(x)$ yields

$$G^T(F(x)) = 0 \qquad (3.34)$$

Taking the partial derivatives with respect to x gives

$$\frac{\partial G^T}{\partial x} = \frac{\partial G^T}{\partial y}\frac{\partial y}{\partial x} = \frac{\partial G^T}{\partial y}\bigg|_{y^0}\frac{\partial F}{\partial x}\bigg|_{x^0} = 0 \qquad (3.35)$$

with $y^0 = F(x^0)$. Premultiplication of (3.24) with $\partial G^T / \partial y = B^T$ finally gives the linearised model of condition equations

$$B^T E\{\Delta \underline{y}\} = 0 \quad D\{\underline{y}\} = Q_y \qquad (3.36)$$

3.2   Quality control

Hydrographers and surveyors have always been interested not only in estimating positions or other parameters, but also in the associated quality control aspects. The quality of an estimated set of parameters consists, amongst others, of precision and reliability. Precision, as described by the covariance matrix, expresses the estimated parameters' characteristics in propagating random errors. Often only the diagonal elements of this matrix are considered, since they describe the variances of the unknown parameters. However, such an approach does not take into account the correlation that exists between the parameters. Sometimes an even further simplification is made. If the observations all have the same variance σ^2, then the covariance matrix of the estimated parameters (3.20) can be written as

$$Q_{\hat{x}} = \sigma^2 (A^T A)^{-1} \qquad (3.37)$$

The Dilution of Precision (DOP) is defined as

$$\text{DOP} = \sqrt{\sum_{i=1}^{m}(A^T A)_{ii}^{-1}} \qquad (3.38)$$

where the subscripts refer to the diagonal elements of the matrix $(A^T A)^{-1}$. In (3.38), all parameters are involved, but often only a subset of parameters is considered as well, see the example below. The DOP values indicate the influence of the geometry (through the design matrix A) on the precision of the parameters to be estimated.

Example 3.3

For GPS positioning using pseudo ranges, parameters to be estimated consist of receiver coordinates (φ, λ, h) and the product of the speed of light c and the receiver clock bias $\delta_r t$. Some of the most commonly used DOP parameters are

GDOP (Geometric DOP): $\quad \text{GDOP} = \sqrt{\sigma_\varphi^2 + \sigma_\lambda^2 + \sigma_h^2 + \sigma_{c\delta_r t}^2} / \sigma$

PDOP (Position DOP): $\quad \text{PDOP} = \sqrt{\sigma_\varphi^2 + \sigma_\lambda^2 + \sigma_h^2} / \sigma$

HDOP (Horizontal DOP): $\quad \text{HDOP} = \sqrt{\sigma_\varphi^2 + \sigma_\lambda^2} / \sigma$

VDOP (Vertical DOP): $\quad \text{VDOP} = \sigma_h / \sigma$

TDOP (Time DOP): $\quad \text{TDOP} = \sigma_{c\delta_r t} / \sigma$

For a station, located in the central part of the Netherlands (latitude 52°, longitude 6°), the DOP values on January 12, 2002, at noon (GPS time) were

GDOP	2.04
PDOP	1.80
HDOP	0.90
VDOP	1.56
TDOP	0.96

Although modern satellite-based positioning systems, like GPS, provide positions in three dimensions, at sea one often is still mainly interested in horizontal (2D) positions and their corresponding precision. The area within which an estimated 2D position is likely to be is called *error ellipse* or *confidence region*. Let the covariance matrix Q of the horizontal position (x, y) be given by

$$Q = \begin{pmatrix} \sigma_x^2 & \sigma_{xy} \\ \sigma_{xy} & \sigma_y^2 \end{pmatrix}$$

then the semi-major axis a, the semi-minor axis b and the orientation angle γ (the angle between semi-major axis and horizontal coordinate axis) of the standard error ellipse follow from

$$a^2 = \lambda_{max}^2 = \tfrac{1}{2}(\sigma_x^2 + \sigma_y^2) + \sqrt{\tfrac{1}{4}(\sigma_x^2 - \sigma_y^2)^2 + \sigma_{xy}^2}$$

$$b^2 = \lambda_{min}^2 = \tfrac{1}{2}(\sigma_x^2 + \sigma_y^2) - \sqrt{\tfrac{1}{4}(\sigma_x^2 + \sigma_y^2)^2 - \sigma_{xy}^2} \qquad (3.39)$$

$$\tan 2\gamma = \frac{2\sigma_{xy}}{\sigma_x^2 - \sigma_Y^2}$$

where λ_{max} and λ_{min} are the largest and smallest eigenvalues of Q, respectively. The probability that the horizontal position is within the standard error ellipse is 39.9%.
Instead of the error ellipse, which is defined by three parameters, in practice it is easier to use scalar quantities. The *Distance Root Mean Squared* (DRMS) is a single number which expresses 2D precision. It is defined as

$$\text{DRMS} = \sqrt{\sigma_x^2 + \sigma_y^2} \qquad (3.40)$$

DRMS is also known as *Mean Squared Position Error* (MSPE), *radial error* or *Root Sum Squared* (RSS). The probability of being within the circle with radius DRMS varies depending on the ratio between σ_x and σ_y. If both are the same, the probability is 63.2%, if their ratio is equal to 10, it is 68.2%. In practice, often 2DRMS (2×DRMS) is used, which corresponds to a probability between 95.4 and 98.2%
The *Circular Error Probable* (CEP) is the radius of the 50% probability circle and is defined as

$$\text{CEP} \approx 0.589 \cdot (\sigma_x + \sigma_y) \qquad (3.41)$$

This expression is valid for the range $0.2 \le \sigma_x / \sigma_y \le 1$, where it is assumed that $\sigma_x \le \sigma_y$.
In three dimensions, the standard error ellipse becomes an ellipsoid, with axes given by the three eigenvalues of the 3×3 covariance matrix. For the three dimensional case, the probability that the position is within the standard error ellipsoid is 19.9%. Expanding the axes by a common scale factor results in an increased probability. For two and three dimensions, some scale factors and probabilities are given in Table 3.1. The *Mean Radial Square Error* (MRSE) is a single number which expresses 3D

Table 3.1: 2D and 3D scale factors.

2D		3D	
Probability level [%]	Scale factor	Probability level [%]	Scale factor
39.4	1.000	19.9	1.000
50	1.177	50	1.538
90	2.146	90	2.500
95	2.447	95	2.700
99	3.035	99	3.368

precision and is defined as

$$\text{MRSE} \approx \sqrt{\sigma_x^2 + \sigma_y^2 + \sigma_z^2} \tag{3.42}$$

where x, y, z are the three components of position. The probability of being in the sphere with radius MRSE is 61%. *Spherical Error Probable* (SEP) is the 3D equivalent of the 2D CEP. It is the so called 50% probability sphere, defined as

$$\text{CEP} \approx 0.51 \cdot (\sigma_x + \sigma_y + \sigma_z) \tag{3.43}$$

Internal reliability describes the ability of the redundant observations to detect and identify specific model errors. *External reliability* expresses the influence of undetected model errors on the parameters of interest, i.e., coordinates.

The *null hypothesis* H_0 describes the case model errors are absent. The *alternative hypothesis* H_a considered here assumes there are one or more biases in the observations. These two hypotheses are defined as

$$H_0 : E\{\underline{y}\} = Ax \qquad\qquad D\{\underline{y}\} = Q_y \tag{3.44}$$

$$H_a : E\{\underline{y}\} = Ax + C\nabla \qquad D\{\underline{y}\} = Q_y \tag{3.45}$$

where C is a known $m \times b$-matrix, which specifies the type of model errors, and ∇ a b-vector containing the bias parameters. Note that $b \leq m - n$. The least squares solution to (3.44) under the null hypothesis and its covariance matrix are given by (3.17) and (3.20).

Testing H_0 against H_a consists of three steps
1. *Detection*: An overall model test is performed to find out if unspecified model errors have occurred.
2. *Identification*: If model errors are detected, their potential sources are identified by testing the original or nominal observation model (3.44) against models extended with bias parameters, such as (3.45).
3. *Adaptation*: After the identification of the most likely source of the model error, the observation model is adapted to eliminate the influence of biases in the parameter vector.

In the detection step the test statistic for testing H_0 against H_a is given as

$$T = \frac{\hat{\underline{e}}^T Q_y^{-1} \hat{\underline{e}}}{m - n} \tag{3.46}$$

The above test statistic T will be referred to as *overall model test statistic*. Under H_0 and H_a, T has the F distribution

$$H_0 : T \sim F(m-n,\infty,0)$$
$$H_a : T \sim F(m-n,\infty,\lambda)$$

(3.47)

where λ is the *non-centrality parameter*.

Once biases have been detected, i.e., if the test statistic T exceeds a threshold, the sources of the possible errors have to be found in the identification step. In practice this is accomplished by testing a number of alternative hypotheses, each describing one model error at a time. The matrix C in (3.45) then reduces to an m-vector c.

In the identification step, the uniformly most powerful test statistic for testing H_0 against H_a is given as

$$t = \frac{c^T Q_y^{-1} \hat{e}}{\sqrt{c^T Q_y^{-1} P_A^\perp c}}$$

(3.48)

Expression (3.48) is known as the *slippage test statistic*. Under H_0 and H_a, the slippage test statistic is normally distributed

$$H_0 : t \sim N(0,1)$$
$$H_a : t \sim N(\sqrt{c^T Q_y^{-1} P_A^\perp c}\nabla,1)$$

(3.49)

The practical procedure to identify model errors is to determine the largest slippage test statistic (in absolute value), remove the corresponding observation and perform another least squares adjustment until the overall model test statistic is accepted. Once the largest slippage test statistic has been found, its likelihood needs to be tested. The likelihood of the identified model error can be tested by comparing the test statistic with the critical value $N_{0.5\alpha_0}(0,1)$, where α_0 is the level of significance.

If the largest slippage test statistic in each cycle exceeds the critical value, i.e., if

$$|t| > N_{0.5\alpha_0}(0,1)$$

(3.50)

then it is likely that a model error has been identified. If not, one should extend the set of alternative hypotheses to consider.

For the adaptation step, several alternatives exist. One way to adapt would be to simply discard the bad observations (as already done, actually, in the iterated identification step), another to extend the vector of unknowns by one or more additional parameters. This means that the columns of the matrix C of (3.45) consist of the c-vectors, corresponding to the identified alternative hypotheses and that the new measurement model under the null hypothesis becomes in fact model (3.45)

The non-centrality parameter λ is defined as

$$\lambda = \nabla^2 c^T Q_y^{-1} P_A^\perp c \tag{3.51}$$

This parameter can be computed once reference values are chosen for the level of significance α_0 (the probability of an error of the first kind, i.e., rejecting H_0 falsely), the detection power γ_0 (the probability of rejecting H_0 when H_a is true) and the number of degrees of freedom $b=m-n$. Statistical testing is based on the B-method, developed at Delft University of Technology. The B-method assumes that an error related to the non-centrality parameter $\lambda_0 = \lambda(\alpha_0, \gamma_0, 1)$ is detected with equal probability, i.e., γ_0, by all tests. In other words from $\lambda_0 = \lambda(\alpha_0, \gamma_0, 1) = \lambda(\alpha, \gamma_0, b)$, with $b>1$, the level of significance α can be computed. This implies that a certain model error can be found with the same probability by both the overall and the slippage test. A consequence of this coupling is that α increases when the redundancy increases. As a result, α may become so large that the null hypothesis is rejected too often.

Once the parameter $\lambda_0 = \lambda(\alpha_0, \gamma_0, 1)$ is known, the corresponding size of the bias that can just be detected follows from (3.51) as

$$|\nabla| = \sqrt{\frac{\lambda_0}{c^T Q_y^{-1} P_A^\perp c}} \tag{3.52}$$

This is the *Minimal Detectable Bias* (MDB). For most practical applications, $\alpha_0 = 0.001$ and $\gamma_0 = 0.80$, resulting in a non-centrality parameter $\lambda_0 = 17.05$. As can be seen from (3.52), the MDB not only depends on α_0 and γ_0, but also on the functional and stochastic model, through the design matrix A and the covariance matrix Q_y, and the alternative hypothesis considered, represented by the vector c. The alternative hypotheses may for example consist of outliers and cycle slips in GPS code and carrier observations, respectively.

The MDB is said to describe the internal reliability of a system. External reliability is defined as the influence of a bias with size equal to the MDB on the estimated parameters

$$\nabla \hat{x} = (A^T Q_y^{-1} A)^{-1} A^T Q_y^{-1} c \nabla \tag{3.53}$$

Since $\nabla \hat{x}$ is a vector and each alternative hypothesis results in such a vector, external reliability as described by (3.53) is in general hard to interpret. There are two alternatives, which allow for an easier interpretation. One is to consider only the largest (in absolute value) element of the vector $\nabla \hat{x}$. This maximum is sometimes referred to as *Minimal Detectable Effect* (MDE). The second alternative is the scalar quantity

$$\lambda_x = \sqrt{\nabla \hat{x}^T Q_{\hat{x}}^{-1} \nabla \hat{x}} \qquad (3.54)$$

This is the *Bias to Noise Ratio* (BNR). It is a dimensionless quantity and a measure for the influence of biases in the observations on the estimated parameters.

Expression (3.54) applies to the entire parameter vector. Usually one is only interested in the influence of biases on a set of linear(-ized) functions of the state vector. For example, in precise relative GPS positioning, estimated parameters consist of coordinates, clock biases and carrier ambiguities, but the parameters of interest are just the coordinates or even one coordinate in particular, such as height. Assuming these linear(-ized) functions are collected in the $r \times n$ matrix F^T, expression (3.54) becomes

$$\lambda_x = \sqrt{(F^T \nabla \hat{x})^T (F^T Q_{\hat{x}} F)^{-1} (F^T \nabla \hat{x})} \qquad (3.55)$$

Finally, it should be noted that for the computation of MDB's and BNR's, no actual data is required. They can already be computed in the design or planning stage of a survey and are important diagnostic tools to infer the strength with which observation models can be validated.

Example 3.4

Consider again the location and observation epoch of Example 3.3. Choosing a level of significance α_0 of 0.1% and a power of test γ_0 of 80%, results in a non-centrality parameter λ_0 of 17.05. The standard deviation of the pseudo range observations was

Satellite	MDB [m]	BNR [-]	MDE [m]
4	19.3	5.0	4.2
5	15.3	3.0	8.3
6	15.0	2.9	8.9
9	24.9	7.3	21.6
14	15.0	2.9	6.9
24	14.9	2.8	3.2
25	17.0	3.9	7.0
29	14.8	2.8	7.9
30	18.3	4.5	15.9

Reliability parameters (left) and satellite distribution for the satellites, visible in the central part of the Netherlands on 12 January 2002 at noon (GPS time).

chosen to be one meter. Forming a linear combination of observations to eliminate the ionosphere results in an observation precision of about three meters. The reliability parameters for the visible satellites (above a cut-off elevation of 10°) are shown in the table above. In addition, the distribution of the satellites in the sky is visualized as well.

3.3 Recursive estimation

Consider the partitioned measurement model

$$E\{\begin{pmatrix} \underline{y}_1 \\ \vdots \\ \underline{y}_{k-1} \end{pmatrix}\} = \begin{pmatrix} A_1 \\ \vdots \\ A_{k-1} \end{pmatrix} x \qquad D\{\begin{pmatrix} \underline{y}_1 \\ \vdots \\ \underline{y}_{k-1} \end{pmatrix}\} = \begin{pmatrix} Q_1 & & \\ & \ddots & \\ & & Q_{k-1} \end{pmatrix} \qquad (3.56)$$

where the subscripts could, e.g., indicate the epochs the observations became available. Note that the observation vectors $\underline{y}_i$ are mutually uncorrelated. The least squares solution to this model is given by

$$\hat{\underline{x}}_{(k-1)} = (\sum_{i=1}^{k-1} A_i^T Q_i^{-1} A_i)^{-1} \sum_{i=1}^{k-1} A_i^T Q_i^{-1} \underline{y}_i \qquad (3.57)$$

and its corresponding covariance matrix

$$Q_{\hat{x}_{(k-1)}} = (\sum_{i=1}^{k-1} A_i^T Q_i^{-1} A_i)^{-1} \qquad (3.58)$$

In the above expressions the notation $\hat{\underline{x}}_{(k-1)}$ means that the parameters have been estimated using the observations up to and including epoch k-1.
If observations at epoch k become available, model (3.56) becomes

$$E\{\begin{pmatrix} \underline{y}_1 \\ \vdots \\ \underline{y}_{k-1} \\ \underline{y}_k \end{pmatrix}\} = \begin{pmatrix} A_1 \\ \vdots \\ A_{k-1} \\ A_k \end{pmatrix} x \qquad D\{\begin{pmatrix} \underline{y}_1 \\ \vdots \\ \underline{y}_{k-1} \\ \underline{y}_k \end{pmatrix}\} = \begin{pmatrix} Q_1 & & & \\ & \ddots & & \\ & & Q_{k-1} & \\ & & & Q_k \end{pmatrix} \qquad (3.59)$$

and its solution with corresponding covariance matrix

$$\hat{\underline{x}}_{(k)} = (\sum_{i=1}^{k-1} A_i^T Q_i^{-1} A_i + A_k^T Q_k^{-1} A_k)^{-1} (\sum_{i=1}^{k-1} A_i^T Q_i^{-1} \underline{y}_i + A_k^T Q_k^{-1} \underline{y}_k) \qquad (3.60)$$

$$Q_{\hat{x}_{(k)}} = (\sum_{i=1}^{k-1} A_i^T Q_i^{-1} A_i + A_k^T Q_k^{-1} A_k)^{-1} \tag{3.61}$$

Using (3.57) and (3.58), expressions (3.60) and (3.61) can be rewritten as

$$\hat{\underline{x}}_{(k)} = (Q_{\hat{x}_{(k-1)}}^{-1} + A_k^T Q_k^{-1} A_k)^{-1} (Q_{\hat{x}_{(k-1)}}^{-1} \hat{\underline{x}}_{(k-1)} + A_k^T Q_k \underline{y}_k) \tag{3.62}$$

$$Q_{\hat{x}_{(k)}} = (Q_{\hat{x}_{(k-1)}}^{-1} + A_k^T Q_k^{-1} A_k)^{-1} \tag{3.63}$$

But (3.62) and (3.63) can be considered the least squares solution of the measurement model

$$E\left\{ \begin{pmatrix} \hat{\underline{x}}_{(k-1)} \\ \underline{y}_k \end{pmatrix} \right\} = \begin{pmatrix} I \\ A_k \end{pmatrix} x \qquad D\left\{ \begin{pmatrix} \hat{\underline{x}}_{(k-1)} \\ \underline{y}_k \end{pmatrix} \right\} = \begin{pmatrix} Q_{\hat{x}_{(k-1)}} & 0 \\ 0 & Q_k \end{pmatrix} \tag{3.64}$$

We may therefore conclude that (3.59) and (3.64) are completeley equivalent. The advantage of (3.64) over (3.59) is that it is not necessary to store all observations from epochs 1…k-1 to compute an updated solution when the observations $\underline{y}_k$ become available. Instead, only the solution $\hat{\underline{x}}_{(k-1)}$ and its covariance matrix need to be stored. Since the dimension of the parameter vector is usually much smaller than the total number of observations, this saves a considerable amount of space. Another aspect is that the computational load is distributed, which is especially important for real-time applications.

Thus, the essence of *recursive estimation* is that in order to compute $\hat{\underline{x}}_{(k)}$ only $\hat{\underline{x}}_{(k-1)}$, $\underline{y}_k$ and their corresponding covariance matrices are required. The recursive estimation is initialized using the standard least squares solution for the estimator $\hat{\underline{x}}_{(1)}$

$$\hat{\underline{x}}_{(1)} = (A_1^T Q_1^{-1} A_1)^{-1} A_1^T Q_1^{-1} \underline{y}_1 \qquad Q_{\hat{x}_{(1)}} = (A_1^T Q_1^{-1} A_1)^{-1} \tag{3.65}$$

From (3.61) it follows that

$$Q_{\hat{x}_{(k-1)}}^{-1} = Q_{\hat{x}_{(k)}}^{-1} - A_k^T Q_k^{-1} A_k \tag{3.66}$$

Substitution into (3.62) results in an expression for the recursive estimation that is more commonly used

$$\hat{\underline{x}}_{(k)} = \hat{\underline{x}}_{(k-1)} + Q_{\hat{x}_{(k)}} A_k^T Q_k^{-1} (\underline{y}_k - A_k^T \hat{\underline{x}}_{(k-1)}) \tag{3.67}$$

Equations (3.67) (or (3.62)) and (3.63) are known as *measurement update* and *covariance update*, respectively, although the measurement update often also comprises both the actual measurement update and the covariance update.

Defining the *predicted residuals* $\underline{v}_k$ as

$$\underline{v}_k = \underline{y}_k - A_k^T \hat{\underline{x}}_{(k-1)} = (- A_k^T \quad I)\begin{pmatrix} \hat{\underline{x}}_{(k-1)} \\ \underline{y}_k \end{pmatrix} \tag{3.68}$$

and the gain matrix K_k as

$$K_k = Q_{\hat{x}_{(k)}} A_k^T Q_k^{-1} \tag{3.69}$$

the measurement update can be written in a more compact form as

$$\hat{\underline{x}}_{(k)} = \hat{\underline{x}}_{(k-1)} + K_k \underline{v}_k \tag{3.70}$$

Note that the predicted residuals (3.68) should not be confused with the least squares residuals (3.10), which, for epoch k are given by

$$\hat{\underline{e}}_k = \underline{y}_k - A_k^T \hat{\underline{x}}_{(k)} \tag{3.71}$$

The covariance matrix of the predicted residuals follows from applying the covariance law and reads

$$Q_{v_k} = Q_k + A_k Q_{\hat{x}_{(k-1)}} A_k^T \tag{3.72}$$

From (3.69) we may conclude that the gain matrix is small if the precision of the estimator $\hat{\underline{x}}_{(k-1)}$ is high or the precisions of the observations $\underline{y}_k$ is poor. On the other hand, the influence of these observations will be large if their precision is high.

Model (3.64) in terms of condition equations can be written as

$$(- A_k \quad I)E\{\begin{pmatrix} \hat{\underline{x}}_{(k-1)} \\ \underline{y}_k \end{pmatrix}\} = 0 \qquad D\{\begin{pmatrix} \hat{\underline{x}}_{(k-1)} \\ \underline{y}_k \end{pmatrix}\} = \begin{pmatrix} Q_{\hat{x}_{(k-1)}} & 0 \\ 0 & Q_k \end{pmatrix} \tag{3.73}$$

The solution of this system follows from straightforward application of (3.29) and is given by

$$\begin{pmatrix} \hat{\hat{x}}_{(k-1)} \\ \hat{y}_k \end{pmatrix} = \begin{pmatrix} \hat{x}_{(k-1)} \\ y_k \end{pmatrix} + \begin{pmatrix} Q_{\hat{x}_{(k-1)}} A_k^T Q_{v_k}^{-1} v_k \\ -Q_k Q_{v_k}^{-1} v_k \end{pmatrix}$$ (3.74)

This expression shows that the relationship between the least squares and predicted residuals is given by

$$\hat{e}_k = y_k - \hat{y}_k = Q_k Q_{v_k}^{-1} v_k$$ (3.75)

The expression for $\hat{\hat{x}}_{(k-1)}$ in (3.74) has a similar structure as (3.67). If it can be shown that $Q_{\hat{x}_{(k-1)}} A_k^T Q_{v_k}^{-1}$ is the same as the gain matrix (3.69), then $\hat{\hat{x}}_{(k-1)} = \hat{x}_{(k)}$. This is done as follows: substituting (3.72) into (3.74) and (3.63) into (3.69), we get

$$Q_{\hat{x}_{(k-1)}} A_k^T (Q_k + A_k Q_{\hat{x}_{(k-1)}} A_k^T)^{-1} \overset{?}{=} (Q_{\hat{x}_{(k-1)}}^{-1} + A_k^T Q_k^{-1} A_k)^{-1} A_k^T Q_k^{-1} \Leftrightarrow$$

$$(Q_{\hat{x}_{(k-1)}}^{-1} + A_k^T Q_k^{-1} A_k) Q_{\hat{x}_{(k-1)}} A_k^T \overset{?}{=} A_k^T Q_k^{-1} (Q_k + A_k Q_{\hat{x}_{(k-1)}} A_k^T) \Leftrightarrow$$ (3.76)

$$A_k^T + A_k^T Q_k^{-1} A_k Q_{\hat{x}_{(k-1)}} A_k^T = A_k^T + A_k^T Q_k^{-1} A_k Q_{\hat{x}_{(k-1)}} A_k^T)$$

from which we may conclude that

$$\hat{x}_{(k)} = \hat{x}_{(k-1)} + Q_{\hat{x}_{(k-1)}} A_k^T Q_{v_k}^{-1} v_k$$ (3.77)

Defining the gain matrix for this model as

$$K_k = Q_{\hat{x}_{(k-1)}} A_k^T Q_{v_k}^{-1}$$ (3.78)

the covariance matrix of $\hat{x}_{(k)}$ follows with (3.30) as

$$Q_{\hat{x}_{(k)}} = (I - K_k A_k) Q_{\hat{x}_{(k-1)}}$$ (3.79)

The major difference between (3.77) and (3.79) on the one hand and (3.67) and (3.63) on the other is the number of matrix inversions that is required: for (3.77) and (3.79) we need only one inversion, whereas for (3.67) and (3.63) we need three. The single matrix inversion even reduces to a simple scalar division in case the number of observations at an epoch is one.

The above models deal with parameters that remain constant from one epoch to the next. For time dependent parameters, such as the position of a moving platform, the measurement model would be of the form

$$E\left\{\begin{pmatrix} \underline{y}_1 \\ \vdots \\ \underline{y}_{k-1} \end{pmatrix}\right\} = \begin{pmatrix} A_1 & & \\ & \ddots & \\ & & A_{k-1} \end{pmatrix}\begin{pmatrix} x_1 \\ \vdots \\ x_{k-1} \end{pmatrix} \qquad D\left\{\begin{pmatrix} \underline{y}_1 \\ \vdots \\ \underline{y}_{k-1} \end{pmatrix}\right\} = \begin{pmatrix} Q_1 & & \\ & \ddots & \\ & & Q_{k-1} \end{pmatrix} \qquad (3.80)$$

Since there is no relationship between the parameters at consecutive epochs, the best that can be done is separately solve each system

$$E\{\underline{y}_i\} = A_i x_i \qquad\qquad D\{\underline{y}_i\} = Q_i \qquad i = 1,\ldots,k-1 \qquad (3.81)$$

Compared to the recursive estimation procedure discussed above, the precision of the parameters, reflected in their covariance matrix, will not improve as time proceeds. Often, however, parameters do not change arbitrarily from one epoch to the next. The relationship between parameters at times t and t_0 will be described by the *transition model*

$$x_t = \Phi_{t,0} x_0 \qquad\qquad (3.82)$$

where the known $n{\times}n$-matrix Φ is the *transition matrix*. With the transition model it is possible to compute the values of the state vector x at any time t, i.e., not only at the times of observation. The transition matrix has the following properties

$$\Phi_{t,t} = I \qquad\qquad\qquad \text{Initial value}$$

$$\Phi_{t,t_0}^{-1} = \Phi_{t_0,t} \qquad\qquad \text{Inverse property}$$

$$\Phi_{t,t_0} = \Phi_{t,t_1}\Phi_{t_1,t_0} \qquad \text{Transition property}$$

Example 3.5
Consider the model

$$\begin{pmatrix} x(t) \\ \dot{x}(t) \end{pmatrix} = \begin{pmatrix} 1 & t-t_0 \\ 0 & 1 \end{pmatrix}\begin{pmatrix} x(t_0) \\ \dot{x}(t_0) \end{pmatrix}$$

The 2×2 matrix on the right-hand side is a valid transition matrix, since all three conditions are fulfilled:

$$\Phi(t_0,t_0) = \begin{pmatrix} 1 & t_0 - t_0 \\ 0 & 1 \end{pmatrix} = \begin{pmatrix} 1 & 0 \\ 0 & 1 \end{pmatrix} = I$$

$$\Phi(t,t_0)^{-1} = \begin{pmatrix} 1 & t - t_0 \\ 0 & 1 \end{pmatrix}^{-1} = \begin{pmatrix} 1 & t_0 - t \\ 0 & 1 \end{pmatrix} = \Phi(t_0,t)$$

$$\Phi(t,t_1)\Phi(t_1,t_0) = \begin{pmatrix} 1 & t - t_1 \\ 0 & 1 \end{pmatrix}\begin{pmatrix} 1 & t_1 - t_0 \\ 0 & 1 \end{pmatrix} = \begin{pmatrix} 1 & t - t_0 \\ 0 & 1 \end{pmatrix} = \Phi(t,t_0)$$

Assume that for the unknown parameters in (3.80) a transition model (3.82) is available. Expressing the parameters in terms of x_{k-1}, i.e.

$$x_i = \Phi_{i,k-1} x_{k-1} \tag{3.83}$$

and substituting into (3.80) yields

$$E\left\{ \begin{pmatrix} \underline{y}_1 \\ \vdots \\ \underline{y}_{k-1} \end{pmatrix} \right\} = \begin{pmatrix} A_1 \Phi_{1,k-1} \\ \vdots \\ A_{k-1} \end{pmatrix} x_{k-1} \qquad D\left\{ \begin{pmatrix} \underline{y}_1 \\ \vdots \\ \underline{y}_{k-1} \end{pmatrix} \right\} = \begin{pmatrix} Q_1 & & \\ & \ddots & \\ & & Q_{k-1} \end{pmatrix} \tag{3.84}$$

The solution up to and including epoch k-1 is denoted by $\hat{\underline{x}}_{k-1|k-1}$, the corresponding covariance matrix by $Q_{\hat{x}_{k-1|k-1}}$. The first part of the subscript indicates that the solution applies to epoch k-1, the second that all observations until epoch k-1 were used to compute the solution.
The solution at epoch k can be *predicted* as

$$\hat{\underline{x}}_{k|k-1} = \Phi_{k,k-1} \hat{\underline{x}}_{k-1|k-1} \qquad Q_{\hat{x}_{k|k-1}} = \Phi_{k,k-1} Q_{\hat{x}_{k-1|k-1}} \Phi_{k,k-1}^T \tag{3.85}$$

This prediction is known as *time update*. If also observations are available at time k, we can set up the observation model

$$E\left\{ \begin{pmatrix} \hat{\underline{x}}_{k|k-1} \\ \underline{y}_k \end{pmatrix} \right\} = \begin{pmatrix} I \\ A_k \end{pmatrix} x_k \qquad D\left\{ \begin{pmatrix} \hat{\underline{x}}_{k|k-1} \\ \underline{y}_k \end{pmatrix} \right\} = \begin{pmatrix} Q_{\hat{x}_{k|k-1}} & 0 \\ 0 & Q_k \end{pmatrix} \tag{3.86}$$

This model has the same structure as (3.64). Its solution, the measurement update, therefore reads (compare with (3.67) and (3.63))

$$\hat{\underline{x}}_{k|k} = \hat{\underline{x}}_{k|k-1} + K_k \underline{v}_k \tag{3.87}$$

$$Q_{\hat{x}_{k|k}} = (Q_{\hat{x}_{k|k-1}}^{-1} + A_k^T Q_k^{-1} A_k)^{-1} \tag{3.88}$$

with the predicted residuals $\underline{v}_k$ defined as

$$\underline{v}_k = \underline{y}_k - A_k^T \underline{\hat{x}}_{k|k-1} = \left(-A_k^T \quad I\right) \begin{pmatrix} \underline{\hat{x}}_{k|k-1} \\ \underline{y}_k \end{pmatrix} \tag{3.89}$$

and the gain matrix K_k as

$$K_k = Q_{\hat{x}_{k|k}} A_k^T Q_k^{-1} \tag{3.90}$$

Alternatively we may also write the gain matrix as

$$K_k = Q_{\hat{x}_{k|k-1}} A_k^T Q_{v_k}^{-1} \tag{3.91}$$

and the the covariance update as

$$Q_{\hat{x}_{k|k}} = (I - K_k A_k) Q_{\hat{x}_{k|k-1}} \tag{3.92}$$

Example 3.6

Consider a vehicle moving along a straight line. Assuming the coordinate function u has a continuous time derivative and that the position at time t_0 is known, the position at time t is given by

$$u(t) = u(t_0) + \int_{t_0}^{t} \dot{u}(\tau) d\tau \tag{3.93}$$

If the function $\dot{u}$ also has a continuous time derivative, we may write

$$\dot{u}(t) = \dot{u}(t_0) + \int_{t_0}^{t} \ddot{u}(\tau) d\tau \tag{3.94}$$

so that

$$u(t) = u(t_0) + \int_{t_0}^{t} \left(\dot{u}(t_0) + \int_{t_0}^{\tau} \ddot{u}(\rho) d\rho\right) d\tau$$
$$= u(t_0) + \dot{u}(t_0)(t - t_0) + \int_{t_0}^{t} \int_{t_0}^{\tau} \ddot{u}(\rho) d\rho d\tau \tag{3.95}$$

The double integral can be rewritten into a single one, using integration by parts, which for two functions f and g is defined as

$$\int_{t_0}^{t} \dot{f}(\tau)g(\tau)d\tau = [f(\tau)g(\tau)]_{t_0}^{t} - \int_{t_0}^{t} f(\tau)\dot{g}(\tau)d\tau \qquad (3.96)$$

For this particular case, we select

$$f(\tau) = \tau \qquad\qquad g(\tau) = \int_{t_0}^{\tau} \ddot{u}(\rho)d\rho$$

which, after substitution into (3.96) yields

$$\int_{t_0}^{t}\int_{t_0}^{\tau} \ddot{u}(\rho)d\rho d\tau = [\tau \int_{t_0}^{\tau} \ddot{u}(\rho)d\rho]_{t_0}^{t} - \int_{t_0}^{t} \tau\ddot{u}(\tau)d\tau$$

$$= \int_{t_0}^{t}(t-\tau)\ddot{u}(\tau)d\tau \qquad (3.97)$$

Substitution of (3.97) into (3.95) and combining with (3.94) finally results in

$$\begin{pmatrix} u(t) \\ \dot{u}(t) \end{pmatrix} = \begin{pmatrix} 1 & t-t_0 \\ 0 & 1 \end{pmatrix}\begin{pmatrix} u(t_0) \\ \dot{u}(t_0) \end{pmatrix} + \int_{t_0}^{t}\begin{pmatrix} t-\tau \\ 1 \end{pmatrix}\ddot{u}(\tau)d\tau$$

$$= \begin{pmatrix} 1 & t-t_0 \\ 0 & 1 \end{pmatrix}\begin{pmatrix} u(t_0) \\ \dot{u}(t_0) \end{pmatrix} + \int_{t_0}^{t}\begin{pmatrix} 1 & t-\tau \\ 0 & 1 \end{pmatrix}\begin{pmatrix} 0 \\ 1 \end{pmatrix}\ddot{u}(\tau)d\tau \qquad (3.98)$$

Ignoring for the time being the second term on the right-hand side, we recognize a transition model of the form (3.82).

Defining the state vector x_k as

$$x_k = \begin{pmatrix} u(t_k) \\ \dot{u}(t_k) \end{pmatrix} = \begin{pmatrix} u_k \\ \dot{u}_k \end{pmatrix}$$

the transition matrix $\Phi_{k,k-1}$ as

$$\Phi_{k,k-1} = \begin{pmatrix} 1 & t_k - t_{k-1} \\ 0 & 1 \end{pmatrix}$$

and the *disturbance vector* d_k as

$$d_k = \int_{t_{k-1}}^{t_k} \begin{pmatrix} 1 & t-\tau \\ 0 & 1 \end{pmatrix} \begin{pmatrix} 0 \\ 1 \end{pmatrix} \ddot{u}(\tau) d\tau = \int_{t_{k-1}}^{t_k} \Phi_{t_k,\tau} \begin{pmatrix} 0 \\ 1 \end{pmatrix} \ddot{u}(\tau) d\tau$$

results in

$$x_k = \Phi_{k,k-1} x_{k-1} + d_k \tag{3.99}$$

which is an extension of the original transition model (3.82)

If we assume that both the state vector x and the vector of disturbances d of Example 3.6 are stochastic quantities and that at time t_{k-1} the solution $\hat{\underline{x}}_{k-1|k-1}$ is available, we get

$$\hat{\underline{x}}_{k|k-1} = \Phi_{k,k-1} \hat{\underline{x}}_{k-1|k-1} + \underline{d}_k \tag{3.100}$$

We are now no longer dealing with a determinsitic transition model, but with a stochastic one, where the uncertainties in the transition model are captured in the covariance matrix Q_{d_k} of the disurbances. Assuming $\hat{\underline{x}}_{k-1|k-1}$ and $\underline{d}_k$ are uncorrelated, the covariance matrix of the predicted state vector $\hat{\underline{x}}_{k|k-1}$ is given by

$$Q_{\hat{x}_{k|k-1}} = \Phi_{k,k-1} Q_{\hat{x}_{k-1|k-1}} \Phi_{k,k-1}^T + Q_{d_k} \tag{3.101}$$

In most practical applications it is assumed that $\underline{d}_k$ is zero on the average, i.e., $E\{\underline{d}_k\} = 0$. The only difference with the time update (3.85) is then the additional covariance matrix of the disturbances Q_{d_k}. Thus, also for a non-deterministic transition model, the recursive expressions for time and measurement update apply equally well. The measurement update (3.67) and (3.63) or (3.77) and (3.79), together with the time update (3.100) and (3.101) are known together as the Kalman filter.

Example 3.7
Consider again the vehicle of Example 3.6. It can be shown that the covariance matrix of the disturbances is given by

$$\begin{aligned} Q_{d_k} &= q_{\ddot{u}} \int_{t_{k-1}}^{t_k} \Phi(t,\tau) \begin{pmatrix} 0 \\ 1 \end{pmatrix} (0 \quad 1) \Phi^T(t,\tau) d\tau \\ &= q_{\ddot{u}} \begin{pmatrix} \frac{1}{3}(t_k - t_{k-1})^3 & \frac{1}{2}(t_k - t_{k-1})^2 \\ \frac{1}{2}(t_k - t_{k-1})^2 & (t_k - t_{k-1}) \end{pmatrix} \end{aligned} \tag{3.102}$$

where q_{ii} is the spectral density, which for this example has the dimension m^2/s^3. In general, it has the dimension of a variance, multiplied by time. For higher order polynomials, the expression for the covariance matrix of the disturbances is derived in a similar way.

Example 3.8
The GPS geometry-free observation model is a very simple model that does not require any a priori knowledge on receiver and satellite positions and velocities, clock behaviour and tropospheric effects. For a single satellite, the simplified observation model for dual-frequency code (pseudo range) C and carrier observations ϕ at an epoch k, expressed in meters, reads

$$C_{1,k} = R_k + c\delta_r t_k + c\delta_s t_k + T_k + I_k$$
$$C_{2,k} = R_k + c\delta_r t_k + c\delta_s t_k + T_k + \gamma I_k$$
$$\phi_{1,k} = R_k + c\delta_r t_k + c\delta_s t_k + T_k - I_k + \lambda_1 N_1$$
$$\phi_{2,k} = R_k + c\delta_r t_k + c\delta_s t_k + T_k - \gamma I_k + \lambda_2 N_2$$

with R_k the distance between satellite and receiver, $\delta_r t_k$ and $\delta_s t_k$ the receiver and satellite clock bias, T_k the tropospheric effect, I_k the ionospheric effect, N_1 and N_2 the carrier cycle ambiguities for the GPS L1 and L2 frequency, c the speed of light, $\gamma = f_1^2 / f_2^2$, f_1 and f_2 the L1 and L2 frequencies, λ_1 and λ_2 the L1 and L2 wavelengths. All time dependent and frequency independent terms can be eliminated by simply subtracting one observation, e.g., the L1 code obervation C_1, from the remaining ones, resulting in

$$\begin{pmatrix} \phi_1 - C_1 \\ \phi_2 - C_1 \\ C_2 - C_1 \end{pmatrix}_k = \begin{pmatrix} -2I_k + \lambda_1 N_1 \\ (-1-\gamma)I_k + \lambda_2 N_1 \\ (-1+\gamma)I_k \end{pmatrix}$$

Introducing the transition model for the ionosphere

$$\begin{pmatrix} I \\ i \end{pmatrix}_k = \begin{pmatrix} 1 & t_k - t_{k-1} \\ 0 & 1 \end{pmatrix}\begin{pmatrix} I \\ i \end{pmatrix}_{k-1}$$

the measurement model becomes

$$\begin{pmatrix} \phi_1 - C_1 \\ \phi_2 - C_1 \\ C_2 - C_1 \end{pmatrix}_k = \begin{pmatrix} 0 & -2 & \lambda_1 & 0 \\ 0 & -1-\gamma & 0 & \lambda_2 \\ 0 & -1+\gamma & 0 & 0 \end{pmatrix}\begin{pmatrix} i_k \\ I_k \\ N_1 \\ N_2 \end{pmatrix}$$

The covariance matrix of the original observations is assumed to be a diagonal matrix

$$diag(\sigma_{C_1}^2,\sigma_{C_2}^2,\sigma_{\phi_1}^2,\sigma_{\phi_2}^2) = diag(0.8^2,0.8^2,0.005^2,0.005^2)$$

and the spectral density of the ionosphere

$$q_i = 10^{-8} \text{ m}^2/\text{s}$$

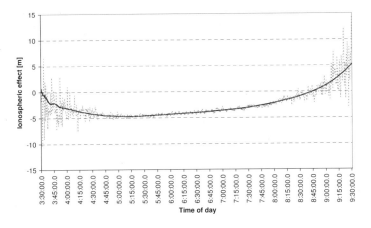

Computed (dotted line) and estimated ionospheric effects.

The figure above shows a time series of the computed (from a linear combination of pseudo range observations) and estimated ionospheric effects for a particular satellite. As can be seen from this figure, the estimated effects are much smoother than the computed ones. Both the estimated and the computed effects are partly negative, due to hardware biases, not taken into account in the simplified model.

3.4 Recursive quality control

The main difference with non-recursive least squares is that for recursive least squares the unknown parameters are updated whenever new observations become available. The null and alternative hypothesis for an epoch k are defined as

$$H_0 : E\{\underline{y}_k\} = A_k x_k \qquad\qquad D\{\underline{y}_k\} = Q_{y_k} \qquad\qquad (3.103)$$

$$H_a : E\{\underline{y}_k\} = A_k x_k + C_k \nabla_k \qquad\qquad D\{\underline{y}_k\} = Q_{y_k} \qquad\qquad (3.104)$$

where C_k now is a known $m_k \times b_k$-matrix, which specifies the type of model errors, and ∇_k a b_k-vector containing the bias parameters. Note that $b_k \leq m_k$ in this case: the redundancy at an epoch is equal to the number of observations.

In real-time situations a bias should in general be detected and identified at the epoch it occurs. In other words, we consider only *local* alternative hypotheses as opposed to global ones, which consider a number of (or even all) epochs before detecting and identifying the bias.

For the detection and identification step, the *Local Overall Model* (LOM) and *Local Slippage* (LS) test statistics are based on the filter's predicted residuals. The LOM test statistic is given by

$$T_k = \frac{\underline{v}_k^T Q_{v_k}^{-1} \underline{v}_k}{m_k} \qquad (3.105)$$

Under H_0 and H_a this test statistic is distributed as

$$\begin{aligned} H_0 &: T_k \sim F(m_k, \infty, 0) \\ H_a &: T_k \sim F(m_k, \infty, \lambda) \end{aligned} \qquad (3.106)$$

If the test statistic exceeds a threshold, the sources of the possible errors have to be found and identified in the identification step. Again, this is accomplished in practice by testing a number of alternative hypotheses, each describing one model error at a time. The matrix C_k in (3.104) reduces to an m_k-vector c. The LS test statistic is given by

$$t_k = \frac{c^T Q_{v_k}^{-1} \underline{v}_k}{\sqrt{c^T Q_{v_k}^{-1} c}} \qquad (3.107)$$

Under H_0 and H_a the LS test statistic is distributed as

$$\begin{aligned} H_0 &: t_k \sim N(0,1) \\ H_a &: t_k \sim N(\sqrt{c^T Q_{v_k}^{-1} c \nabla}, 1) \end{aligned} \qquad (3.108)$$

Example 3.9

Consider again the geometry-free GPS model of Example 3.8. A time series of GPS observations was considered in which a cycle slip was added to the L1 observations of one cycle (0.19 m). Next, data was analysed to see if it was possible to detect and identify the cycle slip and to account for it. The level of significance α_0 was chosen as 0.1% and the power of the test γ_0 80%. The results are shown in the table below.

As can be seen from this table, it was indeed possible to correctly identify the cycle slip, without using any a priori information, except for the a priori stochtastic model of the observations and the spectral density of the ionosphere. This example also shows, however, that it may be hard to distinguish between L1 and L2 cycle slips.

Time		6:07:00-cont
Type of bias		L1 cycle slip of 1 cycle
Critical value LOM test	3.4	
Critical value LS test	3.3	
Detection	LOM test statistic	*71.5*
Identification	Alternative hypothesis	LS test statistic
	L1 cycle slip	*16.9*
	L2 cycle slip	16.8
	P1 outlier	1.5
	P2 outlier	1.6
	C/A outlier	1.5
Adaptation	Estimated bias	1.02 cycle
	Cycle slip after rounding	1.00 cycle

If more than one model error is assumed to be present, it is possible to identify these model errors in a recursive way. Quality control for recursive processing is based on the predicted residuals, which are computed before the measurement update is performed. Therefore, contrary to standard least squares processing, where all observations, except for the ones rejected in the identification step, are processed again to compute a new solution and the corresponding test statistics, this is not required for recursive processing. Both the LOM and the LS test statistics are updated recursively. The procedure for recursive identification is as follows

1) Initialization:

$$p = 0$$

$$c_{i,p+1} = c_i \quad i = 1,\dots,q$$

$$T_{k,m_k} = \frac{v_k^T Q_{v_k}^{-1} v_k}{m_k}$$

where q is the number of alternative hypotheses to be considered.

2) $p = p+1$

3) Compute LS-test statistics and find maximum:

$$t_{k,i,p} = \frac{c_{i,p}^T Q_{v_k}^{-1} \underline{v}_k}{\sqrt{c_{i,p}^T Q_{v_k}^{-1} c_{i,p}}} \quad \text{for all } c_{i,p}$$

$$t_{k,j,p} = \max_i |t_{k,i,p}|$$

4) Carry out the likelihood test (3.50). If $t_{k,j,p} < N_{0.5\alpha_0}(0,1)$ then stop (the model error cannot be described by any of the considered alternative hypotheses).

5) Redundancy test: if $m_k \le p$ then stop (too many errors).

6) Remove the effect of the largest LS-test statistic from the LOM-test statistic:

$$T_{k,m_k-p} = T_{k,m_k-p+1} - \frac{1}{m_k - p}\{(t_{k,j,p})^2 - T_{k,m_k-p+1}\}$$

7) If $T_{k,m_k-p} \ge F_\alpha(m_k - p, \infty, 0)$ then orthogonalize the remaining c-vectors with respect to $c_{j,p}$:

$$c_{i,p+1} = \{I_{m_k} - c_{j,p}(c_{j,p}^T Q_{v_k}^{-1} c_{j,p})^{-1} c_{j,p}^T Q_{v_k}^{-1}\}c_{i,p} \text{ for all } c_{i,p} \ne c_{j,p}$$

and go to 2)

8) Finished.

The above procedure is repeated until the LOM-test is accepted. With the identified alternative hypotheses, the matrix C_k of (3.104) can be constructed. Next, the biases, contained in the vector ∇_k can be estimated as

$$\hat{\underline{\nabla}}_k = (C_k^T Q_{v_k}^{-1} C_k)^{-1} C_k^T Q_{v_k}^{-1} \underline{v}_k \qquad Q_{\hat{\nabla}_k} = (C_k^T Q_{v_k}^{-1} C_k)^{-1} \tag{3.109}$$

The measurement update is performed using the original observations. If these observations contain biases, they are accounted for using the estimates (3.109)

$$\hat{\underline{x}}_{k|k}^a = \hat{\underline{x}}_{k|k} - K_k C_k \hat{\underline{\nabla}}_k$$
$$= \hat{\underline{x}}_{k|k-1} + K_k(\underline{v}_k - C_k \hat{\underline{\nabla}}_k) \tag{3.110}$$

The state vector's covariance matrix is obtained as

$$Q_{\hat{x}_{k|k}}^a = Q_{\hat{x}_{k|k}} + K_k C_k Q_{\hat{\nabla}_k} C_k^T K_k^T \tag{3.111}$$

After adaptation, recursive estimation under H_0 continues.

The expression for the MDB reads

$$| \nabla_k | = \sqrt{\frac{\lambda_0}{c^T Q_{v_k}^{-1} c}} \qquad (3.112)$$

The influence of a bias with size equal to the MDB on the estimated parameters is given as

$$\nabla \hat{x}_k = K_k c \nabla_k \qquad (3.113)$$

The expressions for the BNR, finally, are given by

$$\lambda_x = \sqrt{\nabla \hat{x}_k^T Q_{\hat{x}_{k|k}}^{-1} \nabla \hat{x}_k} \qquad (3.114)$$

$$\lambda_x = \sqrt{(F^T \nabla \hat{x}_k)^T (F^T Q_{\hat{x}_{k|k}} F)^{-1} (F^T \nabla \hat{x}_k)} \qquad (3.115)$$

Example 3.10
Consider again the geometry-free model of Example 3.8. L1 carrier MDB's were computed as a function of the observation interval, ranging from 1 to 60 seconds. The level of significance α_0 was 0.1% and the power of the test γ_0 80%, resulting in a non-centrality parameter λ_0 of 17.05. As can be seen from the figure below, the

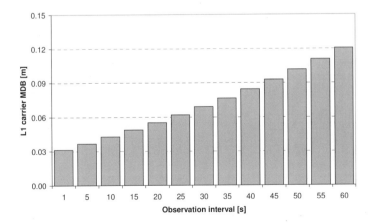

L1 carrier MDB's for the geometry-free observation model as a function of the observation interval.

MDB's are much smaller than one cycle (0.19 m), indicating it is indeed possible to identify even the smallest cycle slip.

3.5 Major references

Teunissen, P.J.G.: *An integrity and quality control procedure for use in multi sensor integration*. Proceedings ION GPS-90, Colorado Springs, 1990, pp. 513-522.

Teunissen, P.J.G.: *Adjustment theory - an introduction*. Delft University Press, Delft, 2000.

Teunissen, P.J.G.: *Testing theory - an introduction*. Delft University Press, Delft, 2000.

Teunissen, P.J.G.: *Dynamic data processing - recursive least squares*. Delft University Press, Delft, 2001.

4 Coordinate systems

4.1 Geodetic datums

The most straightforward way to describe a position in threedimensional space is by means of a cartesian coordinate system. Such a coordinate system is generally known as a *geodetic datum*. The coordinates X, Y, Z are defined with respect to some reference point. Although the reference point can be arbitrarily selected, for a global coordinate system usually the centre of the Earth is chosen. Instead of using a cartesian system it is often more convenient to use a curvilinear system, with coordinates latitude φ, longitude λ and height h. This allows for a separation between 'horizontal' position (φ, λ) and vertical component h.

A *coordinate surface* is defined as the surface on which one of the coordinates is constant. For example, assuming the Earth can be approximated by a sphere with radius R, this sphere is a coordinate surface at which the height is constant. For this simple approximation, the relationships between cartesian and curvilinear (spherical) coordinates are given by, see also Figure 4.1

$$
\begin{aligned}
X &= (R+h)\cos\varphi\cos\lambda \\
Y &= (R+h)\cos\varphi\sin\lambda \\
Z &= (R+h)\sin\varphi
\end{aligned}
\tag{4.1}
$$

The inverse formulae read

$$
\begin{aligned}
\varphi &= \tan^{-1}\left(\frac{Z}{\sqrt{X^2+Y^2}}\right) \\
\lambda &= \tan^{-1}\left(\frac{Y}{X}\right) \\
h &= \sqrt{X^2+Y^2+Z^2} - R
\end{aligned}
\tag{4.2}
$$

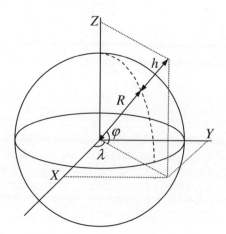

Figure 4.1: Spherical and cartesian coordinates.

Since the Earth is flattened at the poles, a better approximation than a sphere would be an ellipsoid of revolution. Size and shape of such an ellipsoid are determined by two parameters, the *semi-major axis a* and the *semi-minor axis b*. The *flattening f* and the *first eccentricity* e^2 are defined as

$$f = \frac{a-b}{a} \tag{4.3}$$

$$e^2 = \frac{a^2 - b^2}{a^2} = f(2-f) \tag{4.4}$$

For the Earth, the flattening is of the order of 1/300. Instead of *a* and *b*, any pair of the above four parameters can be used to define the size and shape of the ellipsoid, e.g., *a* and *f*.

The position with respect to an ellipsoid of revolution is usually given in *geographic* latitude φ, longitude λ and height (above the ellipsoid) h. A sphere has one constant radius of curvature, whereas an ellipsoid has a radius of curvature that depends on the location on the ellipsoid. This radius is a function of geographic latitude and is different in north-south and east-west direction. The radius of curvature in east-west direction is shown in Figure 4.2 and given by

$$N = \frac{a}{\sqrt{1 - e^2 \sin^2 \varphi}} \tag{4.5}$$

and in north-south direction by

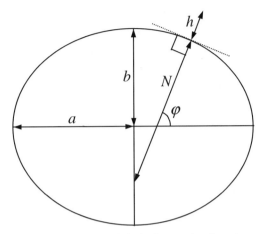

Figure 4.2: Ellipsoidal geographic latitude φ and radius of curvature N.

$$M = \frac{a(1-e^2)}{(1-e^2\sin^2\varphi)^{3/2}} \tag{4.6}$$

Once the geographic coordinates and the parameters defining the ellipsoid are known, the cartesian coordinates can be computed

$$
\begin{aligned}
X &= (N+h)\cos\varphi\cos\lambda \\
Y &= (N+h)\cos\varphi\sin\lambda \\
Z &= (N(1-e^2)+h)\sin\varphi
\end{aligned}
\tag{4.7}
$$

The inverse relationships read

$$
\begin{aligned}
\varphi &= \tan^{-1}(\frac{1}{\sqrt{X^2+Y^2}}(Z+e^2N\sin\varphi)) \\
\lambda &= \tan^{-1}(\frac{Y}{X}) \\
h &= \frac{\sqrt{X^2+Y^2}}{\cos\varphi} - N
\end{aligned}
\tag{4.8}
$$

The latitude φ is computed in an iteration process. In the first iteration, $N\sin\varphi$ is approximated by Z. Usually four iterations are sufficient. For points close to the surface of the Earth, φ can be computed directly

$$\varphi = \tan^{-1}(\frac{Z+e'^2 b\sin^3\mu}{\sqrt{X^2+Y^2}-e^2 a\cos^3\mu}) \tag{4.9}$$

where

$$e'^2 = \frac{a^2 - b^2}{b^2} = \frac{e^2}{1-e^2} = \frac{f(2-f)}{(1-f)^2}$$ (4.10)

and

$$\mu = \tan^{-1}(\frac{aZ}{b\sqrt{X^2 + Y^2}})$$ (4.11)

The quantity e'^2 is known as the *second eccentricity*.

At the end of the 19th and the beginning of the 20th century, many countries developed their own national coordinate systems. These regional and national geodetic datums were based on an ellipsoid of revolution that best fitted the area of interest. As a result, a wide variety of ellipsoids, with different locations and orientations in space exists. For example, after World War II the USA initiated the work on a European first order trigonometric network. The adjustment was completed around 1950 and became known as the European Datum 1950 or ED50. ED50 was established using existing terrestrial and astronomic measurements. ED50 is often used at sea. Until recently it was the datum used for many European nautical charts. Due to the inhomogeneity of the national networks, ED50 is inhomogeneous as well. The inhomogeneities were painfully revealed after the introduction of satellite systems in the second half ot the 20th century.

The advent of these systems, in particular the NNSS/Transit system and its successor GPS, made it possible for the first time to establish truly global geocentric datums. Global because the satellites can be tracked anywhere on Earth and geocentric because the positions of the satellites are by definition determined with respect to the centre of mass of the Earth. The World Geodetic System 1960 (WGS60) was defined by the USA in 1960; the most recent version, WGS84, is used by the GPS community since 1987.

To express coordinates, given in one system, in another system, requires a *datum transformation*. For cartesian coordinates, such a transformation in its most general form consists of three translations, three rotations and a scaling, as shown in Figure 4.3

$$x_{new} = (1 + \Delta\lambda)R_3(\gamma)R_2(\beta)R_1(\alpha)x_{old} + t$$ (4.12)

with

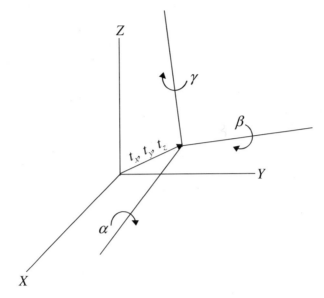

Figure 4.3: Datum transformation.

$t = (t_x \quad t_y \quad t_z)^T$ -   Translation of the origin

$R_3(\gamma)R_2(\beta)R_1(\alpha)$ -   Rotation matrix, the product of three rotations α, β and γ around X, Y and Z-axis, respectively. Each rotation matrix is defined as

$$R_1(\alpha) = \begin{pmatrix} 1 & 0 & 0 \\ 0 & \cos\alpha & \sin\alpha \\ 0 & -\sin\alpha & \cos\alpha \end{pmatrix}$$

$$R_2(\beta) = \begin{pmatrix} \cos\beta & 0 & -\sin\beta \\ 0 & 1 & 0 \\ \sin\beta & 0 & \cos\beta \end{pmatrix}$$

$$R_3(\gamma) = \begin{pmatrix} \cos\gamma & \sin\gamma & 0 \\ -\sin\gamma & \cos\gamma & 0 \\ 0 & 0 & 1 \end{pmatrix}$$

For small rotations, $\sin x$ and $\cos x$ can be approximated by x and 1, respectively. Ignoring second order terms, the rotation matrix in that case becomes

$$R_3(\gamma)R_2(\beta)R_1(\alpha) = \begin{pmatrix} 1 & \gamma & -\beta \\ -\gamma & 1 & \alpha \\ \beta & -\alpha & 1 \end{pmatrix}$$

$\Delta\lambda$ -   Scale factor

Often the datum transformation consists of a translation only, i.e., the scale factor and rotations are zero. The former US Defense Mapping Agency (DMA), now part of the National Imagery and Mapping Agency (NIMA) has published such three-parameter sets for the transformation between WGS84 and a large number of national and regional datums, see http://164.214.2.59/GandG/tr8350_2.html.

For transformations between geographic coordinates, use can be made of the Molodensky transformation formulas

$$\begin{pmatrix} \varphi \\ \lambda \\ h \end{pmatrix}_{new} = \begin{pmatrix} \varphi \\ \lambda \\ h \end{pmatrix}_{old} + \begin{pmatrix} \Delta\varphi \\ \Delta\lambda \\ \Delta h \end{pmatrix} \qquad (4.13)$$

with

$$\Delta\varphi = \frac{1}{(M+h)\sin 1"}\{-t_x \sin\varphi\cos\lambda - t_y \sin\varphi\sin\lambda + t_z \cos\varphi$$

$$+ Ne^2 \sin\varphi\cos\varphi\Delta a + (\frac{a}{b}M/b + \frac{b}{a}N)\Delta f\}$$

$$\Delta\lambda = \frac{1}{(N+h)\cos\varphi\sin 1"}\{-t_x \sin\lambda + t_y \cos\lambda\} \qquad (4.14)$$

$$\Delta h = t_x \cos\varphi\cos\lambda + t_y \cos\varphi\sin\lambda + t_z \sin\varphi - \frac{a}{N}\Delta a + \frac{b}{a}N\sin^2\varphi\Delta f$$

where $\Delta\varphi$ and $\Delta\lambda$ are in seconds of arc and Δh is in metres, $\Delta a = a_{new} - a_{old}$, $\Delta f = f_{new} - f_{old}$. The parameters φ, λ, h refer to the old system.

4.2 Ellipsoidal computations

The shortest line connecting two points in a plane is a straight line. On a sphere, it is a great circle and on an ellipsoid it is a geodesic. Two of the most important problems in which the geodesic is involved, are known as the *direct problem* and the *inverse problem*.

The direct problem is stated as follows: given a point P_1 with position (φ_1, λ_1), the length of the geodesic s between P_1 and another point P_2 and the azimuth α_1 of the geodesic at P_1, find the position (φ_2, λ_2) of P_2 and the azimuth α_2 of the geodesic at P_2.

For the inverse problem, the positions (φ_1, λ_1) and (φ_2, λ_2) are given and the parameters to be determined are the geodesic s and the azimuths α_1 and α_2.

A number of solutions to these problems were developed over the years. Here we will discuss only one for each problem. Introducing the auxiliary parameters

α -   Azimuth of the geodesic at the equator

$u^2 = e^2 \cos^2 \alpha$

$U = \tan^{-1}((1-f)\tan\varphi)$ -   Reduced latitude

Λ -   Difference in longitude on an auxiliary sphere

σ -   Angular distance $P_1 P_2$ on the sphere

σ_i -   Angular distance on the sphere from the equator to P_i

$\sigma_m = \sigma_1 + \tfrac{1}{2}\sigma$ -   Angular distance on the sphere from the equator to the midpoint of the line

the solution to the direct problem follows from

$$\sigma_1 = \tan^{-1}(\frac{\tan U_1}{\cos\alpha_1}) \qquad\qquad\qquad (4.15)$$

$$\alpha = \sin^{-1}(\cos U_1 \sin\alpha_1) \qquad\qquad\qquad (4.16)$$

$$A = 1 + \frac{u^2}{16384}(4096 + u^2(-768 + u^2(320 - 175u^2))) \qquad\qquad (4.17)$$

$$B = \frac{u^2}{1024}(256 + u^2(-128 + u^2(74 - 47u^2))) \qquad\qquad (4.18)$$

Initial value: $\sigma = \dfrac{s}{bA}$

$$\Delta\sigma = B\sin\sigma(\cos 2\sigma_m + \frac{1}{4}B(\cos\sigma(-1+2\cos^2 2\sigma_m)$$
$$-\frac{1}{6}B\cos 2\sigma_m(-3+4\sin^2\sigma)(-3+4\cos^2 2\sigma_m)))$$

(4.19)

$$\sigma = \frac{s}{bA} + \Delta\sigma$$

(4.20)

Expressions (4.19) and (4.20) are iterated until the change in σ is negligible. Next, the remaining parameters are computed

$$\varphi_2 = \tan^{-1}(\frac{\sin U_1\cos\sigma + \cos U_1\sin\sigma\cos\alpha_1}{(1-f)(\sin^2\alpha + (\sin U_1\sin\sigma - \cos U_1\cos\sigma\cos\alpha_1)^2)^{1/2}})$$

(4.21)

$$\Lambda = \tan^{-1}(\frac{\sin\sigma\sin\alpha_1}{\cos U_1\cos\sigma - \sin U_1\sin\sigma\cos\alpha_1})$$

(4.22)

$$C = \frac{f}{16}\cos^2\alpha(4+f(4-3\cos^2\alpha))$$

(4.23)

$$\lambda_2 = \lambda_1 + \Lambda - (1-C)f\sin\alpha(\sigma + C\sin\sigma(\cos 2\sigma_m + C\cos\sigma(-1+2\cos^2 2\sigma_m)))$$

(4.24)

$$\alpha_2 = \tan^{-1}(\frac{\sin\alpha}{-\sin U_1\sin\sigma + \cos U_1\cos\sigma\cos\alpha_1})$$

(4.25)

The solution to the inverse problem is given as

Initial value: $\Lambda = \lambda_2 - \lambda_1$

$$\sigma = \tan^{-1}(\frac{((\cos U_2\sin\Lambda)^2 + (\cos U_1\sin U_2 - \sin U_1\cos U_2\cos\Lambda)^2)^{1/2}}{\sin U_1\sin U_2 + \cos U_1\cos U_2\cos\Lambda})$$

(4.26)

$$\alpha = \sin^{-1}(\frac{\cos U_1\cos U_2\sin\Lambda}{\sin\sigma})$$

(4.27)

$$\sigma_m = \frac{1}{2}\cos^{-1}(\cos\sigma - \frac{2\sin U_1 \sin U_2}{\cos^2 \alpha})$$ (4.28)

$$\Lambda = \lambda_2 - \lambda_1 + (1-C)f \sin\alpha(\sigma + C\sin\sigma(\cos 2\sigma_m + C\cos\sigma(-1+2\cos^2 2\sigma_m)))$$ (4.29)

where C is computed using (4.23). Expressions (4.26)-(4.29) are iterated until the change in Λ is negligible. Next, the remaining parameters are computed

$$s = bA(\sigma - \Delta\sigma)$$ (4.30)

$$\alpha_1 = \tan^{-1}(\frac{\cos U_2 \sin\Lambda}{\cos U_1 \sin U_2 - \sin U_1 \cos U_2 \cos\Lambda})$$ (4.31)

$$\alpha_2 = \tan^{-1}(\frac{\cos U_1 \sin\Lambda}{-\sin U_1 \cos U_2 + \cos U_1 \sin U_2 \cos\Lambda})$$ (4.32)

where the quantities A and $\Delta\sigma$ are obtained from (4.17) and (4.19).

The area within a closed polygon on an ellipsoid, such as $P_1 P_2 P_3 P_4$ in Figure 4.4, can be considered as the algebraic sum of a number of quadrangles, each formed by a side of the polygon, the meridians through its end points and the equator, see also Figure 4.4. The area of the closed polygon is given by:

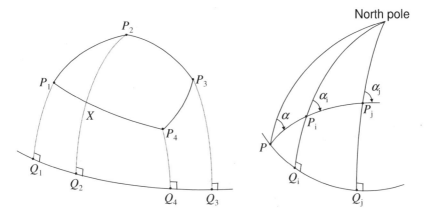

Figure 4.4: Area computations.

$$P_1P_2P_3P_4 = (P_1P_2X + P_1XQ_2Q_1)$$
$$-(P_1XQ_2Q_1 + XP_4Q_4Q_2)$$
$$+(P_2P_3P_4X + XP_4Q_4Q_2 + P_4P_3Q_3Q_4)$$
$$-P_4P_3Q_3Q_4$$
$$= P_1P_2X + P_2P_3P_4X$$

Each quadrangle can be thought of as the difference of two rectangular triangles, e.g. $P_1P_2Q_2Q_1 = PP_2Q_2 - PP_1Q_1$. This difference, denoted A_{ij} for two points P_i and P_j, can be written as

$$A_{ij} = a^2((\alpha_j - \alpha_i) + e'^2 \sin\alpha\cos\alpha(\cos\sigma_j - \cos\sigma_i)) \qquad (4.33)$$

The azimuths α_i and α_j and the angular distances σ_i and σ_j are computed using the expressions for the inverse problem.

4.3 Map projections

The Earth is approximately an ellipsoid. This ellipsoid can never be projected onto a flat surface, like a map, without distortion. A large number of map projections have been developed to map the Earth or parts of it. Each of them has its own characteristics with regard to distortion. For geodetic purposes, only *conformal mapping* functions are of interest, since these mapping functions preserve the angle of intersection between any two curves. The surface of projection can be a cylinder, a cone or a plane. For hydrographic applications the cylindrical Mercator or Transverse Mercator projections are the most widely used. The reason for this popularity is that the Mercator projection is the only projection for which *rhumblines* are mapped onto straight lines (a rhumbline or *loxodrome* is a curve intersecting the meridians at a constant azimuth).

With the *Mercator projection*, the equator is mapped onto the map's x-axis. Distances along the equator preserve their length. The meridians converge towards the poles. In this projection, meridians are mapped parallel to each other. The expressions for the *map coordinates* (x, y), expressed in terms of ellipsoidal coordinates and parameters, read

$$x = a\lambda$$
$$y = aq \qquad (4.34)$$

with

$$q = a \cdot \ln(\tan(\frac{\pi}{4} + \frac{\varphi}{2}) - \frac{1}{2}e \cdot \ln(\frac{1 - e\sin\varphi}{1 + e\sin\varphi}) \qquad (4.35)$$

The *scale factor m* is defined as the ratio between a distance on the map and the corresponding distance on the ellipsoid. It is given by

$$m = \frac{1}{\cos\varphi} \tag{4.36}$$

For the Transverse Mercator projection, the cylinder on which to project is no longer tangent to the equator, but to one of the meridians. As a result, the area within a few degrees of the meridian is projected with relatively small distortions. The projection formulae, however, become much more complex than for the standard Mercator projection, since the meridians and parallel circles no longer coincide with the coordinate axes on the map. For an ellipsoid of revolution, no analytical expressions exist; instead, one has to revert to series' expansions. The general expressions for these expansions are

$$x = \sum_{i=0}^{\infty} (-1)^i a_{2i+1} \Delta\lambda^{2i+1}$$

$$y = \sum_{i=0}^{\infty} (-1)^i a_{2i} \Delta\lambda^{2i} \tag{4.37}$$

where $\Delta\lambda$ is the difference between the longitude λ of the point to be projected and the central meridian λ_{ref}, expressed in radians, and the coefficients a depend on the latitude φ.

The coefficient a_0 is the meridian arc length of the point to be mapped. This is a geodesic, which can be computed using the expressions for the inverse problem using $P_1 = (\varphi, \lambda)$ and $P_2 = (0, \lambda)$. However, for this special case, more straightforward formulae can be used

$$a_0 = \int_0^\varphi M d\varphi = a(1-e^2)\{\varphi + \sum_{j=1}^J \frac{2j+1}{2j} e^{2j} L_{2j}\} \tag{4.38}$$

with

$$L_{2j} = \frac{2j-1}{2j} L_{2j-2} - \frac{1}{2j}\sin^{2j-1}\varphi\cos\varphi$$

$$L_0 = \varphi \tag{4.39}$$

Usually, a maximum number of only four terms in the series expansion in (4.38) needs to be evaluated. The remaining coefficients a_n, with $n \geq 1$, are defined as

$$a_n = \frac{1}{n!}\frac{\partial^n y}{\partial q^n} = \frac{1}{n!}\frac{\partial^n y}{\partial \varphi^n}\frac{\partial \varphi}{\partial q} = \frac{1}{n}\frac{\partial a_{n-1}}{\partial \varphi}\frac{\partial \varphi}{\partial q} \tag{4.40}$$

The partial derivatives are evaluated at the central meridian. Then

$$y = a_0 = \int_0^\varphi M d\varphi \tag{4.41}$$

and

$$\frac{\partial y}{\partial \varphi} = M \tag{4.42}$$

With expression (4.35) for q we get

$$\frac{\partial \varphi}{\partial q} = (\frac{\partial q}{\partial \varphi})^{-1} = \frac{N\cos\varphi}{M} \tag{4.43}$$

resulting in $a_1 = N\cos\varphi$. For $|\Delta\lambda| < 3°$ only the coefficients $a_1 \ldots a_7$ are required to get a precision of (x, y) at the millimetre level. These coefficients are given in Table 4.1.

The *meridian convergence* γ, defined as the angle between map and true north, and the scale factor m can be expressed as a function of the coordinates (φ, λ). Ignoring terms of order $\Delta\lambda^6$ and higher and defining $\eta = e'\cos\varphi$ and $t = \tan\varphi$, the expressions for scale factor and meridian convergence are given as

Table 4.1: First seven coefficients of the series' expansion (4.37) ($\eta = e'\cos\varphi$ and $t = \tan\varphi$).

$$a_1 = N\cos\varphi$$

$$a_2 = \frac{1}{2}N\cos^2\varphi \cdot t \cdot (-1)$$

$$a_3 = \frac{1}{6}N\cos^3\varphi \cdot (-1 + t^2 - \eta^2)$$

$$a_4 = \frac{1}{24}N\cos^4\varphi \cdot t \cdot (5 - t^2 + 9\eta^2 + 4\eta^4)$$

$$a_5 = \frac{1}{120}N\cos^5\varphi \cdot (5 - 18t^2 + t^4 + 14\eta^2 - 58t^2\eta^2)$$

$$a_6 = \frac{1}{720}N\cos^6\varphi \cdot t \cdot (-61 + 58t^2 - t^4 - 270\eta^2 + 330t^2\eta^2)$$

$$a_7 = \frac{1}{5040}N\cos^7\varphi \cdot (-61 + 479t^2 - 179t^4 + t^6)$$

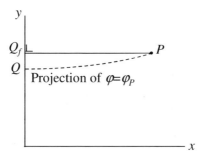

Figure 4.5: Footpoint Q_f of P.

$$m = 1 + \frac{1}{2}\cos^2\varphi(1+\eta^2)\Delta\lambda^2 + \frac{1}{24}\cos^4\varphi(5-4t^2-28t^2\eta^2+14\eta^2)\Delta\lambda^4$$

$$\gamma = \Delta\lambda\sin\varphi + \frac{1}{3}\Delta\lambda^3\sin\varphi\cos^2\varphi(1+3\eta^2+2\eta^4) + \frac{1}{15}\Delta\lambda^5\sin\varphi\cos^4\varphi(2-t^2)$$

$$(4.44)$$

For the inverse mapping we may write

$$\Delta\lambda = \sum_{i=0}^{\infty}(-1)^i b_{2i+1}x^{2i+1}$$

$$(4.45)$$

$$\varphi = \sum_{i=0}^{\infty}(-1)^i b_{2i}x^{2i}$$

The coefficient b_0 is the geographic latitude of the footpoint Q_f, for which the y-coordinate in the map is equal to that of the point P, the point for which latitude and longitude are to be computed. Since x is zero at the footpoint, this latitude can be obtained by inversion of the expression for a_0 , (4.38), using an iteration process

$$\varphi^{(k)} = \frac{a_0\varphi^{(k-1)}}{a(1-e^2)} - \sum_{j=1}^{J}\frac{2j+1}{2j}e^{2j}L_{2j}$$

$$(4.46)$$

This process is started with $\varphi^{(0)} = 0$ and is repeated until no significant change in φ occurs. The remaining coefficients are defined as

$$b_n = \frac{1}{n!}\frac{\partial^n q}{\partial y^n} = \frac{1}{n!}\frac{\partial^n q}{\partial\varphi^n}\frac{\partial\varphi}{\partial y} = \frac{1}{n}\frac{\partial b_{n-1}}{\partial\varphi}\frac{\partial\varphi}{\partial y}$$

$$(4.47)$$

The partial derivatives are evaluated at φ_f and $x = 0$. Since

Table 4.2: First seven coefficients of the series' expansion (4.45)
($\eta = e'\cos\varphi$ and $t = \tan\varphi$).

$$b_1 = (N\cos\varphi)^{-1}$$

$$b_2 = \frac{1}{2}(N^2\cos\varphi)^{-1}\cdot t$$

$$b_3 = \frac{1}{6}(N^3\cos\varphi)^{-1}\cdot(1+2t^2+\eta^2)$$

$$b_4 = \frac{1}{24}(N^4\cos\varphi)^{-1}\cdot t\cdot(5+6t^2+\eta^2-4\eta^4)$$

$$b_5 = \frac{1}{120}(N^5\cos\varphi)^{-1}\cdot(5+28t^2+24t^4+6\eta^2+8t^2\eta^2)$$

$$b_6 = \frac{1}{720}(N^6\cos\varphi)^{-1}\cdot t\cdot(61+180t^2+120t^4+46\eta^2+48t^2\eta^2)$$

$$b_7 = \frac{1}{5040}(N^7\cos\varphi)^{-1}\cdot(61+662t^2+1320t^4+720t^6)$$

$$\varphi_f = b_0 = \int_0^{\varphi_f}Md\varphi \qquad\qquad (4.48)$$

the coefficients b_n are computed in a similar way as the a_n. The coefficients $b_1 \ldots b_7$ are given in Table 4.2.

After World War II a projection system for the entire Earth was developed, based on the Transverse Mercator projection. This system became known as the *Universal Transverse Mercator* (UTM) system. For Europe it is based on Hayford's ellipsoid ($a=6378388$, $f=1/297$). The world is divided into zones along the meridians with a width of 6°. These zones are numbered from 1 to 60. Zone 1 applies to 180°-174° W. Northing is computed from the equator, Easting from the central meridian (for Zone 1: 177° W). Easting is given an offset of 500,000 to avoid negative values. For the same reason, an offset of 10,000,000 is added to Northing on the southern hemisphere. The scale factor at the central meridian is 0.9996. The scale factor for the UTM projection thus becomes $0.9996\cdot m$, with m defined in (4.44).

4.4 Vertical datums

The elevation of a point can only be expressed with respect to the elevation of another point. It could be related to the centre of the Earth, the mean surface of the ocean, the orbit of a satellite or simply a bench mark. The chosen reference to which elevations are referred to is called a *vertical datum*. Currently there are about 100-200 vertical datums in the world.

Orthometric heights are defined with respect to the *geoid* which is an equipotential surface approximated by *Mean Sea Level* (MSL). The elevation of MSL could only be determined by fitting a level surface to observations of the mean level of the sea surface over the oceans. The mean elevation of the sea surface at a particular location is thus not necessarily the same as the elevation of MSL. MSL experiences long term variations due to isostatic and eustatic phenomenae

It is useful to define various average tidal elevations that can be used in comparing tidal characteristics from place to place.

- *MWL*: Mean Water Level is an average of all hourly water levels over the available period of record.
- *MSL*: Mean Sea Level is the ideal equipotential surface that could be obtained by fitting a level surface to observations of the mean level of the sea surface.
- *HHWLT*: Higher High Water, Large Tide is the average of the highest high waters, one from each of 19 years (period of regression of lunar nodes) of prediction.
- *HHWMT*: Higher High Water, Mean Tide is the average of all the higher high waters from 19 years of prediction.
- *LLWMT*: Lower Low Water, Mean Tide is the average of all the lower low waters from 19 years of prediction.
- *LLWLT*: Lower Low Water, Large Tide is the average of the lowest low waters, one from each of 19 years of prediction.
- *LNT*: Lowest Normal Tide is currently synonymous with LLWLT; on older charts, it may refer to a variety of low water Chart Datums.
- *MLLWS*: Mean Lower Low Water Spring, the average of the lower low water heights over a period. It is so low that during average meteorological conditions the occurring depth will seldom be less than charted.
- *LAT*: Lowest Astronomical Tide is not an observed tide, but the lowest tide that can be expected to occur under average meteorological conditions and under any combination of astronomical conditions.

MWL is the only surface whose elevation is determined in practice by the straightforward application of the definition. In Canada, in the adjustment of 1928, the assumption was made that MWL equals MSL. MWL departs from MSL for many reasons: surface slopes due to majors currents (Coriolis effect), prevailing winds, trends in precipitation, evaporation, freezing, melting, heating and cooling, etc. The remaining surfaces were calculated from semi-empirical formulae using the harmonic coefficients of the major tidal constituents. At present, all the surfaces can be generated with 19 years predictions applying directly the definitions.

For reasons of navigational safety, depths and elevations shown on hydrographic charts must be below and above specified datum surfaces

- Depths are referenced to a low water datum.
- Elevations are referenced to a high water datum.

Rarely can there be less depth or less clearance than charted. Water levels and tide predictions are referenced to the same datum as that used for charted depths. Thus the addition of water height (observed or predicted) to the charted depth gives directly the total depth.

Chart Datum is the datum to which each of the following are referenced:

- depths on a published chart
- tide height predictions
- most water level measurements

It was agreed in 1926 by member states of the IHO (International Hydrographic Organization) that the Chart Datum *should be a plane so low that the tide will but seldom fall below it.*

On most Canadian coastal charts LLWLT (LNT on some charts) was adopted as the Chart Datum. On inland water charts, e.g., St Lawrence, Great Lakes, the Chart Datum is usually more difficult to choose because inland waters lack the stabilizing influence the huge ocean reservoir exerts on the mean water level. Therefore the Chart Datum may vary. Several organisations try to adopt one reference system to refer their heights (or depths) to. The IHO and the IMO (International Maritime Organisation) stated in the early 1980's that states should consider adopting an

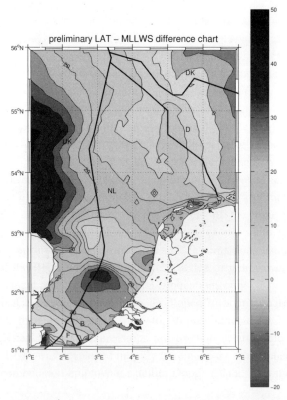

Figure 4.6: Difference in cm between MLLWS and LAT for the North Sea.

astronomical Chart Datum as reference system. For example, in 1995 the Tidal Working Group of the North Sea Hydrographic Commission (NSHC) has proposed to use LAT as Chart Datum in the North Sea. At the 1996 NSHC conference, the North Sea Hydrographic Commission accepted *"...to adopt LAT for Chart Datum in the NSHC region and to encourage its members to implement this adoption at the earliest practicable opportunity."* It was not possible to formally agree on a date of introduction. The NSHC order is now, under good coordinated bilateral and trilateral cooperation, transition to LAT. A consequence of the transition from MLLWS to LAT is that the low-water line along the coast will change, and thus, the baseline, see Chapter 7. The change in position of the baseline depends on the steepness of the seafloor. The difference between MLLWS (the current Chart Datum for the Netherlands) and LAT for the North Sea area is shown in Figure 4.6.

Sounding datum is the intermediate datum chosen during a hydrographic survey using an instantaneous or short term average of water. It is chosen rather arbitrarily to facilitate an immediate start for a sounding survey, and it may or may not remain as the Chart Datum.

Datum for elevations on a chart is the water surface to which the charted elevations of prominent targets (lights, beacons, steeples, chimneys, etc.) and clearances under obstacles (power lines, bridges, etc.) are referenced.

On Canadian coastal charts HHWLT is adopted as datum for elevations. On Canadian charts of non-tidal inland waters the low water Chart Datum is used as a datum for elevations, while a high water surface is used to define the shoreline.

Shown in Figure 4.7 are some of the reference surfaces, discussed above.

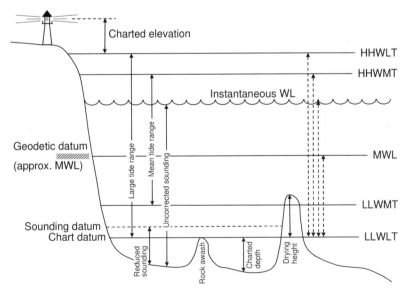

Figure 4.7: Relationship between various reference surfaces.

4.5 Major references

Bakker, G., J.C. de Munck, G.L. Strang van Hees: *Radio positioning at sea*. Delft University Press, Delft, revised edition 1995.

Bowring, B.R.: *Transformation from spatial to geographical coordinates*. Survey Review, 181, 1976, pp. 323-327.

NIMA: *Department of Defense World Geodetic System 1984 - Its definition and relationships with local geodetic systems*. National Imagery and Mapping Agency (NIMA), January 2000. Available from http://164.214.2.59/GandG/tr8350_2.html.

Vincenty, T.: *Direct and inverse solutions of geodesics on the ellipsoid with application of nested equations*. Survey Review XXII, 176, 1975, pp. 88-93.

5 Fundamentals of Radio Frequency propagation and measurements

5.1 Radio Frequency definitions

5.1.1 Electromagnetic waves - general

An electromagnetic wave can be considered as an oscillating (alternating) electric force (E-field) travelling through space (vacuum, atmosphere or solid). This electric force is coupled with a magnetic force (M- or H-field) in a plane at right angle to it.

A varying electric field creates a magnetic field and a varying magnetic field creates an electric field. The combination of the electric and magnetic fields gives an electromagnetic field (EM-field). An EM-field travels as an EM-wave.

The E-field plane in space defines the wave *polarization*. In Figure 5.1 the wave has

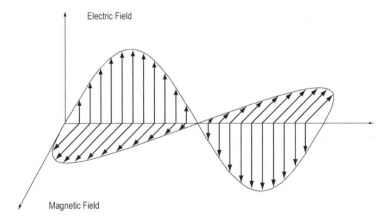

Figure 5.1: Vertically polarized EM-wave.

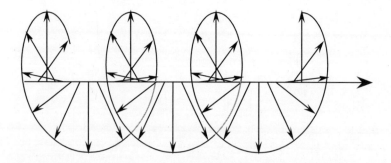

Figure 5.2: Right-hand circular polarization (GPS).

a vertical electric field. Such a wave is therefore vertically polarized.

Radio Frequency (RF) electromagnetic waves are always polarized. The polarization of a plane wave at a fixed point is determined by the time varying behavior of the E-field vector of an EM-wave. EM-waves generally are elliptically polarized with their E-field vector varying periodically in both magnitude and direction. Linear (vertical or horizontal) and circular polarizations are particular cases of elliptical polarization.

In the case of *circular polarization* (left- or right-handed, depending whether the E-field vector rotates counterclockwise or clockwise), the magnitude of the E-field remains constant. An example of right-handed circular polarization (e.g., GPS) is shown in Figure 5.2.

Circular polarization is used to deal with the Faraday effect on trans-ionospheric (e.g., satellite) propagation. The Faraday effect results in the rotation of the polarization of the wave due to the presence of ions. This effect is relatively small at frequencies less than 1 GHz.

Propagation of EM-waves (time varying EM-fields) takes place in the medium according to Maxwell's four laws. The propagation medium is described by its three characteristics: permittivity κ, permeability μ and conductivity σ. The propagation (i.e., radiation) can be assumed to be a sinusoidal wave motion, which can be modulated. The roles of transmitting and receiving antennas are shown in Figure 5.3.

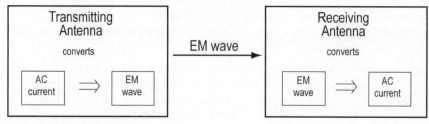

Figure 5.3: RF propagation.

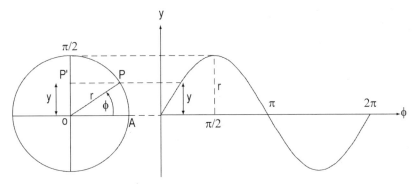

Figure 5.4: Sinusoidal motion (simple harmonic).

5.1.2 Alternating current (AC) signal

An alternating current signal can be easily described using the theory of simple harmonic motion. It corresponds to the motion of a point along the perimeter of a circle with radius r, rotating counterclockwise with a constant speed, as shown in Figure 5.4.

At time t_0 the point is located at A while later, at time t_1, it is located at P. Location of point P is given by the angle ϕ which is called the *phase angle*. The phase angle, which defines the instantaneous position of the moving point on the circle, is a function of time and can be expressed in degrees, radians or *cycles*. The phase can also be expressed in unit of length in which case it is denoted by Φ. It is related to ϕ by

$$\Phi = \phi\lambda \ \text{(or } -\phi\lambda, \text{ depending on the convention)} \tag{5.1}$$

The instantaneous fractional part of ϕ is a measure of the fractional cycle. The location of the moving point with respect to the y-axis is

$$y = r\sin\phi \tag{5.2}$$

The phase angle ϕ varies from 0° to 360° (0 to 2π radians) with respect to time ($\phi = \phi(t)$). One variation of the phase angle by 360° (one total revolution) corresponds to one cycle. The time T needed for one total revolution is called a *period*. Thus

$$\frac{\phi}{2\pi} = \frac{t}{T} \tag{5.3}$$

and

$$y = r\sin 2\pi\frac{t}{T} \tag{5.4}$$

or

$$y = r \sin 2\pi f t \tag{5.5}$$

where f is the *frequency* (inverse of the period) which corresponds to the number of cycles per second

$$f = \frac{1}{T} \tag{5.6}$$

One cycle per second corresponds to 1 Hertz (i.e., 1 cycle/s = 1 Hz). If the period T is in seconds, then the frequency f will be in cycles per second. The point moves along the circumference of a circle with the *angular velocity* ω

$$\omega = \frac{2\pi}{T} = \frac{\phi}{t} \tag{5.7}$$

and thus

$$y = r \sin \omega t \tag{5.8}$$

The circular motion as a function of time (or phase angle) corresponds to the motion along the sine curve with the phase angle being an argument of the function. During one period, a wave travelling with the *velocity of propagation* of an EM-wave c will cover a distance λ, the *wavelength*, which describes the linear length of the wave

$$\lambda = cT = \frac{c}{f} \tag{5.9}$$

The velocity of propagation of an EM-wave in vacuo c_0 is

$$c_0 = 299{,}792{,}458 \text{ m/s}$$

If c is defined in metres per second, T in seconds and f in cycles per second, then λ is in metres. Wavelengths for various frequencies are given in Table 5.1.

Table 5.1: Frequency and wavelength.

Frequency			T	λ
1 Hz			1 s	3×10^8 m
1 kHz =	1 Kilohertz	= 10^3 Hz	1 ms (10^{-3} s)	3×10^5 m
1 MHz =	1 Megahertz	= 10^6 Hz	1 μs (10^{-6} s)	3×10^2 m
1 GHz =	1 Gigahertz	= 10^9 Hz	1 ns (10^{-9} s)	3×10^{-1} m
1 THz =	1 Terahertz	= 10^{12} Hz	1 ps (10^{-12} s)	3×10^{-4} m

---

Example 5.1: Navigation systems.

Omega:	$f = 10$ kHz (VLF)	$\lambda = 30,000$ m
Loran-C:	$f = 100$ kHz (LF)	$\lambda = 3,000$ m
GPS (L1):	$f = 1575.42$ MHz (UHF)	$\lambda = 0.19$ m

Equation (5.8) can be re-written for alternating sinusoidal voltage as

$$V\,(\text{instantaneous voltage}) = V_0\,(\text{maximum voltage}) \cdot \sin \omega t \qquad (5.10)$$

where ωt represents the phase angle ϕ. More generally

$$V = V_0 \sin\left(\omega t - \phi_0\right) \qquad (5.11)$$

where ϕ_0 is the phase shift at time t_0 (lag or lead). A radionavigation receiver measures voltage variations.

5.1.3 Electromagnetic spectrum

The frequencies transmitted from satellites must be in the Radio window, shown in Figure 5.5, to be able to travel down to the Earth through the ionosphere. The ionospheric opaque band is used for some ground-based long range radionavigation systems (e.g., Omega and Loran-C) and some radio stations to increase the range to over-the-horizon through reflection off the ionosphere, e.g., time signals from U.S.A. (Fort Collins, CO) at 5,000 kHz and 10,000 kHz.

Allocations of frequency bands for particular services to regions and/or administrations under special conditions are governed by the International Telecommunications Union (ITU), which includes over 150 member countries. According to ITU Radio Regulations, radio waves belong to frequency band below 3,000 GHz, as shown in Figure 5.6 and Table 5.2

The use of different frequency bands is also governed by internal federal regulations.

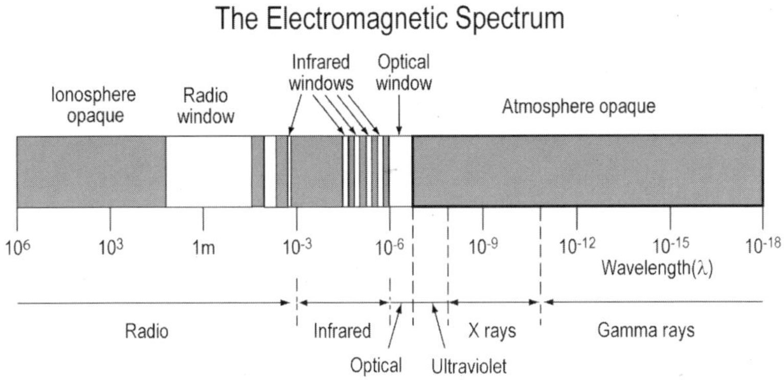

Figure 5.5: Spectrum of electromagnetic radiation.

The Radio Wave Spectrum

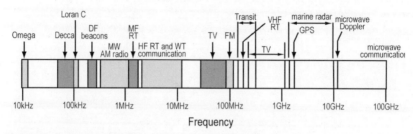

Figure 5.6: Frequency bands used for radionavigation.

Information can be found on the Internet, e.g.,

- *Canada*: Industry Canada http://strategis.ic.gc.ca/SSG/sf01608e.html.
- *U.S.A.*: http://www.ntia.doc.gov/osmhome/osmhome.html.

Many parameters limit the choice of bandwidth for a specific application (e.g., satellite versus ground system). The atmosphere and the ground play important roles in RF propagation. Other parts of the EM spectrum are also used for range measurements, e.g., optical and infrared, see Table 5.3.

5.1.4 Ambiguity of carrier measurements

Many navigation systems (e.g., Omega, Loran-C, and GPS) make use of phase measurements on the carrier because these can be made with an accuracy of a few degrees (typically 1% or less of the carrier wavelength).

The carrier, represented by a sine wave, lacks the time tags necessary to make absolute measurements and the carrier phase measurements are therefore ambiguous. Techniques to determine the ambiguity are different for each system. In some cases, e.g., Loran-C and GPS, pseudorange measurements made on the modulated part of the signal can be used to estimate the ambiguity. To determine the exact ambiguity requires a high ranging accuracy if the wavelength is relatively short (as in the case of GPS).

In the example shown in Figure 5.7, the final carrier phase reading is 180°. A range

Table 5.2: RF designations.

Frequency band	Wavelength	Designation
30 - 300 Hz	10000 - 1000 km	ELF
3 - 30 kHz	100 - 10 km	VLF
30 - 300 kHz	10 - 1 km	LF
300 - 3000 kHz	1000 - 100 m	MF
3 - 30 MHz	100 - 10 m	HF
30 - 300 MHz	10 - 1 m	VHF
300 - 3000 MHz	100 - 10 cm	UHF
3 - 30 GHz	10 - 1 cm	SHF
30 - 300 GHz	10 - 1 mm	EHF
300 - 3000 GHz	1 - 0.1 mm	

Table 5.3: Usable radar frequencies.

Frequency band [GHz]	Wavelength [m]	IEEE radar band
1 - 2	0.30 - 0.15	L
2 - 4	0.15 - 0.075	S
4 - 8	0.075 - 0.0375	C
8 - 12	0.0375 - 0.025	X
12 - 18	0.0250 - 0.0167	Ku
18 - 27	0.0167 - 0.0111	K
27 - 40	0.0011 - 0.0075	Ka
40 - 300	0.0075 - 0.0010	mm

measurement of 1 cycle made with an accuracy of ± 0.5λ (of the carrier) would narrow the possible choices of ambiguity to only two, namely 0.5 or 1.5 cycles. A pseudorange accuracy slightly better than 0.5λ would be required to identify the correct ambiguity. In the case of the GPS L1 frequency (λ = 19 cm), the accuracy required would be better than 9.5 cm. For longer wavelength systems, the pseudorange accuracy requirement would be less (but the phase accuracy would be degraded in units of length).

Assume now that the GPS L1 phase is measured with an accuracy of 5°. In units of length, this corresponds to an accuracy of (±) 0.26 cm. The range accuracy required to resolve the ambiguity should be better than (9.5 – 0.26) cm. In the presence of other noise, e.g., multipath, the accuracy requirement further increases.

Example 5.2: Ambiguity resolution in radionavigation.

A ground-based radionavigation system uses a carrier frequency of 200 kHz. Assume that some type of modulation is used so that ranging is possible in addition to carrier phase measurements. Range resolution is possible with an accuracy of 50 m. The ground wave is used.

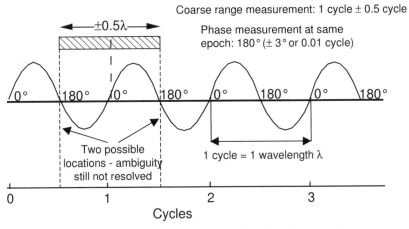

Figure 5.7: Carrier phase ambiguity resolution problem in radionavigation systems.

a) Can the carrier phase ambiguity be resolved exactly?
    The wavelength of a 200 kHz system is $\lambda = c/f = 1500$ m. Since the range
    accuracy (50 m) is better than 1/2 cycle (750 m), the ambiguity can be resolved
    exactly if one neglects the effect of PF + SF + ASF (the effects of the latter will
    be discussed in Section 5.2).

b) What carrier phase accuracy might be expected in unit of length?
    Typically 1° to a few degrees of phase. Assume a worst case of 3.6° or 1/100 of
    a cycle: 0.01 of 1,500 m is 15 m. The instantaneous accuracy would be better
    than 15 m.

5.2   Radiowave propagation

5.2.1 Terminology used in Radio Frequency propagation

The power gain of a system is the ratio of the output power P_o to the input power P_i.
Expressing power ratios in this manner produces frequently either very large or
exceedingly small values. A more convenient method is to express the power gain as
a common logarithm. The unit chosen for the power gain is the *Bel* which is the
logarithm of the ratio of two power levels, i.e.,

$$\text{Bel gain} = \log \frac{P_o}{P_i} \tag{5.12}$$

The Bel is a large unit for most electronic applications; in practical work the
customary unit is the *decibel* [dB], which is one tenth of a Bel

$$\text{dB} = \frac{1}{10} \text{Bel} \tag{5.13}$$

The relationship between power P, voltage V and current intensity I is

$$P = IV \tag{5.14}$$

and according to Ohm's law

$$I = \frac{V}{r} \tag{5.15}$$

where r is the resistance. The power P can be expressed as

$$P = \frac{V^2}{r} \tag{5.16}$$

Thus

$$\text{Bel gain} = \log\frac{P_o}{P_i} = \log\frac{V_o^2/r}{V_i^2/r} = 2\log\frac{V_o}{V_i} \qquad (5.17)$$

and

$$\text{dB gain} = 10\log\frac{P_o}{P_i} = 20\log\frac{V_o}{V_i} = 20\log\frac{I_o}{I_i} \qquad (5.18)$$

which shows the amplification in decibels of power, voltage and current.

Radio Frequency (RF) is a frequency at which EM radiation may be detected/amplified as an electric current.

Absorption is a conversion of the energy of an EM-wave into another form of energy (e.g., heat) as a result of its interaction with matter. Absorption occurs when EM-waves propagate in the atmosphere. The amount of absorption is a function of several variables, including the frequency (the higher the frequency, the larger the absorption in the atmosphere).

Attenuation (*transmission loss*) is a decrease of field strength (i.e., intensity) with increasing distance from the transmitting source, due to geometrical spreading (free-space loss) and absorption (e.g., atmosphere). Attenuation (and gain) is usually expressed in dB

$$\text{Attenuation} = 10\log\frac{P_t}{P_r} \qquad (5.19)$$

where P_t and P_r are transmitted and received power, respectively.

Example 5.3: Attenuation.
   1 dB attenuation : 79% of original power survives.
   3 dB attenuation : 50% of original power survives.
   10 dB attenuation : 10% of original power survives.

Fading is the variation of radio field strength caused by changes in the transmission path with time. It can be frequency sensitive, i.e., it can be restricted to individual frequencies or small bands of frequencies; different frequencies within a signal bandwidth may suffer different amplitude and phase changes. Fading can be caused by:

- The natural cycles of ionosphere (such fading is relatively slow, predictable and may be partially compensated by providing additional signal margin to ensure that the received power does not fall below the required level).

- Unexpected disturbances (e.g., ionospheric storms, which may last from a few minutes to several hours or even days, may only be partially mitigated by frequency changes and may completely interrupt communication).
- Changes in direct and indirect transmission path due to natural and man-made obstructions.

Since fading is a function of frequency, the use of several frequencies simultaneously is sometimes made to increase the chance of successful transmission. This is called *frequency diversity*.

Guided wave is a wave that is guided along or over conducting or dielectric surfaces. The energy of a guided wave is concentrated within or near boundaries between materials of different properties, and is propagated along those boundaries, e.g., ordinary parallel-wire or coaxial transmission line. At VLF frequencies (e.g., Omega), the Earth and the lower layer of the ionosphere act as wave guides.

Scintillation is a rapid fluctuation of the amplitude and phase of a wave passing through a medium with small-scale irregularities (e.g., ionospheric scintillation).

Scattering is the process by which the energy of a wave is dispersed in various directions due to interaction with inhomogeneities of the medium. The sky is blue because of scattering in the atmosphere. Scattering is highest when the particle size is equal to the wavelength of the frequency used.

Diffraction is the deviation of the direction of energy flow of a wave when it passes an obstacle (a wave bends around such obstacles as the Earth's curvature, mountain ranges or large man-made structures), see Figure 5.8. A wavefront can be considered made up of an infinite number of isotropic radiators. A wave does not reflect from a single point but radiates from the entire surface of an obstacle in its path. As a consequence the wave is apparently bent or diffracted around objects as it grazes their surfaces. This is why line-of-sight frequencies can be received when non-line-of-sight conditions occur, e.g., cellular telephones in the 800-900 MHz range.

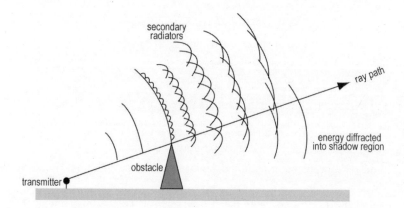

Figure 5.8: Diffraction at an obstacle.

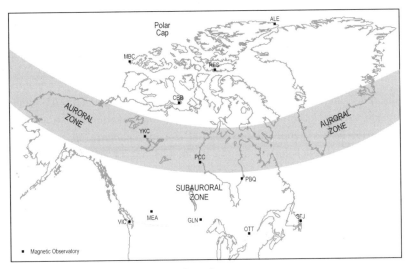

Figure 5.9: Average auroral zone in Canada.

Aurora are optical/electrical phenomena caused by excitation or ionization of the upper atmosphere. The effect of aurora on RF transmission can be significant and is a function of frequency. The auroral zone is located in northern Canada during average solar activity (which is characterized by the 11-year cycle sunspot number) and shown in Figure 5.9.

5.2.2 Characteristics of propagation medium

The character of the medium in which propagation takes place is described by the appropriate values of the medium's permittivity, permeability and conductivity.
Permeability μ is the ability of a material to sustain a magnetic flux in a magnetic field. The permeability μ_0 of a vacuum in SI is

$$\mu_0(\text{free space}) = \frac{c^2}{\kappa_0} = 4\pi \cdot 10^{-7} \text{ N/Ampere}^2$$

where 1 N/Ampere^2 = 1 Weber/(Ampere·m) = 1 Henry/m; κ_0 is defined below. Permeability of a medium is expressed as

$$\mu = \mu_r \cdot \mu_0 \tag{5.20}$$

where μ_r (dimensionless) is the relative permeability. In the CGS (centimeter-gram-second) system $\mu_0 = 1$ and μ and μ_r have the same numerical values.
Permittivity κ is the ability of a material to sustain an electric flux under the influence of the electric field. The permittivity κ_0 of a vacuum in the SI is

$$\kappa_0(\text{free space}) = 8.854187817 \cdot 10^{-12} \text{ farads/m}$$

Table 5.4: Relative permittivity and conductivity of typical surfaces.

Surface	Relative permittivity [-]	Conductivity [S/m]
Sea water	80	4-5
Fresh water	80	0.005
Moist soil	15-20	0.005-0.01
Dry soil	4	0.001-0.01

Permittivity of a medium is expressed as

$$\kappa = \kappa_r \cdot \kappa_0 \tag{5.21}$$

where the dimensionless quantity κ_r is the relative permittivity or dielectric constant of the medium. In Table 5.4 the relative permittivity of some typical surfaces are given. In the case of a vacuum, the relative permittivity $\kappa_r = 1$, and the speed of propagation is maximum. In any substance the value of κ_r is greater than one, and the speed is therefore less than in a vacuum ($\kappa_r = 1.00059$ at a pressure of 1 atm). In the CGS system $\kappa_0 = 1$, and κ and κ_r have the same numerical values.

Conductivity (*conductance*) σ is the reciprocal of resistance. Since resistance is expressed in ohm, conductivity is expressed in reciprocal ohms. The unit of conductivity is the siemens (1/ohm) in the SI system. The siemens is also called the mho (ohm spelled backward). Surface conductivity is given in siemens/m (S/m).

A wave transmitted into the conducting medium may penetrate to lower depths. Energy penetration is a function of the medium characteristics and frequency. Depth of penetration, see Table 5.5, is a quantitative measure of the penetration of a wave into a conducting medium. It corresponds to the distance at which the amplitude of the electromagnetic wave decreases to $1/e$ (i.e., 36.8%). Submerged submarines use frequencies at a few kHz for long-range communication; the antenna can be submerged but has to remain near the surface.

5.2.3 Propagation velocity and refraction

In free-space (vacuo) propagation velocity c_0 is the same and constant for all EM-waves $c_0 = 299,792,458 \pm 1$ m/s . In the Earth's atmosphere, electromagnetic waves are slowed down. The amount of retardation is a function of the medium and the frequency used (depending on the frequency range). The decrease in speed is sometimes referred to as the *primary phase lag* or *primary factor* (especially in the context of ground-based systems).

Table 5.5: Penetration depth at frequencies of 10 kHz, 100 kHz, and 1 MHz.

Material	Conductivity [mS/m]	10 KHz	100 KHz	1 MHz
Sea water	5000	2.5 m	0.7 m	0.25 m
Good ground	30	29.0 m	9.2 m	2.90 m
Poor ground	3	92.0 m	29.0 m	9.20 m

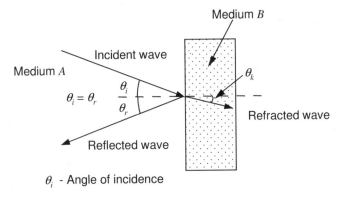

Figure 5.10: Reflection and refraction.

When an electromagnetic wave passes from one medium to another, its velocity changes. This causes the wave to bend from its original trajectory. The refracted wave is transmitted through the new medium. An electromagnetic wave may be completely or partially reflected by the boundary between two media.

The incident wave (from medium A, see Figure 5.10) makes an angle of incidence θ_i with the normal to the boundary between two media. The reflected wave makes an angle of reflection θ_r with the normal to the boundary between two media. The transmitted (refracted) wave makes an angle of refraction θ_k with the normal to the boundary between two media. In a conducting medium, the angle of reflection is equal to the angle of incidence. The relationship between the angle of refraction and the angle of incidence is expressed by Snell's law, which reads

$$n \sin \theta_i = \text{constant} \tag{5.22}$$

where the *index of refraction* (or *refractive index*) n is defined as

$$n = \frac{\text{velocity in vacuo}}{\text{velocity in medium}} = \frac{c_0}{c_m} \tag{5.23}$$

The refractive index n can also be defined in terms of relative permittivity κ_r and relative permeability μ_r as

$$n = \sqrt{\mu_r \kappa_r} \tag{5.24}$$

which gives, for free-space, $n = 1$. Instead of using the index of refraction n, which is close to 1, the *refractivity* N is often used

$$N = (n-1) \cdot 10^6 \tag{5.25}$$

The value of the refractive index depends on the following factors:

- Gaseous composition (troposphere).
- Amount of water vapour (troposphere).
- Temperature and pressure of the gaseous mixture (troposphere).
- Frequency of the electromagnetic signal (troposphere and ionosphere).
- Amount of free electrons (ionosphere).

In the troposphere the refractive index n is

- A function of temperature, atmospheric pressure and water vapour pressure for the RF spectrum (frequencies below 20 GHz) because the troposphere is a non-dispersive medium at these frequencies, i.e., it is independent of frequency for RF.
- A function of temperature, atmospheric pressure, water vapour pressure and frequency for the visible and near-visible spectrum because the troposphere is a dispersive medium at these frequencies, i.e., dependent on frequency for this part of the spectrum.

In the ionosphere the refractive index n is a function of frequency and *Total Electron Content (TEC)* for the RF spectrum because the ionosphere is a dispersive medium. When the refractive index n is dispersive, it can be accurately determined using two-frequency measurements, e.g. L1 and L2 signals for GPS, or two-colour lasers for highly accurate EDM (Electromagnetic Distance Measurement).

5.2.4 Free-space transmission loss

Radio wave free-space transmission loss occurs due to geometrical spreading of the transmitted power P_t. Power density is defined as radiated (transmitted) power per unit area and can be expressed in W/m^2.

If a transmitter with a power P_t is connected to a lossless and totally non-directional antenna (isotropic transmitting antenna), i.e., an antenna radiating equal amounts of power in all directions, the power density P_r of reception at distance r is equal to the transmitted power divided by the surface area of the sphere with radius r

$$P_r = \frac{P_t}{4\pi r^2} \tag{5.26}$$

Note that P_r is in units of power density (W/m^2), while P_t is in units of power (W). The inverse-square law states that power density is inversely proportional to the square of the distance from the source.

If P_{r_1} and P_{r_2} are the power densities at distances r_1 and r_2 from the source point, see Figure 5.11, the relative attenuation α_P of P_{r_2} with respect to P_{r_1} is (using the logarithmic scale)

$$\alpha_P = 10\log\frac{P_{r_1}}{P_{r_2}} = 10\log\frac{P_t/4\pi r_1^2}{P_t/4\pi r_2^2} = 10\log\frac{r_2^2}{r_1^2} = 20\log\frac{r_2}{r_1} \tag{5.27}$$

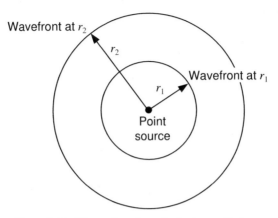

Figure 5.11: Attenuation of a spherical wavefront.

For a reference value of $r_1 = 1$ m, we get

$$\alpha_p = 20\log r_2 \tag{5.28}$$

The relationship between the received field strength of an electric field (i.e., intensity) E (V/m) and power density P_r is

$$E = \sqrt{P_r L} = \sqrt{\frac{P_t}{4\pi r^2}120\pi} = \sqrt{\frac{30P_t}{r^2}} = \frac{\sqrt{30P_t}}{r} \tag{5.29}$$

where L is the characteristic impedance of the medium

$$L = \sqrt{\frac{\mu}{\kappa}} = \sqrt{\frac{\text{permeability}}{\text{permittivity}}} \tag{5.30}$$

In free-space, $\mu_0 = 1.26\cdot 10^{-6}$ henry/m, $\kappa_0 = 8.854\cdot 10^{-12}$ farads/m and $L_0 = 120\pi$. If E_{r_1} and E_{r_2} are the field intensities at distances r_1 and r_2 from the source point, the relative attenuation α_E of E_{r_2} with respect to E_{r_1} is, using the logarithmic scale

$$\alpha_E = 20\log\frac{r_2}{r_1} \tag{5.31}$$

which is the same as α_p in (5.27) and (5.28). Radio wave free-space transmission loss occurs due to the geometrical spreading of the transmitted power P_t. Power density is defined as radiated (or transmitted) power per unit area and can be expressed in Watts per square metre (W/m^2).

In reality, antennas are not totally non-directional. Every antenna focuses its radiation in certain directions. This focusing ability is called the antenna *directivity* or *gain* and is often denoted by D_t. To account for transmitter antenna gain, P_t in (5.26) is multiplied by D_t

$$P_r = \frac{D_t P_t}{4\pi r^2}$$

(5.32)

If losses in the transmitting antenna are also considered, the effective gain G_t is

$$G_t = k \cdot D_t$$

(5.33)

where the coefficient k is usually between 0.3 and 0.8. Effective gain then replaces gain

$$P_r = \frac{G_t P_t}{4\pi r^2}$$

(5.34)

This is the power density "in the air" at a distance r from the transmitter. This power now has to be received by a receiver antenna. The receiver antenna has an effective area A_r, such that the power received by the antenna equals the power density at the receiver antenna multiplied by the effective area of the antenna

$$P_r = \frac{G_t P_t A_r}{4\pi r^2}$$

(5.35)

Note that P_r is now in units of power as opposed to power density. The effective area of a receiver antenna is a function of the antenna's own gain, G_r, and of the antenna's physical size with respect to the wavelength being received

$$A_r = \frac{G_r \lambda^2}{4\pi}$$

(5.36)

where G_r is the receiver antenna gain and λ is the wavelength. We can now express P_r as

$$P_r = \frac{G_t G_r P_t \lambda^2}{(4\pi r)^2}$$

(5.37)

Free-space loss L_0 can be defined as the portion of the above equation relating transmitted power and received power that is independent of the gains of the two antennas. If L_0 is defined as

$$L_0 = (\frac{4\pi r}{\lambda})^2 \qquad (5.38)$$

we can write P_r as

$$P_r = \frac{G_t G_r P_t}{L_0} \qquad (5.39)$$

For the simple case where the gain G_r of the receiving antenna is equal to one (isotropic case), A_r is given by

$$A_r = \frac{\lambda^2}{4\pi} \qquad (5.40)$$

and

$$P_r = \frac{P_t \lambda^2}{(4\pi r)^2} = \frac{P_t}{L_0} \qquad (5.41)$$

Expressed in dB, the free-space loss will be $10\log L_0$.

GPS signal free-space loss

For GPS, the relative attenuation α_p is

$$\alpha_p = 10\log\frac{P_t}{P_r} = 10\log L_0 = 10\log(\frac{4\pi r}{\lambda})^2 = 20\log\frac{4\pi r}{\lambda} \qquad (5.42)$$

where r = 25,092 km (maximum distance between the ground station and a satellite) and $\lambda_{L1} \approx 0.19$ m (wavelength of the GPS L1 carrier), such that

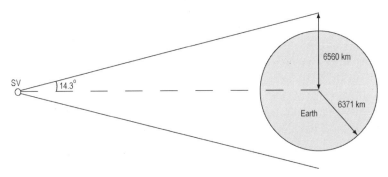

Figure 5.12: GPS space vehicle (SV) effective antenna beam.

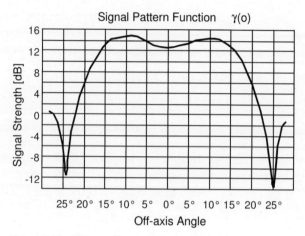

Figure 5.13: GPS satellite antenna beam pattern.

$$10\log L_0 = 184.4 \ \text{dBw}$$

This is the greatest source of signal attenuation. In addition, 2 dB is lost due to atmospheric attenuation. The satellite antenna signal beam is 14.3° off-axis, see Figure 5.12, and is shaped to conform to Earth's surface with a variable beam pattern, as shown in Figure 5.13. This results in a gain of 13.4 dB. Other effects result in a signal power of -160 dBw at the receiver on the Earth's surface.

5.2.5 The atmosphere - general

The structure of the atmosphere can be described through concentric layers of atmospheric domains, shown in Figure 5.14, with different physical and chemical properties. Considering the electromagnetic signal propagation, a subdivision into troposphere and ionosphere is advisable because the particular propagation conditions are very different in these two regions. The troposphere is the lowest part of the Earth's atmosphere. For RF applications, it extends from the Earth's surface to about 50-60 km above the Earth. The signal propagation depends on the temperature of the atmospheric layers, the pressure and the water vapour content. The troposphere consists of practically neutral gas.

The ionosphere is the upper part of the Earth's atmosphere. It extends from approximately 60-70 km to 1,000-1,500 km above the Earth. The signal propagation depends primarily on the number and distribution of free charged particles. The ionosphere has sufficient amount of electrons and ions to affect the propagation of electromagnetic signals. Both the troposphere and the ionosphere cause propagation delays.

A medium in which the propagation velocity of electromagnetic signals depends on the frequency is a dispersive medium. In such a medium, the index of refraction is a

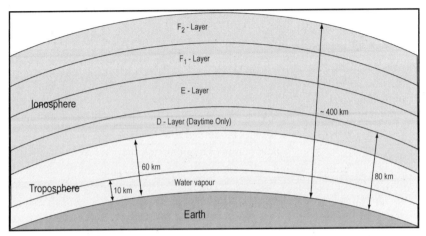

Figure 5.14: Structure of the atmosphere.

function of frequency (and, therefore, wavelength). Resonance occurs when the atomic frequency of the medium and the frequency of the penetrating wave are similar. This resonance generates a frequency-dependent influence on the propagation velocity. In a dispersive medium different propagation velocities for sinusoidal waves (phases) and groups of waves are observed.

The ionosphere is dispersive for the RF band of frequencies, and the index of refraction n varies with frequency such that

$$v_g \neq v_\phi$$

where v_g is group velocity and v_ϕ phase velocity. The troposphere is non-dispersive in the RF band, where frequencies are below 20 GHz, but dispersive at higher frequencies.

5.2.6 The troposphere

The troposphere extends from the Earth's surface up to altitudes of approximately 50-60 km. It consists of the following layers:

- 0-10 km: the tropospheric layer with most of the water vapour or humidity.
- Tropopause: the transition layer between the tropospheric and stratospheric layers.
- 10-50 km: the stratospheric layer.

The density at sea level with normal pressure (1 atm) ranges from 1.13 kg/m^3 (40°C) to 1.29 kg/m^3 (0°C). The pressure decreases with increasing altitude. Variations of pressure with altitude are shown in Figure 5.15. At sea level, the normal pressure is (at 15°C)

1013.246 mbar = 760 mm Hg = 29.9213 inch Hg = 101.3246 kPa

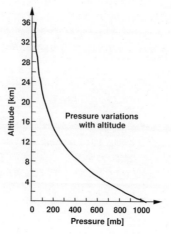

Figure 5.15: Pressure variation with altitude.

where 1 mbar = 1×10^{-3} bar = 10^2 Pa = 10^2 N/m^2 (1 mbar = 0.75006 mm Hg = 0.029530 inch Hg).

The temperature varies with increasing altitude as shown in Figure 5.16. The troposphere is divided into four horizontal layers based on the temperature profiles in these regions:

• 0-10 km: normal lapse rate $dT / dh = -6.5\,°C/km$

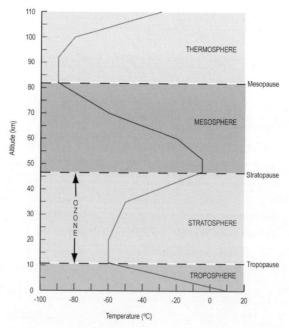

Figure 5.16. Thermal structure of the atmosphere (after Lutgens and Tarbuck, 1995).

Table 5.6: Water vapour capacity at average sea level pressure.

T [°C]	Capacity [g/kg]
-40	0.1
-30	0.3
-20	0.75
-10	2.0
0	3.5
10	7.0
15	10.0
20	14.0
25	20.0
30	26.5

- 11-20 km: normal lapse rate $dT / dh = 0 \,°C/km$
- 20-31 km: normal lapse rate $dT / dh = 1 \,°C/km$
- 32-47 km: normal lapse rate $dT / dh = 2.8 \,°C/km$

The first layer (0-10 km), which is called the troposphere in meteorology, is the main focus of meteorologists; all phenomena that are collectively referred to as weather occur in this layer. Within the troposphere the atmospheric properties are readily transferred by large-scale turbulence and mixing. In the stratosphere they are much more regular.

Humidity is used to describe the amount of water vapour in the air. Several methods are used to express humidity quantitatively, e.g., absolute humidity, mixing ratio, relative humidity. The water vapour capacity at sea level is given for specific temperatures in Table 5.6.

- *Absolute humidity* is expressed as the mass of water vapour in a given volume of air (e.g., g per m³). It is difficult to monitor the water vapour content of a moving mass of air if the absolute humidity is being used (volume changes occur).
- *Mixing ratio* is expressed as the mass of water vapour in a unit mass of dry air (e.g., g per kg). Since it is measured in units of mass, the mixing ratio is not affected by the changes in pressure and temperature.
- *Relative humidity* is expressed as the ratio of the air's actual water vapour content to its water vapour capacity at a given temperature T (saturation mixing ratio) in percent.

The water vapour capacity at 25°C is 20 g per kg. If the air contains 10 g per kg at that temperature, the relative humidity is expressed as 10g/20g or 50%. Assume now that at 15°C the air contains 10 g per kg. Using Table 5.6, the relative humidity is then 10g/10g or 100%. Relative humidity therefore changes with temperature during the course of a day, as shown in Figure 5.17, and dew is often present in the early morning.

A variety of instruments, called hygrometers, can be used to measure relative humidity *RH*, defined as

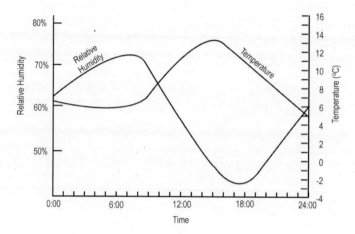

Figure 5.17: Daily variation of temperature and relative humidity.

$$RH = \frac{\text{vapor pressure}}{\text{saturation vapor pressure}} \times 100 \ [\%] \qquad (5.43)$$

One of the simplest hygrometers is called a psychrometer, which consists of two thermometers mounted side by side. One thermometer has a dry bulb, the other a wet bulb. The wet bulb is covered with cotton fabric, which is soaked with distilled water. A continuous current of air circulates over the wet cotton fabric, either by swinging the psychrometer freely in the air or by fanning air past it. The air streaming past the wet bulb vapourizes water, causing evaporation and cooling of the bulb. The wet-bulb thermometer reading is T_w, while the dry-bulb reading is T_d. The drier the

Table 5.7: Relative humidity [%] from a wet-and-dry bulb psychrometer (after Moran and Morgan, 1989).

Dry bulb temperature	Wet bulb depression [°C]										
[°C]	0.5	1.0	1.5	2.0	2.5	3.0	4.0	5.0	7.5	10	15
-10.0	85	69	54	39	24	10	-	-	-	-	-
-7.5	87	73	60	48	35	22	-	-	-	-	-
-5.0	88	77	66	54	43	32	11	-	-	-	-
-2.5	90	80	70	60	50	41	22	3	-	-	-
0.0	91	82	73	65	56	47	31	15	-	-	-
2.5	92	84	76	68	61	53	38	24	-	-	-
5.0	93	86	78	71	65	58	45	32	1	-	-
7.5	93	87	80	74	68	62	50	38	11	-	-
10.0	94	88	82	76	71	65	54	44	19	-	-
15.0	95	90	85	80	75	70	61	52	31	12	-
20.0	95	91	87	82	78	74	66	58	40	24	-
25.0	96	92	88	84	81	77	70	63	47	32	7
30.0	96	93	89	86	82	79	73	67	52	39	16
35.0	97	93	90	87	84	81	75	69	56	44	23
40.0	97	94	91	88	85	82	77	72	59	48	29

air, the greater the evaporation and the lower the reading will be on the wet-bulb thermometer as compared with the dry-bulb thermometer. The temperature difference between the two thermometers is called the wet-bulb depression. Wet-bulb depression is a function of the air dryness and of the dry temperature (since saturation is a function of T_d) Relative humidity can be obtained from the measured temperatures using a conversion table (psychrometric table) such as Table 5.7.

The partial water vapour pressure e is often required to calculate the index of refraction in the troposphere

$$e = \frac{h}{100} E \tag{5.44}$$

where E is the *saturation water vapour pressure* in mbar at temperature T_d and h is the relative humidity in percent. The value of E is obtained from a table or computed (e.g., Rueger, 1990). The value of e can also be calculated as

$$e = E'_w - 0.000662 \cdot p \cdot (T_d - T_w) \text{ for } T_d > 0\,°C \text{ and } T_w > 0\,°C$$

$$e = E'_{ice} - 0.000583 \cdot p \cdot (T_d - T_w) \text{ for } T_d < 0\,°C \text{ and } T_w < 0\,°C \tag{5.45}$$

where E'_w is the saturation water vapour pressure for T_w over water, E'_{ice} is the saturation water vapour pressure for T_w over ice, and p is the atmospheric pressure in mbar. Values of E'_w and E'_{ice} are obtained from a table (e.g., Rueger, 1990).

Example 5.4: Test conducted by M. Petovello on June 8, 1998, in the Department of Geomatics Engineering, University of Calgary, using a psychrometer.

Psychrometer in the room: Dry bulb 22.8°C and wet bulb 12.7°C. The relative humidity, using Table 5.7, is 28%. The value of E is 27.75 mbar [Rueger (1990), Appendix B] and e is therefore 7.8 mbar. The value of E'_w is 14.68 mbar [Rueger (1990), Appendix B] and $e = E'_w - 0.000662 \cdot p \cdot (T_d - T_w)$ is 8.0 mbar, assuming an atmospheric pressure of 1,000 mbar.

The psychrometer was then put in a low temperature freezer and the following readings were observed: dry bulb -14.0°C and wet bulb -13.0°C. The second term of the partial water vapour pressure ($0.000583 \cdot p \cdot (T_d - T_w)$) is 0.6 mbar and $E'_{ice} \approx 2$ mbar. The value of e is therefore approximately 1.5 mbar.

Due to variations of pressure p, temperature T, and humidity h with altitude, the index of refraction for the troposphere varies as a function of position (especially altitude). A standard atmosphere is sometimes used to model the index of refraction as a function of altitude. The U.S. Standard Atmosphere is given in Table 5.8.

The atmospheric parameters of the U.S. Standard Atmosphere as functions of altitude z can be approximated by the following analytical formulae (Bogush, 1989). The pressure is given as

$$p(z) = p_0 e^{-z/Z_p} \tag{5.46}$$

where z is the height above sea level, p_0 is the sea level pressure, Z_p is a constant "scale height" or "thickness of the atmosphere".

The temperature is given for different atmospheric layers

$$
\begin{aligned}
T(h) &= T_0 - ah & 0 \le h \le 11\,\text{km} \\
T(h) &= T_1 & 11 \le h \le 20\,\text{km} \\
T(h) &= T_1 + (h-20) & 20 \le h \le 32\,\text{km}
\end{aligned}
\tag{5.47}
$$

where $a = 6.5°C/1{,}000$ m (the temperature lapse rate), T_0 is temperature at sea level and T_1 is temperature at 11 km (-56°C). The water vapour is expressed in exponential form as function of wet and dry temperature.

Table 5.8: U.S. Standard Atmosphere.

Height [km]	Temperature [°C]	Pressure [mbar]
0	15	1013.2
0.5	12	954.6
1.0	9	898.8
1.5	5	845.6
0.0	2	795.0
2.5	-1	746.9
3.0	-4	701.2
3.5	-8	657.8
4.0	-11	616.6
5.0	-17	540.4
6.0	-24	472.2
7.0	-30	411.0
8.0	-37	356.5
9.0	-43	308.0
10.0	-50	265.0
12.0	-56	194.0
14.0	-56	141.7
16.0	-56	103.5
18.0	-56	75.65
20.0	-56	55.29
25.0	-51	25.49
30.0	-46	11.97
35.0	-36	5.75
40.0	-22	2.87
50.0	-2	0.798

Tropospheric refractivity

The refractive index n, see (5.23), in the troposphere is larger than one, and this results in a measured range that is too large. For RF frequencies, the refractivity N, as defined by (5.25), is independent of frequency since the troposphere is not dispersive in this frequency range. Thus refractivity N can be calculated using a formula of the general form

$$N = N(P, T_d, e)$$

i.e., N is a function of total atmospheric pressure p, partial pressure of water vapour e and dry bulb temperature T_d. The Essen-Froome formula is usually preferred (Rueger, 1990)

$$N = (p - e)\frac{77.624}{273.15 + T_d} + e\frac{64.70}{273.15 + T_d}(1 + \frac{5748}{273.15 + T_d}) \qquad (5.48)$$

where p and e are in mbar and T_d is in °C. The addition of 273.15° converts the temperature from degrees Celsius into Kelvin. The first term accounts for the dry part of the atmosphere and the second term accounts for the wet (partial water vapour pressure) part. Assume a normal pressure of 1,013.15 mbar and a very cold winter temperature of $T_d = -35$ °C. In such a case, e is practically zero and N is 330. Now assume a summer temperature of 20°C. Water vapour will be present; if we assume $e = 10$, N is 312. As a consequence, for normal seasonal conditions, an average value of 320 is often used for N ($n = 1.000320$) on the Earth's surface. Under extreme circumstances, e can reach about 4% of the total atmospheric pressure, namely about

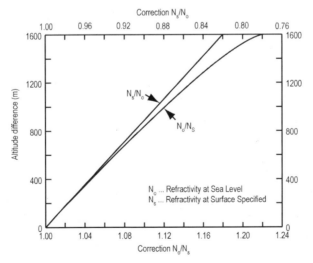

Figure 5.18: Variation of refractivity N with height (after Segal and Barrington, 1977).

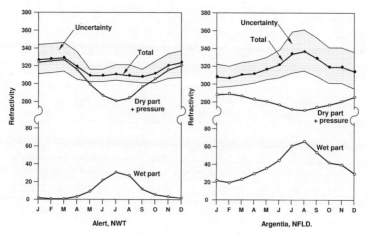

Figure 5.19: Seasonal variations of refractivity.

40 mbar.

A simpler formula to calculate N is that of Smith and Weintraub

$$N = 77.6 \frac{p}{273.15 + T_d} + 3.73 \cdot 10^5 \frac{e}{(273.15 + T_d)^2} \tag{5.49}$$

where p and e are in mbar and T_d is in °C.

The difference in the calculated N from (5.48) and (5.49) decreases from about 0.6 at sea level to 0.1 at an elevation of 5000 m. For RF navigation applications, the choice of the formula is not critical because an average N is required along the propagation path and the errors caused by unknown variations in p, T and e are greater than those caused by the use of a specific formula.

Variation of refractivity N with height can be expressed in terms of the correction representing the ratio of refractivity at sea level N_0 to refractivity at the specified surface N_s, or by its inverse, as shown in Figure 5.18.

Seasonal variations of the dry and wet components are shown in Figure 5.19 for two locations in Canada, namely Alert in the high Arctic and Argentia, NF. Note that, during winter in Alert, the wet component is nearly zero. During the same period however, the dry component is greater, resulting in an overall N near 320 for all seasons.

Warm, dry winds in the western part of North America which sometimes move down the east slopes of the Rockies are called *chinooks* (a Native American word which means "snow eater"). Chinooks are often created when a pressure pulls air over the mountains, as shown in Figure 5.20. As the air descends the leeward slopes of the mountains it is heated by compression. Because condensation may have occurred as the air ascended the windward side, releasing the latent heat, the air descending the leeward side will be warmer and drier than at a similar elevation on the windward side. The temperature of a chinook is generally less than 10°C. Chinooks usually

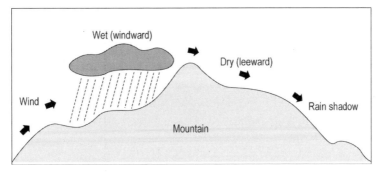

Figure 5.20: Profile of a chinook wind.

occur in winter and spring when the affected area may be experiencing subfreezing temperatures. Thus, these dry, warm winds frequently bring drastic temperature changes. Within minutes of the arrival of a chinook, the temperature may climb 20°C in extreme cases. Chinooks can change tropospheric refractivity significantly for precise applications.

Mirages are one of the most interesting optical events common to our atmosphere. They can actually be experienced anywhere, not only in the desert. One type of mirage occurs when the air near the ground is much cooler than the air aloft. Such an effect is observed in polar regions or over cool ocean surfaces, as shown in Figure 5.21. The light bends towards the Earth. This effect allows ships to be seen where ordinarily the Earth's curvature would block them from view. This phenomenon is known as *looming*, since sometimes the refraction of light is so great that the object appears suspended above the horizon (the image is seen above its true position).

Another type of mirage occurs on very hot days when the air near the ground is much less dense than the air aloft. A change in the density of air causes a gradual bending of the light rays, as shown in 5.22. The rays will develop a curvature in a direction opposite to the Earth's curvature. This will cause the light reflected from a distant object to approach the observer from below eye level. Because the brain perceives the light as following the straight path, the object appears below its original position

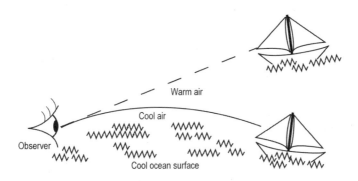

Figure 5.21: Looming mirage.

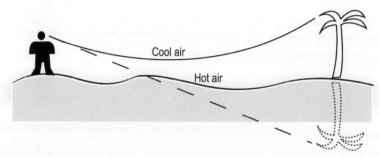

Figure 5.22: Inferior mirage.

and is frequently inverted. The palm tree in Figure 5.22 will appear inverted when the rays that originate near the top of the tree are bent more than those that originate near the base of the tree. The observed palm trees are real, but the shimmering water surface on which the reflection of the palms appears to be seen, as well as the reflected palms, are part of the mirage. Such desert mirages are called inferior mirages since the images appear below the true location of the observed object. Other optical and radio anomalies in the atmosphere are described in Corliss (1995).

Satellite tropospheric delay (RF band)

Incoming satellite signals propagate through the troposphere, from 60 km above the Earth to the Earth's surface. The refractivity N in the troposphere changes continuously along the path due to variations in temperature T, pressure p, and partial water vapour pressure e. As a consequence, the signals do not travel along straight lines and variations (delays) in the propagation velocity occur. Since time observables are converted to ranges or range differences using the signal velocity, changes in the velocity affect the range accuracy.

The actual delay in a signal from the satellite is also a function of the satellite elevation. The closer the satellite is to the horizon, the longer the path of the signal through the troposphere and the larger the delay. The tropospheric delay is caused by both retardation of the signal and path curvature. The total range error Δs due to the tropospheric delay can be expressed by the integral

$$\Delta s = 10^{-6} \int_{0}^{t} N(s)ds \qquad (5.50)$$

where the integration takes place along the signal path from the ground station ($s = 0$) to the height of the upper troposphere ($s = t$). If the refractivity N is expressed as a function of the height h above sea level, an elevation angle mapping function is introduced to map $N(h)$ onto the signal path (slant range) and the above equation can be rewritten as

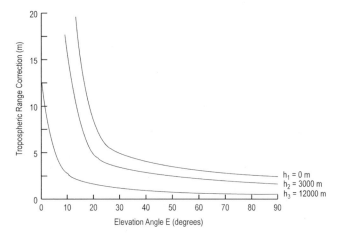

Figure 5.23: Tropospheric delay versus elevation angle for receivers at various heights.

$$\Delta s = 10^{-6} \int_{h_1}^{h_2} N(h)(dl/dh)dh \qquad (5.51)$$

where h_1 is the height of the receiver, h_2 is the height of the upper troposphere (e.g., approximately 60 km), $N(h)$ is the vertical refractivity profile model, l is the slant range signal path and dl/dh is the elevation angle mapping function.

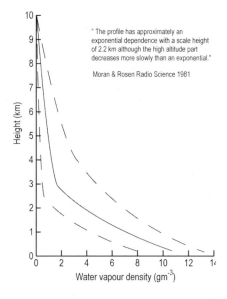

Figure 5.24: Water vapour density ρ_v [10^{-6}g/cm^3] (solid line) and one sigma error bounds (dashed lines).

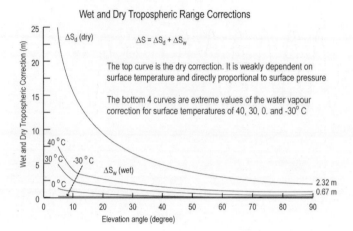

Figure 5.25: Dry and wet tropospheric effects (after Black and Eisner, 1984).

The total tropospheric effect for average conditions is shown in Figure 5.23 for different heights of the receiver. This effect remains the same for any RF frequency.

The total tropospheric effect can be represented by two separate effects:

- Wet (water vapour) effect - 10% of total effect.
- Dry (temperature and pressure) effect - 90% of total effect.

Water vapour mostly occurs in the first 10 km of the atmosphere, as shown in Figure 5.24. Some dry and wet effects of the troposphere are shown in Figure 5.25.

The dry term of the tropospheric delay can usually be well-modelled because the dry temperature and pressure are relatively stable. The wet term is more difficult to model because of the variability of the water vapour content.

Predictability of tropospheric delay (for elevations of 10° or higher):

- The dry term contributes 80 to 90% of the total effect. The accuracy of the predicted dry term at the zenith is better than 1% (less than 0.9% of total error).
- The wet term contributes 10 to 20% of the total effect. The accuracy of the predicted wet term at the zenith is 10 to 20% (less than 4% of total error).

One way of determining the water vapour content of the atmosphere along the propagation path is direct measurement with water vapour radiometers (WVR). A WVR accurately measures water vapour in specific directions using frequencies at the high end of the RF spectrum, i.e., above 20 GHz. It is however a complex and expensive instrument and is used for special applications only.

Several empirical expressions have been developed to approximate the integral in (5.51) for the total range error due to tropospheric delay (e.g., Hopfield, Saastamoinen, Black). These expressions are used in satellite navigation. Black's model (Black, 1978) was developed initially to remove the tropospheric range effects in navigation computation employing satellite Doppler data. This model is given as follows

$$\Delta s = \Delta s_d + \Delta s_w$$
$$\Delta s_d = 2.343 \cdot p \cdot ((T - 4.12)/T) \cdot l(h = h_d, E)$$
$$\Delta s_w = k_w \cdot l(h = h_w, E) \tag{5.52}$$
$$l(h, E) = \sqrt{1 - \frac{\cos^2 E}{(1 + (1 - l_c) \cdot h/r_s)^2}}$$

where $h_d = 148.98 \cdot (T - 4.12)$ m above the station, $h_w = 13,000$ m, $l_c = 0.85$, r_s is distance in m from the Earth's centre of mass to the station, p is surface pressure in standard atmospheres, T is surface temperature in Kelvin and k_w depends on latitude and season: it is 0.28 for summer in the tropics or in mid-latitudes, 0.20 for spring and fall in mid-latitudes, 0.12 for winter in maritime latitudes, 0.06 for winter in continental mid-latitudes, and 0.05 for polar regions.

Comparison of RF and light/laser wave refractivity (after Rueger, 1990)

To determine tropospheric refractivity for RF, the temperature T, atmospheric pressure p, and water vapour pressure e are measured on the ground as close to the line-of-sight as possible (and at as many points as possible). Average values of T, p and e are used to obtain N (e.g., from (5.48)).

For the visible and near-visible bands, the refractivity or refractive index in the troposphere is a function of frequency f (or the wavelength λ). Let n_s be the refractive index of air at 0°C, 1013.25 mbar and 0.03% carbon dioxide content. Then the refractivity is given by

$$N = (n_s - 1) \cdot 10^6 = 287.604 + 3 \cdot \frac{1.6288}{\lambda^2} + 5 \cdot \frac{0.0136}{\lambda^4} \tag{5.53}$$

where the wavelength λ is in micrometres (μm). The refractive index n_T at temperature T (°C), pressure p (mbar) and water vapour pressure e (mbar) is then

$$n_T - 1 = (n_s - 1) \cdot \frac{273.15}{273.15 + T} \cdot \frac{p}{1013.25} - \frac{11.27 \cdot 10^{-6}}{273.15 + T} e \tag{5.54}$$

for the visible and near-visible bands.

In order to understand limitations in the use of the various formulae for refractivity, it is interesting to carry out a simple error propagation analysis.

For RF signals, differentiation of the Essen-Froome formula (5.48) for $T = 10\,°C$, $p = 1013.25$ mbar, and $e = 13$ mbar gives

$$dn_{RF} \cdot 10^6 = -1.4 dT + 0.3 dP + 4.6 de \tag{5.55}$$

Table 5.9: Accuracies of p, T and e required to obtain one ppm accuracy for the refractive index.

Parameter	Light/laser	RF
T	1.0°C	0.80°C
p	3.6 mbar	3.80 mbar
e	26.0 mbar	0.23 mbar

which means that an error of 1°C in temperature affects the refractive index and range by 1.4 ppm, an error of 1 mbar in pressure by 0.3 ppm and an error of 1 mbar in water vapour pressure by 4.6 ppm.

Differentiation of the visible/laser formula (5.54) using initial values of $T = 15$ °C, $p = 1007$ mbar, $e = 13$ mbar and a refractive index n_s of 1.0003045 gives

$$dn_T \cdot 10^6 = -1.00dT + 0.28dp - 0.04de \tag{5.56}$$

which means that an error of 1°C in temperature affects the refractive index and range by 1 ppm, an error of 1 mbar in pressure by 0.3 ppm and an error of 1 mbar in water vapour pressure by 0.04 ppm.

In order to maintain a precision of 1 ppm in the value of the refractive index, T, p and e must be measured with the accuracies given in Table 5.9. The humidity must be measured with an accuracy 100 times higher for RF waves than for optical/laser waves. This is very difficult to achieve because humidity is very unevenly distributed within the first 10 km of the troposphere. The average humidity is usually less than the allowable error in the case of light/laser measurements and e is often neglected in the calculation of n_L. Ground-based laser EDM (Electromagnetic Distance Measurements) are more accurate than microwave equipment but are limited to line-of-sight.

5.2.7 Ionosphere

The ionosphere (Banks and Kockarts, 1973) is the region of the atmosphere extending from heights of approximately 60 km to 1,000-1,500 km in which the ionization of gases, i.e., the concentration of free electrons, is particularly intense.

At frequencies from 5 MHz to 50 MHz, RF waves are almost entirely reflected by ionospheric layers. The actual frequency at which waves will reflect is a function of electron content and angle of incidence.

Solar ultra-violet radiation results in the ionization of gases (release of free electrons). Since the molecular density at ionospheric heights is relatively low, the recombination (or de-ionization) process is not rapid. The ionosphere contains free, neutral and charged particles, mainly electrons and ions. These electrons and ions form a *plasma*. The level of ionization is controlled by solar radiation.

Plasma of solar origin (solar wind) interacts with the Earth's magnetic field, leading to a compression of the geomagnetic field on the dayside, and a stretching of the geomagnetic field into a magnetotail on the nightside, see Figure 5.26. The resulting configuration is referred to as the *magnetosphere*.

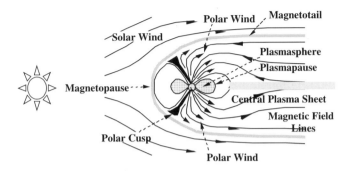

Figure 5.26: Earth's plasma shaped by the solar wind.

The *plasmasphere* is a region of high ion and electron density in the vicinity of the Earth, located primarily at geomagnetic (gm) latitudes below $55°_{gm}$. Magnetic field lines for geomagnetic latitudes in the range $55°_{gm}$-$70°_{gm}$ map to the *central plasma sheet* (CPS). Plasma instabilities in the CPS can accelerate energetic electrons towards the Earth, along magnetic field lines, where collisions with ions and neutrals create visible emissions referred to as the aurora borealis/australis (Northern and Southern lights). Geomagnetic lines above $70°_{gm}$ are referred to as the polar cap, where magnetic field lines are open to the polar wind – resulting in structured irregularities in electron density.

There are three main ionization layers designated by the symbols D, E, and F, in ascending height order. They vary in height and intensity according to time of day, time of year, and latitude. The lower and thinner part of the F layer (up to an altitude

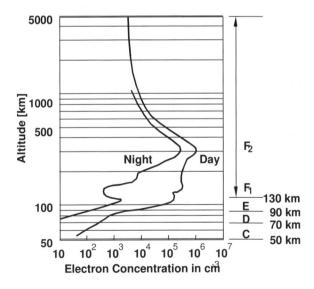

Figure 5.27: Vertical electron distribution in the ionosphere.

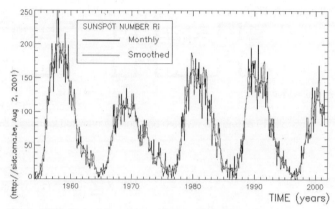

Figure 5.28: Sunspot number variation with solar cycle.

of 180-200 km) is known as the F1 layer. It shows large variations that correspond to the sunspot number. The remaining upper part of the F layer, called F2, has the greater electron density due to a lower rate of recombination. The daytime and nighttime electron distributions in mid-latitudes for a sunspot minimum are shown in Figure 5.27.

At night, the D layer vanishes due to the recombination of ions and electrons. The degree of ionization is also a function of the 11-year solar cycle (sunspot number). A maximum was reached in 1990 and mid-2000. Figure 5.28 shows variations in sunspot number for previous solar cycles.

There are several ionospheric effects on RF waves:

- *Group (or time) delay*: This is the effect of the ionosphere on a measured range using a modulated signal. The range derived from the measured code data is always too long.

- *Carrier phase advance*: Effect of the ionosphere on carrier phase data. The range derived from the measured phase data is always too short.

- *Amplitude and phase scintillation*: Short-term signal variations in amplitude and phase caused by irregularities in electron density in the ionosphere. This effect mainly occurs in the equatorial zone (i.e., in a belt of 30° on either side of the magnetic equator) and in the polar cap and auroral zone.

- *Polarization rotation*: The Faraday effect which causes the polarization of the signal to rotate as it passes through the ionosphere due to the presence of ionized particles and the Earth's magnetic field. For this reason, GPS EM-waves are circularly polarized.

- *Angular refraction*: Effect of bending of the ray due to the varying refractive index, e.g., astronomic refraction - very small at satellite frequencies.

Ionospheric propagation (after Rohan, 1991)

The refractive index n_ϕ of the ionosphere can be expressed by the Appleton formula

$$n_\phi = \sqrt{1 - \frac{80.6M}{f^2}} \qquad (5.57)$$

where f is the frequency of the signal in Hertz and M is the number of electrons per m^3. The refractive index n must be real if signal propagation is to take place. Moreover it must have a value between zero and one (propagation velocity in the medium is positive). At the bottom of the ionosphere where the electron density M is zero the refractive index $n = 1$. As the signal propagates into the ionosphere from the bottom (for a signal transmitted from the ground), the electron density increases and the refractive index n decreases.

The refractive index for the ionosphere is dependent on the frequency f of the signal (the ionosphere is a dispersive medium) and on the electron content. As a wave from the Earth penetrates the ionospheric regions of higher electron densities, n decreases and the angle of refraction θ increases according to Snell's law

$$n_{\phi,1} \sin \theta_1 = n_{\phi,2} \sin \theta_2 \qquad (5.58)$$

The path of the signal may become horizontal (i.e., $\theta_2 = 90°$) for some frequency and electron density, and the wave will be returned to the Earth as shown in Figure 5.29. At the highest point of the trajectory reached by the wave, $\sin \theta_2 = 1$ and

$$n_{\phi,1} \sin \theta_1 = n_{\phi,2}$$

Since at the bottom of the ionosphere the number of electrons is zero and $n = 1$, it follows that

$$n_{\phi,2} = \sqrt{1 - \frac{80.6M}{f^2}} = \sin \theta_1 \qquad (5.59)$$

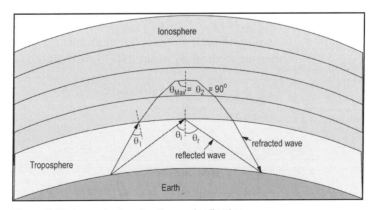

Figure 5.29: Ionospheric refraction and reflection.

The maximum electron density M_{Max} at the level of refraction will be

$$M_{Max} = \frac{f^2 \cos^2 \theta_1}{80.6} \qquad (5.60)$$

If the frequency f is sufficiently low and the electron density M sufficiently high, the ionosphere will become opaque and the wave will be reflected.

The *critical frequency* f_c at which reflection occurs (angle of incidence of 0°) is

$$f_c = 9\sqrt{M_{Max}} \qquad (5.61)$$

The critical frequency f_c generally varies between 5 and 12 MHz depending on M. As the angle of incidence increases, higher frequencies will be reflected back towards the ground. The frequency f_c is called critical in the context of over-the-horizon ground-to-ground communication.

The *Maximum Usable Frequency* (MUF) is the maximum frequency at which reflection takes place for a given angle of incidence. MUF is related to the critical frequency by

$$\text{MUF} \approx \frac{f_c}{\cos\theta_2} \approx \frac{f_c}{\cos 74°} \approx 3.6 f_c \qquad (5.62)$$

Because

$$f_c^2 = 80.6 M_{Max}$$

and, using (5.60)

$$\frac{f_c^2}{80.6} = \frac{f^2 \cos^2 \theta}{80.6}$$

then

$$f = \frac{f_c}{\cos\theta} \qquad (5.63)$$

MUF typically reaches 8-50 MHz (below these frequencies, over-the-horizon ground-to-ground communication becomes possible). The largest angle of incidence of 74° is a function of the Earth's curvature and the height of the ionosphere, as can be derived from Figure 5.30.

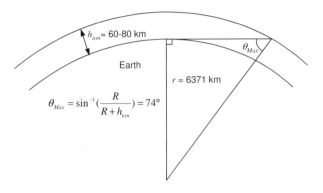

Figure 5.30: Greatest incidence angle on the ionosphere.

Group and phase velocities in the ionosphere

Modulated waves can be considered as the result of mixing different frequencies. Propagation of such waves in a dispersive medium (e.g., RF waves in the ionosphere) results in different group and phase velocities, as shown in Figure 5.31. Because the refractive index is a function of frequency, each frequency travels at a different velocity, creating a specific group velocity for the modulation envelope (e.g., code in the case of GPS). The group velocity v_g is lower than that of the speed of light (c_0). The phase velocity of the basic carrier frequency, however, is increased by an amount equal to the absolute value of the group delay. The refractive index is also a function of the electron content.

If signals are transmitted at two sufficiently separate frequencies (as in the case of GPS), the overall group delay or carrier phase advance can be calculated.

As shown in Figure 5.32, $\beta = 2\pi / \lambda$, $\omega = 2\pi f$ and the group velocity v_g, which is the local tangent of the dispersion curve, is

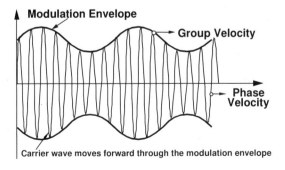

Figure 5.31: Group and phase velocities.

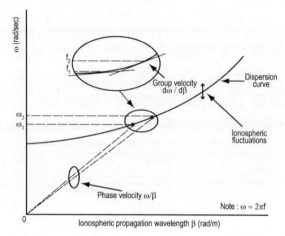

Figure 5.32: Group and phase velocities in the ionosphere.

$$v_g = d\omega / d\beta \tag{5.64}$$

while the phase velocity v_ϕ is given by the slope of the line joining the origin to the point where v_ϕ is required. Values of v_g and v_ϕ are related through the equation

$$v_g = v_\phi + \beta dv_\phi / d\beta \tag{5.65}$$

and the phase and group indices of refraction are given by

$$n_\phi = c_0 / v_\phi \tag{5.66}$$

$$n_g = c_0 / v_g \tag{5.67}$$

where c_0 is the speed of light in vacuo. Values of n_ϕ and n_g are related through the equation

$$n_g = n_\phi + f dn_\phi / df \tag{5.68}$$

The following conditions apply

$$v_\phi > v_0 > v_g$$

In vacuo, $v_\phi = v_0 = v_g$.
The group delay ΔR and carrier phase advance $\Delta \phi$ can be calculated using the following formulas

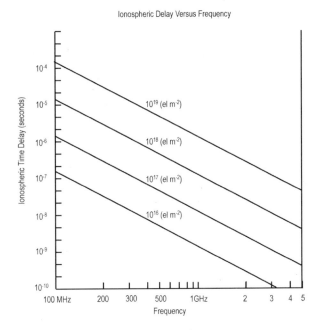

Figure 5.33: Ionospheric delay versus frequency.

$$\Delta R = \frac{40.3}{f^2} \text{TEC} \quad [\text{m}] \tag{5.69}$$

$$\Delta \phi = \frac{f}{c_0} \frac{40.3}{f^2} \text{TEC} = \frac{1.34 \times 10^{-7}}{f} \text{TEC} \quad [\text{cycles}] \tag{5.70}$$

where c_0 is the speed of light in vacuo (approximately $3 \cdot 10^8$ m/s), f is the frequency in Hertz and TEC the Total Electron Content in electrons/m^2. TEC is defined as the total number of electrons in a column with a cross-sectional area of 1 m $\times$ 1 m along the signal path through the ionosphere. For the vertical path of the signal, TEC is typically 10^{16} to 10^{18} electrons per m^2. The vertical TEC (VTEC) depends on solar cycle, diurnal effect, and geomagnetic latitude.

The actual group delay is a function of frequency, as illustrated in Figure 5.33. At the GPS L1 frequency, vertical group delay is typically between 0 and 50 ns. At an elevation angle less than 90°, the delay increases and is typically three times larger for a signal near the horizon.

Variations in ionospheric TEC

Values of vertical TEC can vary significantly, with a dependence on several factors:

- Local time: The number of free electrons depends on the production rate (which is a function of the level of ionization) and the loss rate (which depends on the

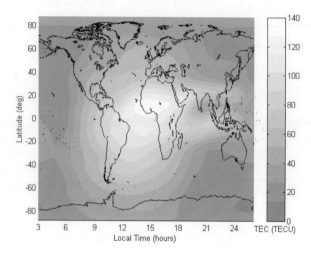

Figure 5.34: Average global distribution of TEC for March 2000. One TECU (TEC Unit) is defined as 10^{16} el/m^2.

rate of recombination of electrons and ions). The level of ionization increases with the intensity of solar radiation. The strongest solar radiation is observed at local noon. The maximum TEC occurs at 1400 local time – where the number of electrons created through ionization processes, versus loss through recombination, is maximized.

- Geographic location: In general, the magnitude of ionospheric TEC decreases at

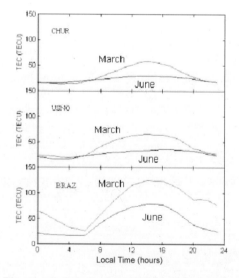

Figure 5.35: Diurnal variations in vertical TEC for March 2000 versus June 1999, for high- (CHUR), mid- (USNO) and low- (BRAZ) latitude stations.

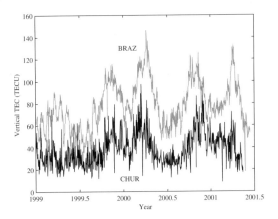

Figure 5.36: Vertical TEC variations at 1400 local time for
high- (CHUR) and low- (BRAZ) latitude regions.

higher latitudes. The low latitudes are characterized by a feature called the
equatorial anomaly. This feature consists of a double-peaked distribution in
TEC, with maxima at ±15° magnetic latitude (Figure 5.34). This feature is
particularly enhanced in the local time sector 2000-2400 at the equinoxes during
solar maximum.

- Season: Seasonal variations in TEC occur at mid- and high-latitudes, with TEC
  values being larger in the winter, versus summer, months. Annual peaks in TEC
  are also observed during the equinoctial months. Figure 5.35 shows variations in
  vertical TEC at three geographic locations for the equinoctial versus summer
  months. TEC values are enhanced by a factor two during the equinoxes, for all
  three locations.

- Solar cycle: TEC values are enhanced by a factor of 2-3 during solar maximum
  versus solar minimum. Enhancements in TEC are observed at all latitudes due to
  the overall increased solar radiation. A solar maximum occurred mid-2000, see
  also Figure 5.28, with corresponding variations in TEC. Both seasonal and solar
  cycle variations in TEC are shown in Figure 5.36

Dual-frequency corrections (RF band)

Assume that GPS pseudorange measurements p are made simultaneously on two
frequencies, namely L1 and L2. The ionospheric effects on $p(L1)$ and $p(L2)$ are

$$\delta p_{ion}(L1) = \frac{40.3}{f_{L1}^2} TEC \qquad (5.71)$$

$$\delta p_{ion}(L2) = \frac{40.3}{f_{L2}^2}\text{TEC} \tag{5.72}$$

The ionospherically corrected pseudorange $p(L1/L2)$ can thus be obtained as

$$p(L1/L2) = p(L1) - \delta p_{ion}(L1) \text{ or}$$
$$p(L1/L2) = p(L2) - \delta p_{ion}(L2) \tag{5.73}$$

Combination of the above formulae eliminates the unknown TEC. The ionospheric correction to $p(L1)$ is therefore

$$\delta p_{ion}(L1) = \frac{p(L1) - p(L2)}{1 - \dfrac{f_{L1}^2}{f_{L2}^2}} \tag{5.74}$$

In the case of GPS, L1 = 1575.42 MHz and L2 = 1227.6 MHz, and

$$\delta p_{ion}(L1) = -1.546 \cdot (p(L1) - p(L2)) \tag{5.75}$$

The above linear combination, however, increases the error on the individual ionospherically corrected pseudorange. Assuming the same standard deviation σ_p for the L1 and L2 pseudoranges and applying the covariance law results in

$$\sigma_p(L_1/L_2) \approx 3\sigma_p \tag{5.76}$$

Ionospherically corrected data should therefore be used only when the effect is significant. The carrier phase ionospheric correction using dual-frequency data can be derived in a similar way. It is expressed (in cycles) as

$$\delta\phi_{ion}(L1) = \frac{f_{L2}^2}{f_{L2}^2 - f_{L1}^2}\left(\phi(L1) - \frac{f_{L1}}{f_{L2}}\phi(L2) - N_{L1} - \frac{f_{L1}}{f_{L2}}N_{L2}\right) \tag{5.77}$$

The total ionospheric delay $\delta\phi_{ion}(L1)$ at an epoch cannot be determined due to the ambiguities N_{L1} and N_{L2}. If both L1 and L2 carriers are tracked without any cycle slips over an interval (t_1, t_2) the differential ionospheric delay $\Delta\delta\phi_{ion}(L1)$ over (t_1, t_2) can be determined because the ambiguities remain unchanged over this time interval.

Scintillation effects

Phase and amplitude *scintillations* can cause degraded tracking of RF signals by GPS receivers. The rapid phase variations (phase scintillations) cause a Doppler shift in the GPS signal, which may exceed the bandwidth of the phase lock loop (PLL), resulting in a loss of phase lock. Additionally, amplitude fades can cause the signal-to-noise ratio (SNR) to drop below receiver threshold, resulting in loss of code lock. These effects have a larger impact on tracking loops employing codeless and semicodeless technologies (to extract the encrypted L2 signal) versus full code correlation. Availability of the L2 signal is particularly important for positioning applications that require formation of widelane and/or ionosphere-free observables. The magnitude and frequency of low latitude scintillations are well-correlated with seasonal enhancements of the equatorial anomaly. High latitude scintillations are generally associated with aurora at high latitudes.

Figure 5.37 shows the hourly percentage of L2 phase cycle slips and missing observations due to scintillations in three latitude regions. No data were available for NLGN until mid-1999. The larger percentages of corrupt observations are derived for the low latitude station BRAZ, where a clear seasonal dependence exists. The largest low latitude percentages are found in winter months. Degraded GPS receiver tracking performance is observed relatively regularly at the high latitude station CENA – these values are associated with the aurora. Tracking performance is considerably better at the mid-latitude station NLGN, where scintillation effects are rarely observed.

5.2.8 Atmospheric attenuation

At frequencies greater than 3 GHz, rain, clouds or fog may cause significant

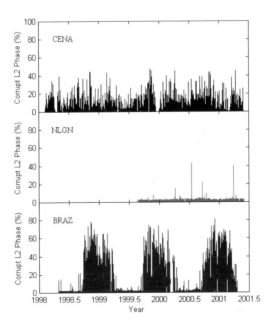

Figure 5.37: L2 tracking performance for GPS receivers in high- (CENA), mid- (NLGN) and low- (BRAZ) latitude regions.

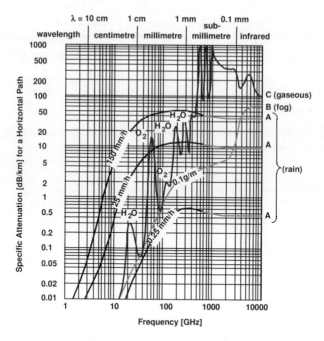

Figure 5.38: Attenuation due to rain, fog and atmospheric gases.

absorption and scattering of radio energy. Such absorbing media also generate thermal noise which frequently needs to be considered in Earth-space systems. Scattering from clouds or precipitation may be a source of substantial interference between systems. Even in clear air, the absorption by atmospheric gases alone and the associated noise radiation may strongly affect frequencies greater than 20 GHz.

The *specific attenuation* (in dB/km) due to rain, fog and atmospheric gases for transmission through the atmosphere (temperature 20°C, pressure at sea level 1 atm, water vapour content 7.5 g/m^3) is shown in Figure 5.38 for frequencies in the range 1-10,000 GHz (after Hall and Barclay, 1989). The figure shows the relative importance of rain, fog and atmospheric gases in the cm wavelength to visible region of the spectrum. It also shows a relatively low level of attenuation for GPS frequencies (1.2 and 1.5 GHz). GPS is an all-weather system. A system working in the infra-red part of the spectrum (e.g., satellite laser ranging) would obviously not function in all weather.

The specific attenuation [dB/m] of RF waves up to 30 MHz propagating between two points on the Earth's surface is shown in Figure 5.39 (after Hall and Barclay, 1989). Attenuation is generally lower for lower frequencies. Nighttime attenuation is lower than daytime attenuation because the D layer of the ionosphere disappears at night.

The magnitude of attenuation (due to rain, fog, snow and ice) depends on the frequency of the wave, the elevation angle, and the intensity of the meteorological phenomena. Specific attenuation as a function of rain rate is given in Figure 5.40 for the frequencies 10, 30 and 100 GHz. The lower the frequency of the propagated

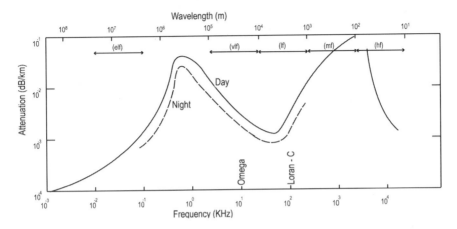

Figure 5.39: RF attenuation on the Earth's surface.

signal, the smaller the attenuation. In the case of GPS, the attenuation is relatively low since satellite-based waves cross only a few km of rain (rain clouds are below a few thousand metres) and the frequency of the signal is on the order of 1.2 GHz. Therefore the attenuation due to rain is negligible for GPS.

Example 5.5: Effect of ice on a GPS antenna.
For up to a few cm of dry fresh water ice, the attenuation is less than a few dBs. If the ice surface is wet, the attenuation is larger but still insignificant (the attenuation would be much larger for sea water ice).
Ref: O'Keefe, K., J. Stephen, G. Lachapelle and R. Gonzales: Effect of Ice Loading on a GPS Antenna. Proceedings of National Technical Meeting, The Institute of Navigation, January 25-27, San Diego, CA, pp. 861-869, 1999.

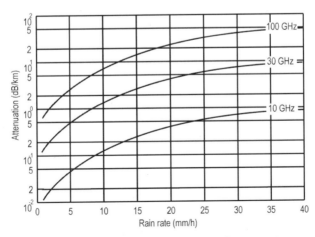

Figure 5.40: Specific RF attenuation due to rain.

Fog is a visibility restricting suspension of tiny water droplets or ice crystals in the atmospheric layer next to the Earth's surface. Fog with lower visibility restriction is called a suspended mist. Heavy fog with a 150 m visibility has a water content of approximately 0.32 g/m^3. The attenuation caused by fog is related to the attenuation caused by the rain. At frequencies of 7 and 75 GHz, the specific attenuation due to fog is 0.1 and 1 dB/km, respectively.

Ice crystals cause relatively low attenuation. *Wet snow* causes higher attenuation than rain, e.g., 2 dB/km at 35 GHz for a precipitation of 5 mm/h. *Dry snow* results in attenuation at least one order of magnitude less than wet snow. *Hail* is mainly formed by the accretion of supercooled cloud droplets, giving rise to large, high-density particles of roughly spherical shape. Although hail has higher apparent permittivity than snow, attenuation below 30 GHz is weak and can be neglected.

Example 5.6: Snow and ice experiments.

An experiment carried out by a group of undergraduate students in Winter 1996, where up to 1.5 m of loose dry snow was put on the top of a GPS antenna, showed practically no lost of signal strength. A few cm of solid ice shaped in the form of a cone (created using two bowls and a freezer) resulted in very significant signal attenuation. A controlled experiment with 0.5 inch (1.25 cm) of solid ice on GPS antennas in Spring 1998 resulted in a signal strength attenuation of typically 3 dB.

5.2.9 RF propagation at various frequencies

Electromagnetic waves travel in straight lines, except where the Earth and the atmosphere alter their path. Frequencies above the HF range ($f > 30$ MHz), i.e., VHF, UHF, etc., generally travel along straight lines (except for refraction due to varying atmospheric density). These are *space waves* or *direct waves* (e.g., satellite signals).

Frequencies in the HF band (3 MHz $< f <$ 30 MHz) are reflected by the ionized layers of the atmosphere. These are known as *sky waves* or *ionospheric waves*. Frequencies below the HF range ($f < 3$ MHz), i.e. MF, LF, etc., propagate along the Earth's surface. They travel around the curvature of the Earth, sometimes traveling around the globe. Their travel mode is constrained by the combination of diffraction and the waveguide effect formed by the Earth's surface and the lowest ionized layer of the atmosphere. Such waves are called *ground waves* or *surface waves* (e.g., Omega).

Various wave propagation modes are shown in Figure 5.41. The effect of the ionosphere is a function of frequency, electron content and angle of incidence, as discussed earlier. Below a certain penetration frequency, and for given elevation angle, the signal will be reflected back to the Earth. The ionospheric refraction decreases with increasing frequency and elevation angle. With the increase of elevation angle the height of reflection becomes greater, reaching a maximum for vertical incidence. If the frequency is increased, the height of reflection increases,

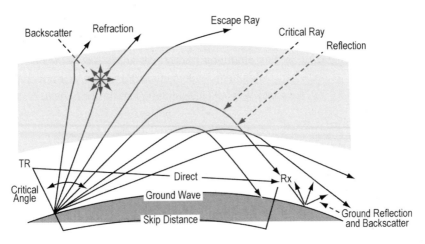

Figure 5.41: RF wave propagation modes.

and at the critical frequency (dependent on the maximum electron density of a layer) the ray will penetrate the ionospheric layer.

For frequencies below the critical frequency, rays transmitted with a zenith angle below a certain critical angle will be reflected back to Earth. Some energy is scattered from the ground back to the transmitter site, some is scattered (reflected) forward and some is absorbed. High rays and low rays may arrive together at distances beyond a skip distance within which no signals are received.

At night, the electron content in the ionosphere is lower (no D layer) and RF waves bouncing off the F layer will be subject to less absorption, resulting in a stronger sky wave. This is why radio reception is generally better at night. However, there may be a skip distance within which reception is poor or null.

Phase factors for ground waves

The Earth is not a perfect conductor. Some of the EM energy is absorbed into the ground or water. It results in bending of a wave and an observable phase lag which increases with the distance from the transmitter and decreases with increasing conductivity and frequency up to an altitude of five times the signal wavelength. The phase factors are:

- *Primary Factor* (PF): Correction for propagation through the atmosphere as opposed to free space – this is the effect of refractivity.
- *Secondary Factor* (SF): Additional delay when the signal is assumed to propagate over an all sea-water (conductivity $\sigma = 5$ S/m) path.
- *Additional Secondary Factor* (ASF): Additional delay caused by propagation over terrain. The ASF depends on the terrain conductivity.

The phase factors are expressed in units of time (usually μs) or length (m). The combined effect of SF + ASF, which increases as the frequency decreases, is shown in Figure 5.42 for various terrain conductivities and for a frequency of 100 kHz

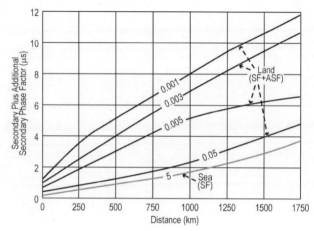

Figure 5.42: Combined effect of SF + ASF at 100 kHz for various terrain conductivities.

(Loran-C). The average conductivity for good soil (in term of conductivity) is 0.05 S/m and 0.001 S/m for relatively poor soil.

The total attenuation of a surface wave will depend on frequency f and conductivity σ. The field strength in dB referred to 1 μV/m for 100 kHz (Loran-C) is given in Figure 5.43 as a function of range from the transmitter for various surfaces. As to whether a signal can be measured will also depend on the receiver sensitivity and the level of atmospheric radio noise.

Mixed conductivity paths (e.g., sea water/land) occur over grounds with varying conductivity. Millington has designed a method to estimate the field strength for mixed path propagation (Hall and Barclay, 1989). This method is summarized in

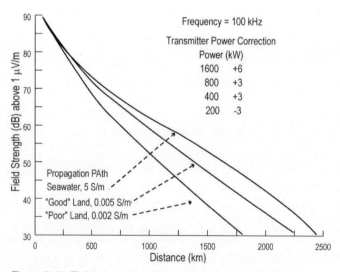

Figure 5.43: Field attenuation of a surface wave at 100 kHz.

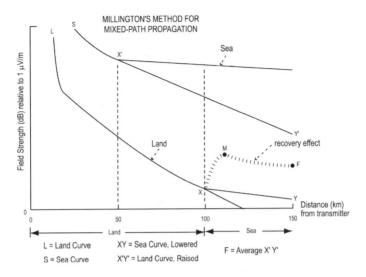

Figure 5.44: Millington's method to calculate field strength for a mixed path.

Figure 5.44.

Propagation from land to sea:

L + (XY) curve: in this case, the first 100 km on the x-axis is the curve for land, followed by the 50 km curve for the sea moved downwards to join the land curve at X to give a point Y at 150 km.

Propagation from sea to land:

S + (X'Y') curve: in this case, the first 50 km on the x-axis is the curve for the sea, followed by the 100 km curve for the land moved upwards to join the sea curve at X' to give a point Y' at 150 km.

Y and Y' are at different locations. However, the field strength must be independent from the direction of propagation. An average of Y and Y' gives the actual field strength F.

When traveling from land to sea, the field strength increases as the distance increases from the transmitter. This *recovery effect* (shown with the dotted line) is due to the better conductivity of sea water.

Mixed sea-land transmission requires us to consider the additional phase lag caused by the land. Plessey's method (Samaddar, 1979) of determining phase change over a mixed path is illustrated in Figure 5.45. The phase at a distance R (D(land) + d(sea)) from the transmitter T is needed. In order to estimate the effect of propagation from land to sea, the curve (b) must be shifted upwards to join with curve (a) at B; the dotted line gives θ_1 at R. In order to estimate the effect of propagation from sea to land, shift the curve (a) downwards to join with the curve (b) at B'; the dotted line gives θ_2 at R. The resulting phase θ at R is simply

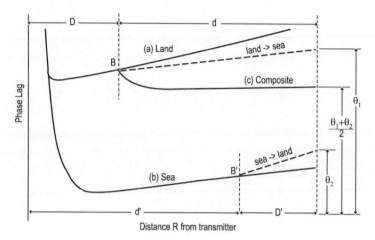

Figure 5.45: Plessey's method to calculate phase lag for a mixed path.

$$\theta = \frac{\theta_1 + \theta_2}{2} \tag{5.78}$$

The phase change between terrain with three types of conductivity, namely $\sigma_1 = 0.005$ S/m, $\sigma_2 = 0.0005$ S/m and $\sigma_3 = 5$ S/m, is shown in Figure 5.46 (after Pisano et al., 1991). The areas with different conductivity, as well as the location of the transmitter and the three receivers, are shown - as well as the phase recovery for the three transmission paths.

Example 5.7: Ambiguity resolution.
A ground-based radionavigation system uses a carrier frequency of 200 kHz. Assume that some type of modulation is used such that ranging is possible in addition to carrier phase measurements. Range resolution is possible with an accuracy of 50 m. The ground wave is used.
a) Can the carrier phase ambiguity be resolved exactly?

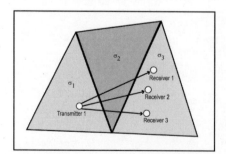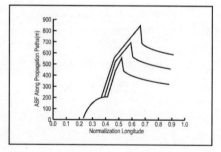

Figure 5.46: ASF for various paths with three types of conductivity ($\sigma_1 = 0.005$ S/m, $\sigma_2 = 0.0005$ S/m and $\sigma_3 = 5$ S/m).

The wavelength of a 200 kHz system is $\lambda = c/f = 1,500$ m. Since the range accuracy (50 m) is better than 1/2 cycle (750 m), the ambiguity can be resolved exactly if one neglects the effect of PF + SF + ASF. However, PF + SF + ASF becomes significant as the distance from the transmitter increases. At 200 kHz, the effect is less than at 100 kHz. PF can be easily estimated (320 ppm of distance). SF is also easily estimated because it is for a uniform conductivity of 5 S/m, but ASF is difficult to estimate - especially over terrain due to conductivity variations and topography. Once a cumulated error due to PF+PF+ASF of 750 m (2.5 μs) occurs, an incorrect ambiguity would result.

b) What carrier phase accuracy might be expected in unit of length?
   Typically 1° to a few degrees of phase. Assume a worst case of 3.6° or 1/100 of a cycle: 0.01 of 1,500 m is 15 m. The instantaneous accuracy would be 15 m or better.

c) Are a) and b) important in view of the primary, secondary and additional secondary phase lags?
   Generally yes, both for predictable (i.e., absolute) and repeatable accuracy. Although PF, SF and ASF might be in excess of 750 m (1/2 cycle) for long distances, PF and SF can be easily estimated. Over flat terrain with relatively constant and/or known conductivity, ASF can also be estimated or measured. If the conductivity is unknown, however, and in mountainous areas, the ASF could easily exceed 750 m preventing the user from fully benefitting from the high resolution of the measurements if predictable accuracy is required. Since ASF due to conductivity and/or topography is more or less constant, a high measurement resolution would in any case benefit the repeatable accuracy.

Example 5.8: Propagation effects.
a) An RF ground wave is propagating over 2,000 km of sea which has a conductivity of 5 S/m. Calculate the phase factors PF, SF and ASF.
   The frequency is not specified but for propagation to occur over 2,000 km an LF system has to be used, in addition to a powerful transmitter. Since we have SF and ASF effects for 100 kHz (Figure 5.42), we will assume that the frequency is 100 kHz. The calculations are straightforward:
   PF $\approx$ 320 ppm $\approx$ 640 m
   Assuming f = 100 kHz, we can use the graph in Figure 5.42 (extrapolation) and SF $\approx$ 4.5 μs (in metres: 4.5 $\times$ 300 = 1,350 m) and ASF $\approx$ 0 because the propagation is over sea water.

b) Assume that the same ground wave is now propagating over land with a conductivity of 0.005 S/m. Re-calculate the PF, SF and ASF for this case.
   PF $\approx$ 320 ppm $\approx$ 640 m (same)
   SF $\approx$ 4.5 μs (in metres: 4.5 x 300 = 1,350 m) (same)
   SF + ASF $\approx$ 7 μs (from Figure 5.42)
   ASF $\approx$ 7 μs - 4.5 μs (SF) $\approx$ 2.5 μs (750 m)

c) Discuss the effects of atmospheric refraction on both Loran-C (100 kHz) and Omega (10 kHz).

Loran-C: Ground wave used, tropospheric refraction applies and average is 320 ppm. A lower ionosphere will affect the sky wave - could cause interference, depending on distance from transmitter. Also, mixed path propagation will mean that atmospheric conditions could change quite drastically. Weather fronts could also affect accuracy.

Omega: Diurnal variation of the lower ionospheric layer will cause variation in the wave velocity. This will affect the range or range difference accuracy, the more since the transmission distances are very long. This effect can largely be accounted for using standard correction tables.

5.3 Time keeping

Time and navigation (e.g., longitude) are intrinsically related. The difference of time measured between two points and related to the same time scale corresponds to the difference of longitudes between these points. The more precise the time measurement, the more precise the determination of longitude difference. The progress in the precision of time measurement during the past few centuries can be illustrated as follows:

- 1714: British Board of longitude offered £20,000 for navigation accuracy of 30 nautical miles (nM), i.e., 0.5° of longitude at the Equator after six weeks at sea.
- 1760's: John Harrison - portable chronometer with accuracy of 1 s/day.

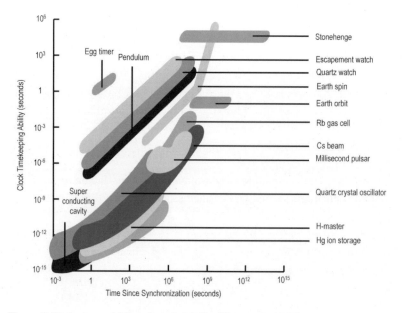

Figure 5.47: Accuracy of time keeping (after Allan et al., 1997).

- 1760's: modern chronometer by Pierre Le Roy.
- 1980s: GPS - 1 s every 100,000 years.

A detailed overview of the accuracy of time keeping is shown in Figure 5.47.

5.3.1 Time scales

Two basic groups of time scales can be distinguished:
- *Astronomical*: derived from the relatively uniform motion of celestial bodies, e.g., diurnal rotation of the Earth, or orbital motion of the Earth, Moon and planets.
- *Atomic*: derived from the highly uniform electromagnetic oscillations produced by the quantum transition of an atom.

Astronomical time scales

a) Time scales based on the diurnal rotation of the Earth:

Sidereal time is based on the Earth's rotation with respect to stars (vernal equinox) – as measured by the hour angle of the vernal equinox. *Solar time* is based on the Earth's rotation with respect to the Sun – as measured by the hour angle of the Sun. Both sidereal and solar time depend on the geographic location of the point (hour angle determines the position of the local astronomic meridian with respect to vernal equinox).

Universal time is the mean solar time of Greenwich as measured by the Greenwich hour angle of the mean Sun. Universal time can be considered as a special form of sidereal time. The difference in the length of the sidereal and solar day is of the order of four minutes. The universal time scale is not a uniform scale and several universal times have been defined:
- UT0 is the raw universal time obtained from observations at a particular station (referred to the actual rotation axis and instantaneous pole).
- UT1 is UT0 reduced to the Conventional Terrestrial Pole (CTP), i.e., with the polar motion removed (referred to the actual rotation axis and the CTP).
- UT2 is UT1 with seasonal (periodic) variations in the Earth rotation removed (referred to the mean rotation axis and the CTP).

b) Time scale based on Earth orbital motion:

Ephemeris time (ET) is based on the Earth's orbital motion around the Sun as opposed to the Earth's rotation. The rotation random fluctuations are removed. Formally the ephemeris second was defined as a certain fraction of the Tropical Year 1900, and hence it was strictly uniform. The availability of ET is delayed in order to use dynamic time to remove the fluctuations.

c) Time scale based on the orbital motion of the celestial bodies:

Dynamic time (DT) is based on the orbital motion of the celestial bodies described in adequate reference frames. DT fulfills at best the conceptual idea of inertial time and it is used for calculations in satellite geodesy.

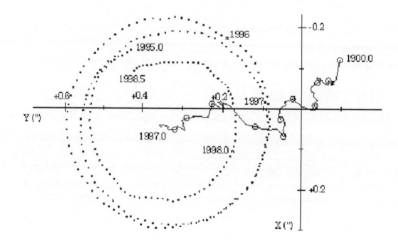

Figure 5.48: Polar motion 1995-98 and mean pole displacement since 1900 (IERS, 2001).

Polar motion

Astronomically observed positions (latitude, longitude) or time are referred to the instantaneous (actual) rotation axis of the Earth which defines the instantaneous (actual) pole. The position of the instantaneous rotation axis with respect to the Earth's crust varies in time. The position of the instantaneous pole changes in time up to a few tenths of one arcsec. A suitable Earth-fixed reference system must be connected in a well-defined way with the Earth's crust. Such a system constitutes a Conventional Terrestrial System (CTS).

Figure 5.48 shows the periodic variation of the position of the pole in 1995-1998 as

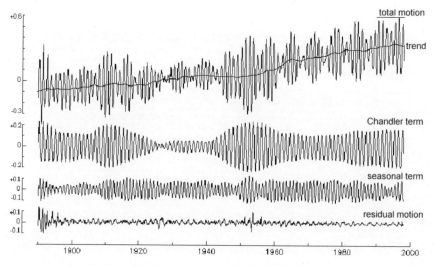

Figure 5.49: Variation of y-coordinate of polar motion (IERS, 2001).

derived by the International Earth Rotation Service (IERS) from its worldwide network. The small circles correspond to the average pole position in different epochs from 1900 until 1997. The displacement of the mean pole illustrates the secular effect in the polar motion. The periodicity of the polar motion is represented by a Chandler term (period about 1.2 years), a seasonal term (period of 1 year), as well as a secular effect (trend), as shown in Figure 5.49.

Time interval (time unit)

The time interval between two consecutive phenomena forms the scale measure of the particular time scale. A certain fraction of the time scale measure is called the time unit. Conventionally the *second* (s) is used as the basic time unit. Larger time units, e.g., days, years, are derived from the second.

Definitions of the second:

- Prior to 1956: 1 s = 1/86,400 of a *mean solar day*.
- Between 1956 and 1967: 1 s = 1/31,556,925.9747 of the Tropical Year 1900.
- Since 1967: 1 s = 9,192,631,770 *periods of the radiation* of the transition between the two hyperfine levels of the ground state of the cesium-133 atom. Such a second is called the ephemeris second.

The ephemeris second is also used as the unit of time of the International System of Units (SI).

Atomic time scale

The *Atomic Time Scale* was introduced on 1 January 1958 to meet the needs for an easily accessible and strictly uniform time scale. The ephemeris second was selected

Table 5.10: Laboratories with independent atomic time scales (after Moritz and Mueller, 1987).

Laboratory (i)	Designation	TAI-TA (i) [s]	
		10/01/1982	26/12/1982
Commission Nationale de l'Heure, Paris, France	F2	-47.24	-33.14
National Bureau of Standards, Boulder, Colorado, U.S.A.	NBS	-45064.41	-45063.48
NRC/CNRC, Ottawa, Canada	NRC	23.03	23.18
Office Fédéral de Météorologie, Berne, Switzerland	OFM	-	-4.77
Physikalisch-Technische Bundes-anstalt, Braunschweig, Germany	PTB	-363.21	-363.53
Royal Greenwich Observatory Herstmonceux, U.K.	RGO	64.51	58.37
Radio Research Laboratories, Tokyo, Japan	RRL	10.3	8.2
U.S. Naval Observatory, Washington, D.C., U.S.A.	USNO	-34459.96	-34472.53

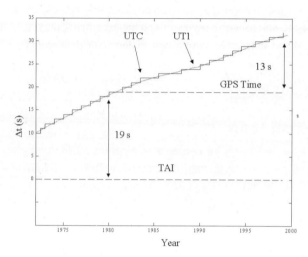

Figure 5.50: Overview of time scales (after Seeber, 1993).

as the unit of the atomic time. The atomic time scale is based on the readings of a large number of atomic clocks in different laboratories, see Table 5.10. Practically, the atomic time scale is derived from groups of commercial cesium standards which generate time intervals, based on the definition of the SI second.

TAI (Temps Atomique International) is based on the average of some 220 cesium clocks located in many parts of the world. Intercomparison of the clocks was maintained through Omega in the 1960's (2-20 μs) and Loran-C (100-300 ns) in the late 1960's and 1970's. Nowadays it is mostly done with geostationary satellites (e.g., GOES) and GPS with an accuracy of a few ns.

The epoch of TAI agreed with the epoch of UT1 on January 1, 1958. Since the Earth's rotation is slowing down and the two scales are not identical, the difference between the TAI and UT1 time scales is increasing. For many applications, including navigation, a time scale is required which provides a highly uniform time unit as well as the best possible adaptation to UT1 (to the Earth rotation). Therefore the UTC time scale was introduced in 1972.

UTC (Universal Time Coordinated) has the same rate as TAI but differs from TAI by an integer number of seconds (leap seconds) due to periodic corrections. The epoch of UTC is adapted to UT1 by inserting (or removing) leap seconds either on January 1 or July 1 when it is necessary, i.e., in order to have $DUT1 = |\, UT1 - UTC\,| \leq 0.9$ s. DUT1 is published in the bulletins of the IERS.

The Global Positioning System uses its own time scale, namely *GPS time*. It differs from TAI by several seconds (GPS time was identical to UTC (USNO) on January 5, 1980). The relation between UTC and GPS time is disseminated through the GPS navigation message. Figure 5.50 gives an overview of the relationship between different time scales.

The constant difference of 32.184 s between the dynamic time and TAI is due to the fact that the ephemeris second used in the dynamic time scale since January 1, 1984 has been derived from the mean duration of the solar day between 1756 and 1895, when Earth rotation was faster than today.

5.3.2 Timing accuracies and RF measurements

For RF and precise time measurements, an oscillator of high stability (with frequency as constant as possible) is required. The oscillator generates pulses at equal time intervals, say every 1 ms. The oscillator converts the DC voltage and current into AC. The sinusoidal variations generate RF waves. The RF frequency required is obtained by multiplying/dividing the oscillator's output.

In atomic clocks, the conversion of the oscillator cycles to the scale unit (second) is achieved via electronic counters or divisors. The Basic Time Standard (atomic clock) consists of an oscillator and a pulse counter. Since RF waves are propagated with the speed of light, i.e., 3×10^8 m/s, time interval measurements are required with a very high level of accuracy.

Conventionally the oscillator frequency f corresponds to the number of "events" per unit of time. For an ideal clock, the relation between the oscillation period (cycle period) T, i.e., time between events, and the oscillator frequency f is

$$f = \frac{1}{T} \tag{5.79}$$

The ratio of the total number of events to the number of events per unit of time gives the accumulated clock time, i.e.,

$$\text{accumulated clock time} = \frac{\text{total number of events}}{\text{number of events per unit of time}} \tag{5.80}$$

A frequency standard is required to generate a highly stable and regular number of events per unit of time.

Frequency and time standards (FTS)

FTS are devices which emit EM-waves at a relatively stable frequency when excited by an electric field. FTS error sources include:

- Long term drift due to the aging of material (the change in frequency with time due to internal changes in the oscillator).
- Environmental effects, mostly temperature (many FTS are ovenized to function at a constant temperature).

Primary standards are FTS which require no other reference(s) for calibration. Two types of primary standards are used:

- *Cesium beam* clocks which provide high accuracy and high short- and long-term

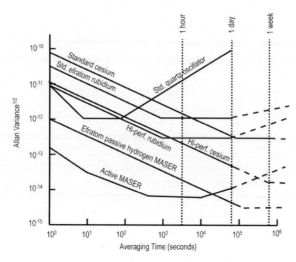

Figure 5.51: Comparison of High Performance Oscillator Frequency Stability (after Ball Corporation, 1991).

stability. They are currently used together with rubidium standards to realize the time base in the GPS satellites. Modern commercial standards provide a stability of a few parts in 10^{13}.

- *Hydrogen maser* provides the highest stability and accuracy (about 1-2 orders of magnitude better than cesium beam FTS), but they are relatively expensive.

Secondary standards include:

- *Rubidium clocks* that are approximately one order of magnitude less stable and less accurate than cesium beam FTS. They are however very portable and much less expensive (less than $10k).
- *Quartz clocks* that are relatively low cost (from less than $100 up to $1,000) and have an excellent short-term ($\Delta t < 100$ s) stability. There is a wide range of quartz oscillators on the market, from relatively low to relatively high accuracy. Quartz oscillators are used in most GPS receivers.

A comparison of high performance oscillator frequency stability is given in Figure 5.51, while the history and trend of timekeeping performance is shown in Figure 5.52.

Allan variance: measure of frequency and/or time stability (Allan et al., 1997)

The frequency of a precision clock is not strictly constant and the need arises to characterize its stability. The behavior of the frequency (or time) can be modelled and the parameters of the model can be estimated through comparison with other clocks. The relative frequency errors show repeatable behaviors for different types of precision clocks. A suitable measure for the relative frequency errors in the time domain is the *Allan variance*.

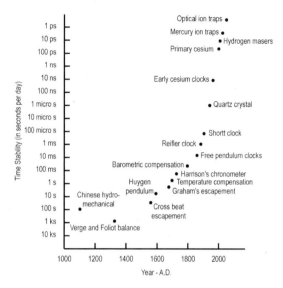

Figure 5.52: Timekeeping performance history and trend
(after Allan et al., 1997).

The Allan variance is a statistical measure to characterize the stability of an FTS over
a specified time interval. Consider three sequential time error measurements of a
clock x_n, x_{n+1} and x_{n+2}, each spaced by a time interval τ. The normalized frequency
departure averaged over the interval n to $n+1$ is

$$y_n = (x_{n+1} - x_n)/\tau \qquad (5.81)$$

or $y_n = \Delta x_n/\tau$ in terms of finite difference notation where Δ denotes the first
difference for the nth interval. Note that the normalized frequency departure or
instability is written as a dimensionless number (Allan et al., 1997). For the next
interval τ, we have

$$y_{n+1} = (x_{n+2} - x_{n+1})/\tau = \Delta x_{n+1}/\tau \qquad (5.82)$$

The instability of the clock frequency averaged over the first interval to the next can
be represented by the change in frequency Δy_n

$$\Delta y_n = y_{n+1} - y_n = (x_{n+2} - x_{n+1})/\tau - (x_{n+1} - x_n)/\tau \qquad (5.83)$$

The Allan variance, for the interval τ, is defined as

$$\sigma_y^2(\tau) = \frac{1}{2(M-1)}\sum_{n=1}^{M-1}(y_{n+1} - y_n)^2 \qquad (5.84)$$

or

$$\sigma_y^2(\tau) = \frac{1}{2\tau^2(N-1)} \sum_{n=1}^{N-2} (x_{n+2} - 2x_{n+1} + x_n)^2 \qquad (5.85)$$

where M is the number of y_n samples and N is the number of x_n samples. The right-hand sides of the above equations are divided by two such that the Allan variance is equal to the classical variance in the case where the y_n samples are random and uncorrelated (as in the case for classical cesium-beam and rubidium gas-cell frequency standards). The variance $\sigma_y^2(\tau)$ is therefore defined for an interval τ and it is a dimensionless number, e.g. 10^{-12}.

Example 5.9: Allan variance computation.
The seven (N=7) time measurement errors x_n of a clock with $\tau = 2$ s are

$$x_1 = 5 \quad x_2 = 3 \quad x_3 = -2 \quad x_4 = 4 \quad x_5 = -1 \quad x_6 = -2 \quad x_7 = 2 \quad (\times 10^{-9} \text{ s})$$

The six (M=6) normalized frequency instability values y_n are

$$y_1 = -1 \quad y_2 = -2.5 \quad y_3 = 3 \quad y_4 = -2.5 \quad y_5 = -0.5 \quad y_6 = -2 \quad (\times 10^{-9})$$

Applying (5.84) to the y_n yields

$$\sigma_y^2(2\,\text{s}) = ((-1.5)^2 + (5.5)^2 + (-5.5)^2 + (2)^2 + (2.5)^2) \cdot (10^{-9})^2 / 10 = 7.3 \cdot 10^{-18}$$

The Allan variance can also be computed by applying (5.85) to the x_n

$$\sigma_y^2(2\,\text{s}) = ((-3)^2 + (11)^2 + (-11)^2 + (4)^2 + (5)^2) \cdot (10^{-9})^2 / 40 = 7.3 \cdot 10^{-18}$$

The corresponding standard deviation, which is a measure of the frequency or time instability of the clock, is therefore 2.7 x 10^{-9}.

Clock bias error variance
The clock bias error variance σ_b^2 can be represented as follows

$$\sigma_b^2(t) = \sigma^2(t_0) + (t-t_0)^2 \cdot \sigma_y^2(\tau) \qquad (5.86)$$

where $\sigma^2(t_0)$ is the clock variance at t_0, t_0 and t are the initial and current epochs and $\sigma_y^2(\tau)$ is the Allan variance over the interval $\tau = t - t_0$.

Example 5.10: Clock bias.
Quartz clock: $\sigma_y(1\,\text{day}) = \sigma_y(86400\,\text{s}) = 10^{-10}$

Assume perfect synchronization at t_0: $\sigma^2(t_0) = 0$

$$\sigma_b^2(24\,\mathrm{h}) = (t - t_0)^2 \cdot \sigma_y^2(t - t_0)$$
$$= 86,400^2 \cdot (10^{-10})^2$$
$$= 74.65 \cdot 10^{-12}\ \mathrm{s}^2$$
$$\sigma_b(24\,\mathrm{h}) = 8.64 \cdot 10^{-6}\ \mathrm{s}$$

The equivalent range error $\sigma_R(24\,\mathrm{h})$ for a RF system would be

$$\sigma_R(24\,\mathrm{h}) = \sigma_b(24\,\mathrm{h}) \cdot c$$
$$= (8.64 \cdot 10^{-6}) \cdot (3 \cdot 10^8)$$
$$= 2,592\ \mathrm{m}$$

Example 5.11: Allan variance and positioning accuracy.
A shore-based two-transmitter range system has a ranging accuracy of 5 m. Assume an HDOP of 2.0 for the position. Since only two transmitters are available, the receiver must maintain time with a relatively high accuracy. Assume that at some reference epoch t_0, the receiver clock time can be perfectly synchronized with the transmitter clocks which themselves are error free. Calculate the Allan variance required for the user receiver clock to maintain a horizontal (2DRMS) position accuracy of 30 m after 2 hours.
The range accuracy is 5 m (1σ). At the beginning (no clock error), DRMS = 5 m × HDOP = 10 m and 2DRMS (95%) = 20 m. If there were no clock drift, the 30 m (2DRMS) accuracy objective could be achieved. After 2 hours (7,200 s), the receiver clock will have drifted. The URE will consist of the 5 m range accuracy + the effect of the clock drift. The maximum allowable value for the URE is derived as follows

2DRMS is 30 m → DRMS is 15 m → URE (1σ) × 2 (HDOP) = 15 m

and URE = 7.5 m. The URE is also related to the measured range accuracy and clock bias

$$\mathrm{URE} = 7.5 = \sqrt{\sigma^2 + \sigma_b^2(\Delta t)} = \sqrt{5^2 + \sigma_b^2(\Delta t)} \qquad \Delta t = 7,200\ \mathrm{s}$$

from which it follows that

$$\sigma_b^2(7,200\,\mathrm{s}) = (7.5^2 - 5^2)/(3 \cdot 10^8)^2 = 346 \cdot 10^{-18} = 7,200^2 \cdot \sigma_y^2(7,200\,\mathrm{s})$$

where σ_y^2 is the Allen variance, which is equal to

$$\sigma_y^2(7,200\,\mathrm{s}) = 6.7 \cdot 10^{-24}$$

A rubidium clock would meet this requirement.

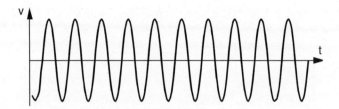

Figure 5.53: Continuous unmodulated wave.

5.4 RF-wave measurements

Continuous Wave (CW) - Unmodulated

The continuous sine wave signal (CW) shown in Figure 5.53 does not include any information but can be used as a carrier for a variety of information. A modulated CW is called *carrier wave*. An unmodulated wave is contained in a narrower bandwidth than a modulated wave.

Measurements on the phase of the wave are nominally within one wavelength only; if the complete number of cycles on the beat frequency is counted, a range difference (over time) can be derived (e.g., GPS carrier phase measurements on the beat signals produced by the Doppler effect). Phase measurements are relatively accurate (0.1-1% of a cycle). The range difference accuracy achievable using the Doppler effect is a function of the frequency f; as f increases, the wavelength λ decreases and the range difference accuracy increases.

Unmodulated pulsed wave (PW)

In this case, shown in Figure 5.54, the pulses are precisely time synchronized and are transmitted at predetermined and known time intervals to assist in the ambiguity resolution (determination of the total number of cycles between the transmitter and the receiver). Omega is an example of a positioning system that used unmodulated pulse waves. Since a pulse consists of many cycles, the carrier phase ambiguity must still be resolved. This is possible using a widelaning technique if λ is very long (e.g., 30 km in the case of Omega) and provided the position is approximately known.

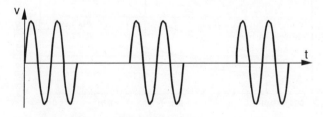

Figure 5.54: Unmodulated pulsed wave.

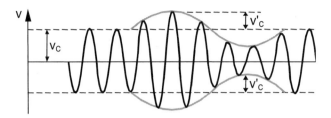

Figure 5.55: Amplitude modulation.

5.4.1 Signal modulation (AM, FM, PM)

Modulation is the superimposition of a desired wave (additional information) onto the carrier wave CW or PW. Several types of modulation are used in navigation or distance measurement techniques, namely

- Amplitude modulation (AM).
- Frequency modulation (FM).
- Phase modulation (PM) such as bi-phase (GPS).

Amplitude modulation (AM)

In amplitude modulation, neither the frequency nor the phase of the carrier wave changes in the modulation process but the amplitude or strength of the carrier wave

$$V(t) = V_c \sin \omega_c t \tag{5.87}$$

alternates sinusoidally with a magnitude

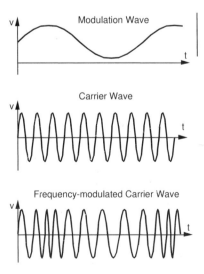

Figure 5.56: Frequency modulation.

$$V'_c = \alpha V_c \qquad\qquad (5.88)$$

where V'_c is the amplitude of the modulation wave, V_c is the strength or amplitude of the carrier, and α is the degree of modulation (the depth), given by

$$\alpha = \frac{V'_c}{V_c} \qquad\qquad (5.89)$$

After modulation, the amplitude of the carrier wave alternates between $V_c + V'_c$ and $V_c - V'_c$ or between $V_c(1+\alpha)$ and $V_c(1-\alpha)$, as shown in Figure 5.55.

Frequency modulation (FM)

In frequency modulation, the amplitude of the carrier wave is constant but the frequency f varies with the amplitude and polarity of the modulation signal. The frequency f is lowest when the modulation is least positive, as shown in Figure 5.56.

Phase modulation (PM)

Phase modulation has many similarities with frequency modulation, e.g., the amplitude of the carrier wave remains constant. In phase modulation, the phase of the carrier wave is varied according to the phase of the modulation wave. The phase change causes compression and spreading of the modulated wave, increasing or decreasing the modulating signal accordingly.

The main difference between FM and PM is that, in the case of FM, the frequency deviation is proportional to the instantaneous amplitude of the modulation signal, while in the case of PM the frequency deviation is proportional to both the instantaneous amplitude and the frequency of the modulation signal.

5.4.2 GPS: Bi-phase modulation

Binary (0 and 1) phase shift keying (BPSK) is used to modulate GPS signals. The modulating signal consists of 0 and 1's which cause a 180° phase reversal (bi-phase modulation). The specific modulating signal used is a PRN (Pseudo Random Noise) signal. After signal reception, the modulating signal and original carrier are separated; pseudorange measurements are made on the modulating signal (code) and (cumulated) phase measurements on the carrier.

The combination of two frequencies to vary voltage simultaneously is called *frequency mixing* or *frequency conversion*. Frequency mixing is used extensively in receivers to make precise measurements at a lower frequency than the nominal one. If one radio frequency is mixed with another radio frequency, the process is known as a *heterodyne* action (two similar frequencies are mixed producing a complex combination of basic frequencies, their sums, differences, i.e., beat frequencies (see Section 5.4.3), and higher order harmonics).

In a GPS receiver, the received signal is heterodyned (mixed) with the signal produced by a local oscillator at a nominal frequency. The resulting frequency difference (IF - Intermediate Frequency) is much lower and can be amplified more effectively. The phase difference $\Delta\phi$ of the difference frequency is equal to the difference in phase between the two higher frequencies prior to heterodyning. Heterodyning is used extensively with a variety of systems. Phase measurements are made more accurately on the relatively lower beat frequencies.

Pseudo-random noise (PRN) measurements

Unwanted electric signals and interference originating from a variety of sources constitute noise. Noise which has a random character, i.e., a flat spectral density over a wide range of frequencies with all frequency components in equal proportion, is called *random noise* or *white noise*. The autocorrelation function of the random noise is zero, except at zero delay where it is unity. Random noise does not carry any information.

The *autocorrelation function* $r(\tau)$ for a function $g(t)$ describes the degree of linear dependence for values of the function g a time τ apart

$$r_{gg}(\tau) = \lim_{T \to \infty} \frac{1}{T} \int_{t=0}^{T} g(t)g(t-\tau)dt \tag{5.90}$$

Pseudo-random noise signals behave like random noise but are deterministic (predictable) and contain specific information (e.g., a reading of the transmitter clock). Their autocorrelation function is a sharp edge which results in accurate time (range) measurements. The autocorrelation function is small except at zero delay. An example of a PRN code is shown in Figure 5.57. PRN codes are used for GPS pseudoranging (PRN C/A and P codes) and for certain shore-based systems (e.g., Sercel's Geoloc in the late 1980's).

In case the function X is a binary data stream, its autocorrelation function can be expressed as

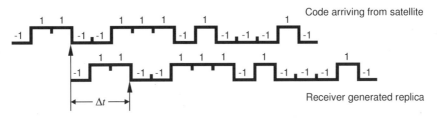

Figure 5.57: Pseudo-random noise (PRN).

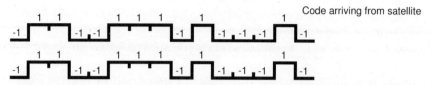

Figure 5.58: Alignment between arriving and receiver-generated PRN code.

$$\frac{1}{T}\int_{t=0}^{T} X(t)X(t-\tau)dt = \frac{1}{N}\sum_{i=1}^{N} X_i X_{i-k} \qquad (5.91)$$

where T is the time interval over which the correlation is determined, k is the number of time units by which the function is shifted and N is the number of binary states of the function in the interval T. In Figure 5.57, N is 15, i.e., there are 15 states of the function X which are considered (available in the receiver-generated replica to the right of the left arrow), and $\tau = \Delta t = 3$, i.e., the shift of the receiver-generated replica with respect to the code arriving from the transmitter has three time units. The autocorrelation function is

$$\frac{1}{15}\sum_{i=1}^{15} X_i X_{i-3} = \frac{1}{15}((-1)(-1)+(-1)(+1)+...) = \frac{-3}{15} = 0.2$$

The maximum correlation is 1. Since $0.2 \ll 1$, further shifting is required for matching.

With the correct alignment shown in Figure 5.58 ($\Delta t = 0$), the autocorrelation is equal to 1:

$$\frac{1}{15}\sum_{i=1}^{15} X_i X_{i-0} = \frac{1}{15}((-1)(-1)+(+1)(+1)+...) = \frac{15}{15} = 1$$

The normalized theoretical autocorrelation function for a 1023-bit (GPS C/A code type) binary PRN code is shown in Figure 5.59.

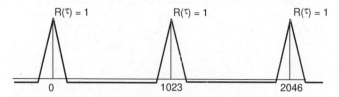

Figure 5.59: Normalized autocorrelation function for 1023-bit PRN code.

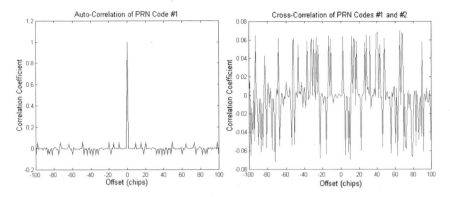

Figure 5.60. GPS auto-correlation and cross-correlation functions.

The autocorrelation of the actual GPS PRN #1 is shown in Figure 5.60, together with the cross-correlation between PRN #1 and PRN #2. As expected, the autocorrelation is unity at zero while the cross-correlation is random and very small.

Sharp peaks make the correlation of the incoming and receiver-generated code relatively precise. Distortion at the peak occurs, however, if a pre-correlation bandwidth of only 2 × C/A code (namely 2.046 MHz) is used due to the spectral power outside ±1 code (±1.023 MHz), as shown in Figure 5.61. The use of a Narrow Correlator™ spacing technique can overcome this limitation.

The GPS C/A code chipping rate is 1.023 MHz or megabits/s, and the length per bit is therefore equal to $(3{\times}10^8$ m/s)/(1.023 megabits/s) or 293 m/bit. The distance measurement accuracy is a function of the chipping rate of the PRN code and the correlation method used. It is typically between 0.05 and 1% of a bit, namely between 0.1 m and a few metres for the GPS C/A code.

5.4.3 Doppler effect

A *Doppler effect* occurs when the distance between the transmitter and the receiver is changing with respect to time. The effect (Doppler shift) is a difference between the frequency of the signal received at a point and the frequency of the same signal transmitted at its source, when the observer and the source are moving with respect to each other. For shore-based systems, the Doppler effect is relatively small. For satellite-based systems, the effect has been (e.g., Transit) and is still (e.g., GPS) used very much. It is the basis of GPS carrier phase measurements.

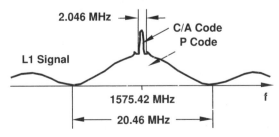

Figure 5.61: Power spectrum of phase-modulated GPS L1 carrier.

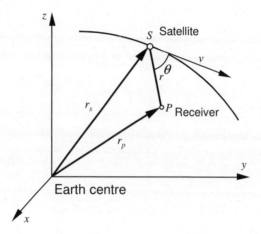

Figure 5.62: Relative motion between satellite and receiver.

In Figure 5.62, S is the satellite, v is its (along track) velocity, P is the observer, r_s and r_p are the position vectors of S and P, and r is the distance (slant range) between S and P. The Doppler effect is a frequency shift observed in the transmitted frequency f_s of S at P. The Doppler shifted frequency received at P is f_r. The relationship between the two is given by the Doppler equation

$$\frac{f_r}{f_s} = \frac{1 - \frac{v}{c}\cos\theta}{\sqrt{1 - \frac{v^2}{c^2}}} \tag{5.92}$$

where c is the speed of light and θ is the angle between the velocity vector of the satellite and the vector between satellite and receiver. If $v = 0$, $f_r = f_s$ (i.e., the Doppler shift is 0). The Doppler effect is therefore a measure of the relative velocity or range rate between S and P. The relative velocity between S and P is

$$\frac{dr}{dt} = -v\cos\theta \tag{5.93}$$

The explicit relationship between f_r and f_s is

$$f_r \approx f_s \cdot (1 - \frac{1}{c}\frac{dr}{dt}) \tag{5.94}$$

Considering that

$$f = \frac{d\phi}{dt} \tag{5.95}$$

and assuming that f_s can be generated inside the receiver as f_g using a sufficiently stable oscillator, the *Integrated Doppler Count* (IDC) over an interval (t_i, t_j) is given by

$$\text{IDC}_{i,j} = \int_{t_i}^{t_j} (f_g - f_r)dt \qquad (5.96)$$

where $\text{IDC}_{i,j}$ is a derived phase measurement in cycles. The difference $f_g - f_r$ is also called the *beat frequency* (from the theory of audible acoustic waves where beats are fluctuations in amplitude produced by two sound waves of slightly different frequency).

In the case of GPS, the beat phase measurement ϕ_i at time i is obtained directly

$$\phi_i = \phi_r - \phi_g \qquad (5.97)$$

as shown in Figure 5.63 where ϕ_r is the phase of the received Doppler shifted frequency, and ϕ_g is the phase of the receiver-generated frequency. The beat phase ϕ_i contains an ambiguity term which is constant over time. $\text{IDC}_{i,j}$ can be simply formed by

$$\text{IDC}_{i,j} = \phi_j - \phi_i \qquad (5.98)$$

The beat phase measurements at times t_i and t_j are ϕ_i and ϕ_j

$$\begin{aligned} \phi_i &= \phi_{r,i} - \phi_{g,i} \\ \phi_j &= \phi_{r,j} - \phi_{g,j} \end{aligned} \qquad (5.99)$$

where ϕ_i and ϕ_j each contain a fractional and an integer number of cycles and a common (if phase lock is maintained between i and j) phase ambiguity term N. Over the interval (t_i, t_j), $\phi_j - \phi_i$ is a measure of the range rate, expressed in m/s

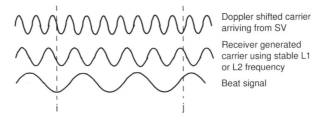

Doppler shifted carrier arriving from SV

Receiver generated carrier using stable L1 or L2 frequency

Beat signal

Figure 5.63: Beat signal.

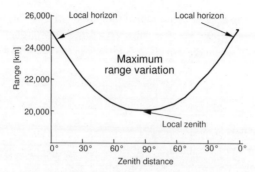

Figure 5.64: Range variation on a typical GPS satellite.

$$\frac{\lambda \cdot (\phi_j - \phi_i)}{t_j - t_i} \qquad\qquad\qquad (5.100)$$

The range variation for a GPS satellite and a stationary user is shown in Figure 5.64 and the resulting range rate (Doppler effect) in Figure 5.65.

Practical use of Doppler effect

Both Transit and GPS satellites used for satellite navigation are placed in circular orbits. Due to Kepler's laws of orbital motion, the velocity v_c of a satellite in a circular orbit ($r = a = r_c$) is

$$v_c = \sqrt{\frac{GM}{r_c}} = 631.348 / \sqrt{r_c} \quad \text{km/s} \qquad\qquad (5.101)$$

where $GM = 398600 \ \text{km}^3/\text{s}^2$, and r_c is the orbit radius. The period T of the satellite is

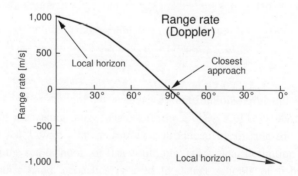

Figure 5.65: Range rate on a typical GPS satellite.

$$T = \frac{2\pi}{\sqrt{GM}} a^{3/2} \qquad (5.102)$$

where the semi-major axis a is the same as r_c. Thus, in the case of a GPS satellite ($a \approx 26,000$ km), $v_c \approx 4$ km/s, $T \approx 12$ h, and angular velocity $\approx 360°/T \approx 30°/h$. T increases as a function of increasing r_c and the angular velocity decreases as a function of increasing r_c.

Consider a receiver on the Earth's surface and a satellite in a circular orbit around it. The Doppler measurements, once integrated (IDC) over a time interval $\Delta t = t_2 - t_1$, are a measure of the range difference between the receiver-satellite position at t_1 and the receiver-satellite position at t_2. In the case of a high satellite (low angular velocity), if the IDC is large, it means that the time interval Δt is relatively long and that the angular displacement is relatively large. When solving for positions (e.g., in range difference mode), the geometry implied by the receivers and the successive satellite positions will be relatively strong because the positions at t_1 and t_2 will be relatively far apart.

Example 5.12: Computation of the Doppler shift.

a) A GPS satellite crosses the local zenith of a stationary receiver on the Earth's surface, as shown in the figure below. At time t_1 the satellite is rising and is 10° above the horizon. At time t_2, the carrier phase difference (IDC) between t_1 and t_2 is measured as 18,000,000 cycles. What is the impact on geometry?

Assume an average Doppler shift of about 4 kHz (4,000 cycles/s). It means that the interval $t_2 - t_1$ is about 4,500 s. The angular displacement of the satellite is about 37.5° (4500/43200×360°). The geometry implied by such a displacement can be estimated using a range difference approach (hyperbolic mode).

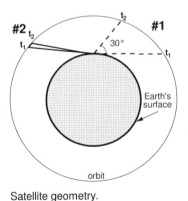

Satellite geometry.

b) Now assume that at time t_2 the carrier phase difference (IDC) between t_1 and t_2 is measured as 18,000 cycles. What is the impact on geometry?

Assume again an average Doppler shift of about 4 kHz (4,000 cycles/s). The interval $t_2 - t_1$ is now 4.5 s. The angular displacement of the satellite is about 0.04°. It is difficult to solve for a position using range differences from transmitters which subtend an angle of 0.04° at the receiver. The solution will be very unstable and will be nearly singular.

Example 5.13: Doppler effect.
a) In the case of a geostationary satellite, what could the Doppler effect be used for?
    In the case of no Doppler shift, no relative motion would be inferred. A non-zero Doppler shift could be used to detect platform motion.
b) Consider the Omega system. Is or could the Doppler shift be used?
    No, because the Doppler shift is practically zero. Omega is an unmodulated pulsed system. The phase measurements are made on the carrier directly, not on a beat frequency produced by a Doppler effect.
    If a Doppler effect was induced by the receiver's motion, the velocity of the platform could in principle be calculated. Let us now assume that the phase could be observed on the beat frequency. The accuracy could be assumed to be a few degrees. If we assume 3.6°, this would result in an accuracy of 1/100 of a wavelength, i.e., 1/100 of 30,000 m or 300 m - very poor accuracy.
c) What are the advantages/disadvantages of large Doppler effects on a satellite-based radionavigation system?
    Advantages: good geometry to obtain range differences over short periods of time. Range differences obtained through Doppler (phase) measurements are more accurate than corresponding values obtained directly through range measurements. Also, lower clock stability is required than for a long period of time. Velocity can also be determined. However, a large Doppler effect (versus a small one) has no particular advantage in this case. Other applications include code multipath detection and cycle slip detection.
    Disadvantages: a more sophisticated receiver phase lock loop is required to track the large Doppler shift, and a more sophisticated frequency search would be required.
d) What could the use be of observing the Doppler effect on a ship using a shore-based radionavigation system?
    The moving platform's horizontal velocity, which is important for many applications, could be derived more accurately than for the case using range measurements, provided the geometry is good. Attitude motion of the ship could be a problem, however, if the Doppler effect is large. Lane counting could be done in the case of certain systems.

5.5 Major references

Allan, D., N. Ashby, C. Hodges: *The Science of Timekeeping, Application Note 1289*. Hewlett Packard, 1997, available from www.allanstime.com.

Appleyard, S.F., R.S. Linford: *Marine Electronic Navigation*. 2nd edition, Routledge, 1988.

Ball Corporation: *Telecommunications Products Division, Precision Time and Frequency Handbook, Efratom Time and Frequency Products*. 8th edition, 1991.

Banks, P.M., G. Kockarts: *Aeronomy*. Academic Press, 1973.

Black, H.D.: *An Easily Implemented Algorithm for the Tropospheric Range Correction*. Journal of Geophysical Research, Vol. 83, No. B4, pp. 1825-1828, 1978.

Black, H.D., A. Eisner: *Correcting Satellite Doppler Data for Tropospheric Effects*. Proceedings of International Symposium on the Use of Artificial Satellites for Geodesy and Geodynamics, National Technical University of Athens, pp. 1-31, 1984.

Bogush, A.: *Radar and the Atmosphere*. Artech House, 1989.

Burnside, C.D.: *Electromagnetic Distance Measurement*. 3rd edition, Granada, 1991.

Carlson, A.B.: *Communication Systems*. McGraw-Hill, 3rd edition, 1991.

Collin, R.E.: *Antennas and Radiowaves*. McGraw-Hill, 1985.

Corliss, W.R.: *Handbook of Unusual Natural Phenomena*. Gramercy Books, New York, 1995.

Frank, R.: *Current Developments in Loran-C*. Proceedings of the IEEE, Vol. 71, No. 10, 1983.

Hall, M.P.M., L.W. Barclay: *Radiowave Propagation*. IEE, London, 1989.

International Earth Rotation Service (IERS): http://www.iers.org/iers/earth/rotation/-polmot/polmot.html, 2001.

Kraus, J.D.: *Electromagnetics*. 4th edition, McGraw-Hill, 1992.

Laurila, S.H.: *Electronic Surveying and Navigation*. John Wiley and Sons, 1976.

Lutgens, F.K., E.J. Tarbuck: *The Atmosphere*. 6th edition, Prentice-Hall, 1995.

Moran, J.M., M.D. Morgan: *Meteorology*. 2nd edition, MacMillan Publishing Co., New York, 1989.

Moritz, H., I.I. Mueller: *Earth Rotation – Theory and Observation*. The Ungar Publishing Company, New York, 1987.

Pisano, J.J., P.K. Enge, P.L. Levin: *Using GPS to Calibrate Loran-C*. IEEE Transactions on Aerospace and Electronic Systems, Vol. 27, No. 4, pp. 696-708, 1991.

Rohan, P.: *Introduction to EM Propagation*. Artech House, Boston, 1991.

Rueger, J.M.: *Electronic Distance Measurement*. 3rd edition, Springer-Verlag, 1990.

Samaddar, S.N.: *Theory of Loran-C Ground Wave Propagation*. Navigation: Journal of the Institute of Navigation, 26, 3, pp. 173-187, Fall 1979.

Seeber, G.: *Satellite Geodesy*. Walter de Gruyter and Co., 1993.

Segal, B., R.E. Barrington: *The Radio Climatology of Canada - Tropospheric Refractivity Atlas for Canada*. Communications Research Centre Report No. 1315-E, Communications Canada, 1977.

6 Underwater acoustics

6.1 Introduction

Acoustics may be defined as the generation, transmission and reception of energy in the form of vibrational waves in matter. The displacement of the atoms or molecules of a fluid or solid from their normal configuration causes an internal elastic restoring force, e.g., springs or fluid compression. The most common acoustic phenomenon is the sound wave which is a longitudinal wave. As sound waves travel through a medium, the particles of the medium vibrate to produce density and pressure changes along the path of motion of the wave. The change in pressure, known as *acoustic* or *excess pressure*, is defined as

$$p_e = p - p_0 \tag{6.1}$$

where p is the instantaneous pressure and p_0 the hydrostatic pressure, i.e., the pressure without the disturbance.

Due to the excess pressure, the particles in the medium will start moving. As a result, the distance between the particles will change as a function of time and location. In order for sound to propagate through a medium, the medium should be compressible. This *compressibility* s, expressed in m^2/N (or Pa^{-1}), is the volumetric strain per unit applied stress

$$s = -\frac{\Delta v / v_0}{p_e} \tag{6.2}$$

where Δv is the change in the original volume v_0 when an acoustic pressure p_e is applied. If s is constant, (6.2) is known as *Hooke's law*. The reciprocal of the compressibility is known as the *bulk modulus* (or *volume elasticity*) κ. For low amplitude acoustic waves, considered here, compressibility and bulk modulus can be considered constant.

Since a local disturbance of a medium cannot be transferred instantaneously, the propagation of sound waves, which occur together with the disturbance, will take place with a finite velocity c. This speed of sound depends on the bulk modulus κ and the density ρ_0 of the medium and is given by

$$c = \sqrt{\kappa / \rho_0} = \sqrt{1/(s\rho_0)} \tag{6.3}$$

For water $\kappa \approx 2.2 \cdot 10^9$ Pa and $\rho_0 \approx 1000$ kg/m^3, resulting in a speed of sound that is approximately 1480 m/s. For comparison, the speed of sound in steel is approximately 5050 m/s, whereas in air it is about 330 m/s.

6.2 Wave equation

6.2.1 Physics

Underlying the propagation of sound is a number of basic equations of physics. The *equation of continuity* states that no mass of fluid can be created or destroyed. In other words, any difference between the amounts of fluids entering and leaving a given volume must be accompanied by a change in density

$$\frac{\partial \rho}{\partial t} = -\nabla \cdot (\rho u) \tag{6.4}$$

where ρ is the density of the fluid, t time, u the particle's velocity vector and $\nabla \cdot (\rho u)$ the divergence of ρu.

According to *Newton's second law*, force equals mass times acceleration

$$f = \frac{\partial(\rho u)}{\partial t} \tag{6.5}$$

The *equations of force* state that the force in a given direction equals the negative of the rate of change of pressure in that direction

$$f = -\nabla p \tag{6.6}$$

Using the *elastic properties* of the medium, it follows that for small changes in density and pressure

$$\rho = \rho_0 + d\rho$$
$$v = v_0 + dv \tag{6.7}$$

Since the mass of the fluid does not change, we have $\rho_0 v_0 = \rho v$ or, using (6.7) and neglecting second order terms

$$-\frac{d\rho}{\rho_0} = \frac{dv}{v_0} \tag{6.8}$$

From (6.8) and the expression for the compressibility (6.2), it follows that

$$s = -\frac{1}{v_0}\frac{\partial v}{\partial p}\bigg|_T = \frac{1}{\rho_0}\frac{\partial \rho}{\partial p}\bigg|_T \tag{6.9}$$

From the Taylor series' expansion for $\rho = \rho(p)$, we get

$$\rho = \rho_0 + \frac{\partial \rho}{\partial p}\bigg|_{T,p_0} (p - p_0) + \dots$$

or, neglecting second and higher order terms

$$\rho - \rho_0 = \rho_e \approx \frac{\partial \rho}{\partial p}\bigg|_{T,p_0} p_e \tag{6.10}$$

The above expressions will be used to derive the *wave equation*, which describes the behaviour of a wave as a function of time and location. Substituting (6.10) into (6.9) yields

$$\rho_e = s\rho_0 p_e \tag{6.11}$$

Combining (6.5) and (6.6) gives

$$-\nabla p = \frac{\partial \rho u}{\partial t}$$

or

$$-\nabla^2 p = \nabla \cdot \{\frac{\partial (\rho u)}{\partial t}\} = \frac{\partial}{\partial t}\{\nabla \cdot (\rho u)\} \tag{6.12}$$

After substituting (6.4) and (6.11) into this equation and realising that p_0 is a constant, we get

$$\nabla^2 p_e = s\rho_0 \frac{\partial^2 p_e}{\partial t^2}$$

which, using (6.3), finally results in the wave equation

$$\nabla^2 p_e - \frac{1}{c^2} \frac{\partial^2 p_e}{\partial t^2} = 0 \qquad (6.13)$$

The wave equation is a partial differential equation, which relates the variation of pressure in space at a particular instant of time, to the variation of pressure with time that occurs at a particular point in space. The wave equation can be solved in two ways. A set of boundary or initial conditions should be available for a solution based on *wave theory*. These conditions are hard to define in the real world. *Ray theory*, on the other hand, does not require such conditions. This theory can only be applied to relatively high frequencies. Fortunately the frequencies used in underwater acoustics usually meet this condition.

6.2.2 *Wave theory*

In one dimension, the wave equation reads

$$\frac{\partial^2 p_e}{\partial x^2} - \frac{1}{c^2} \frac{\partial^2 p_e}{\partial t^2} = 0 \qquad (6.14)$$

The general solution to (6.14) is given by

$$f(x,t) = f_1(t - x/c) + f_2(t + x/c) \qquad (6.15)$$

which can be verified by substituting (6.15) into (6.14). The first term on the right-hand side of (6.15) represents a plane wave, travelling in positive x-direction, the second term a plane wave travelling in negative x-direction. Each function with argument $t \pm x/c$ satisfies (6.14), provided this solution does not conflict with the assumptions made in the derivations in Section 6.2.1.

A possible simple solution to (6.14) that is often used is

$$p_e(x,t) = \hat{p}_e \cos\{\omega(t - x/c)\} \qquad (6.16)$$

or in complex notation

$$p_e(x,t) = \hat{p}_e \exp(j\{\omega(t - x/c)\}) \qquad (6.17)$$

In these expressions, $\hat{p}_e$ is the wave's amplitude and ω its angular velocity. The complex form is useful for mathematical manipulations, whereas the cosine form (6.16) (or the real part of (6.17)) represents the physical wave.

Using (6.5), (6.6) and (6.16), the particle velocity $u(x,t)$ follows as

$$u(x,t) = \frac{\hat{p}_e}{\rho_0 c} \cos\{\omega(t - x/c)\} \qquad (6.18)$$

Integration of this equation yields the particle displacement $\zeta(x,t)$

$$\zeta(x,t) = \frac{\hat{p}_e}{\omega \rho_0 c} \sin\{\omega(t - x/c)\} \qquad (6.19)$$

Finally, the variation in density $\rho_e(x,t)$ is obtained from (6.11) as

$$\rho_e(x,t) = \rho_0 s \hat{p}_e \cos\{\omega(t - x/c)\} \qquad (6.20)$$

From the periodic properties of the cosine function, it follows that (6.16) will repeat itself each 2π radians. The equality

$$\hat{p}_e \cos\{\omega(t_0 - x_1/c)\} = \hat{p}_e \cos\{\omega(t_0 - x_2/c) + 2\pi\}$$

is fulfilled if

$$\frac{\omega}{c}(x_2 - x_1) = 2\pi \qquad (6.21)$$

The distance $x_2 - x_1$ is defined as the wavelength λ of the acoustic signal and $\omega/c = 2\pi/\lambda$ as the wave number k. In a similar fashion, for a fixed location x_0 and at two different times t_1 and t_2

$$\omega(t_2 - t_1) = 2\pi \qquad (6.22)$$

Defining $T = t_2 - t_1$ as the signal's period, we get $\omega = 2\pi/T = 2\pi f$, with f the signal's frequency. From (6.21) and (6.22) it follows that $c = \lambda f$.

Expression (6.13) is the equation for a plane wave: the disturbance is assumed to propagate in layers. At long distances from a source, the sound characteristics resemble that from a point source rather than an infinite plane. It can therefore be more convenient to express the wave equation in spherical rather than cartesian coordinates. This is accomplished by substitution of

$$x = r \sin \theta \cos \phi$$
$$y = r \sin \theta \sin \phi$$
$$z = r \cos \theta$$

into the Laplace operator ∇^2. The result is

$$\nabla^2 = \frac{\partial^2}{\partial r^2} + \frac{2}{r}\frac{\partial}{\partial r} + \frac{1}{r^2 \sin \theta}\frac{\partial}{\partial \theta}(\sin \theta \frac{\partial}{\partial \phi}) + \frac{1}{r^2 \sin^2 \theta}\frac{\partial^2}{\partial \phi^2}$$

If we assume spherical symmetry, the partial derivatives of θ and ϕ will be zero, resulting in the wave equation

$$\frac{\partial^2 p_e}{\partial r^2} + \frac{2}{r}\frac{\partial p_e}{\partial r} - \frac{1}{c^2}\frac{\partial^2 p_e}{\partial t^2} = 0 \Leftrightarrow$$
$$\frac{1}{r}\frac{\partial^2 r p_e}{\partial r^2} - \frac{1}{c^2}\frac{\partial^2 p_e}{\partial t^2} = 0 \Leftrightarrow \tag{6.24}$$
$$\frac{\partial^2 r p_e}{\partial r^2} - \frac{1}{c^2}\frac{\partial^2 r p_e}{\partial t^2} = 0$$

The general solution to this equation reads (compare with (6.15))

$$f(x,t) = \frac{1}{r}f_1(t - r/c) + \frac{1}{r}f_2(t + r/c) \tag{6.25}$$

The two components on the right-hand side represent diverging and converging waves, respectively. The converging wave can be ignored, as it corresponds to a wave that starts out at some negative time with great radius and contracts into the point $(x,y,z) = (0,0,0)$. The diverging wave is physically valid, since it implies spherical waves spreading out from a point source into ever-increasing spheres with radius r and speed c.

A possible solution to (6.24) is given by

$$p_e(x,t) = \frac{\hat{p}_e}{r}\cos\{\omega(t - r/c)\} \tag{6.26}$$

or in complex form

$$p_e(x,t) = \frac{\hat{p}_e}{r} \exp(j\{\omega(t - r/c)\}) \tag{6.27}$$

Sources that transmit equal power in all directions are called omni- or non-directional.

6.2.3 Ray theory

Ray theory is based on the *eikonal equation* (from the Greek word for image, eikon). The eikonal equation can be derived from the wave equation by inserting a special solution to this equation, which has the form

$$p_e(x,y,z,t) = A(x,y,z)\exp\{j(\omega t - \frac{\omega}{c_0}W(x,y,z))\}$$

In this expression the functions A and W depend on position only, the quantity c_0 is a constant velocity. Inserting this equation into the wave equation (6.13) results in

$$\nabla^2 A - \frac{\omega^2}{c_0^2} A |\nabla W|^2 + \frac{\omega^2}{c^2} A - j\{\frac{\omega}{c_0}\nabla A \cdot \nabla W + \frac{\omega}{c_0}A\nabla^2 W\} = 0$$

In order for this equation to be valid, both the real and the imaginary part should be zero. For the real part, we get, using $\omega/c_0 = 2\pi/\lambda_0$

$$|\nabla W|^2 - \frac{c_0^2}{c^2} = \frac{\lambda_0^2 \nabla^2 A}{4\pi^2 A}$$

If the wavelength λ_0 is small (if the corresponding frequency f_0 is high) and if A is not a strong function of position, we may write

$$|\nabla W|^2 - n^2 = 0 \tag{6.28}$$

with $n = c_0/c$ the *index of refraction*.

Equation (6.28) is called the eikonal equation and the function W the eikonal. The expression $W(x,y,z) = $ constant is a surface in three-dimensional space that coincides with the signal's wavefronts (wavefronts are surfaces that have constant phase). This can be understood by keeping the phase fixed, i.e.

$$\omega t_0 - \frac{\omega}{c_0}W(x,y,z) = \text{constant}$$

from which it follows that

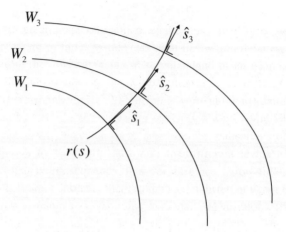

Figure 6.1: Wavefronts W and acoustic rays r. The vectors
$\hat{s}$ are perpendicular to W and tangent to r.

$$W(x, y, z) = (t_0 - \frac{\text{constant}}{\omega})c_0$$

is a surface at which the phase is constant. Acoustic energy is propagated along curved lines, the acoustic rays. These rays are normal to the wavefronts and therefore described by (6.28) as well, see Figure 6.1.

With (6.28) we are in the position to derive *Snell's law*. The unit vector $\hat{s}$ tangent to the normal of the surface $W(x, y, z) = \text{constant}$ is given by

$$\hat{s} = \frac{1}{n} \nabla W$$

Defining the vector $r = r(s)$ as the representation of the acoustic ray, with s the arc length along the ray, the unit vector along the line tangent to this ray follows as

$$\frac{dr}{ds} = \hat{s} = \frac{1}{n} \nabla W \tag{6.29}$$

From the definition

$$\frac{dW}{ds} = \hat{s} \cdot \nabla W \tag{6.30}$$

it follows that

$$\frac{dW}{ds} = n \tag{6.31}$$

which can be verified by substituting (6.29) into (6.30) and the resulting expression into (6.28). Combination of (6.29) and (6.31) yields

$$\frac{d}{ds}(n\frac{dr}{ds}) = \frac{d}{ds}(\nabla W) = \nabla(\frac{dW}{ds}) = \nabla n \qquad (6.32)$$

For a horizontally layered medium, the index of refraction $n = n(z)$ is a function of the vertical z-coordinate only. Using (6.32) and denoting the unit vector along the z-axis by i_z gives

$$\frac{d}{ds}(n\frac{dr}{ds}) = \frac{\partial n}{\partial z}i_z$$

or

$$\frac{d}{ds}(n\frac{dx}{ds}) = \frac{d}{ds}(n\frac{dy}{ds}) = 0 \qquad (6.33a)$$

$$\frac{d}{ds}(n\frac{dz}{ds}) = \frac{\partial n}{\partial z} \qquad (6.33b)$$

From (6.33a) it follows that

$$n\frac{dx}{ds} = \text{constant} \qquad n\frac{dy}{ds} = \text{constant} \qquad (6.34)$$

In other words, the horizontal component of the unit vector s tangent to the acoustic ray has a constant direction. In a horizontally layered medium, the acoustic rays are

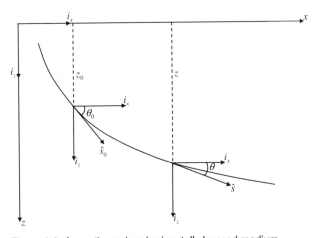

Figure 6.2: Acoustic ray in a horizontally layered medium.

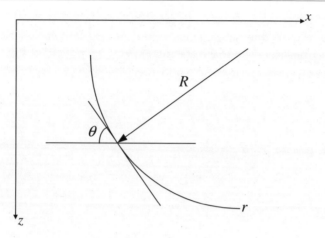

Figure 6.3: Trajectory of an acoustic ray in a medium with constant velocity gradient.

therefore plane curves in a vertical plane, parallel to the z-axis, as shown in Figure 6.2. If $\theta = \theta(z)$ is the angle between tangent and horizontal line, it can be concluded that along the acoustic ray

$$n(z)\cos\theta(z) = n(z_0)\cos\theta(z_0) \qquad (6.35)$$

This is Snell's law in a horizontally layered medium.

If the velocity keeps increasing and if the medium is sufficiently extended, then at some point the acoustic ray will have reached a depth z_v where it will propagate horizontally, i.e., $\theta(z_v) = 0$. The corresponding velocity c_v is known as the *vertex velocity*. Snell's law can be reformulated as

$$\frac{\cos\theta(z)}{c(z)} = \frac{1}{c_v} \qquad (6.36)$$

If we now consider a medium in which the velocity changes linearly with depth as

$$c(z) = c(z_0) + g \cdot (z - z_0) \qquad (6.37)$$

with g (s^{-1}) a constant gradient, the acoustic ray will be an arc of a circle with curvature g/c_v and radius $R = |c_v/g|$. This can be explained using Figure 6.3, from which it can be concluded that

$$\frac{dz}{dx} = \tan\theta = \frac{\sqrt{1 - \cos^2\theta}}{\cos\theta}$$

After substitution of (6.36) we get, using (6.37)

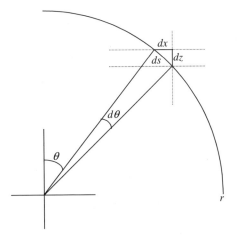

Figure 6.4: Horizontal and vertical displacements
along an acoustic ray r.

$$\frac{dz}{dx} = \frac{\sqrt{1-(c/c_v)^2}}{c/c_v} = \frac{\sqrt{1-\{(c(z_0)+g\cdot(z-z_0))/c_v\}^2}}{(c(z_0)+g\cdot(z-z_0))/c_v} \tag{6.38}$$

Writing this expression as

$$dx = \frac{(c(z_0)+g\cdot(z-z_0))/c_v}{\sqrt{1-\{(c(z_0)+g\cdot(z-z_0))/c_v\}^2}}dz$$

and integrating yields

$$x^2 + (z-z_0+\frac{c_0}{g})^2 = (\frac{c_v}{g})^2 \tag{6.39}$$

which is the equation of a circle with radius R

$$R = \left|\frac{c_v}{g}\right| = \left|\frac{c(z)}{g\cos\theta(z)}\right| \tag{6.40}$$

The gradient g is positive when the speed of sound increases with depth z. The curvature is then also positive and the ray is bent upwards.

From Figure 6.4 we see that

$$dx = R\cos\theta d\theta$$
$$dz = R\sin\theta d\theta \tag{6.41}$$

For two arbitrary points (x_1, z_1) and (x_2, z_2), it thus follows that

$$x_2 - x_1 = \int_{\theta_1}^{\theta_2} R\cos\theta d\theta = R(\sin\theta_2 - \sin\theta_1)$$

$$z_2 - z_1 = \int_{\theta_1}^{\theta_2} R\sin\theta d\theta = -R(\cos\theta_2 - \cos\theta_1)$$

(6.42)

Using (6.37) and (6.40) the second expression can also be written as

$$z_2 - z_1 = \frac{c_2 - c_1}{g}$$

(6.43)

Example 6.1

At the surface of an imaginary ocean the speed of sound $c_0 = 1500$ m/s and for depths up to 750 m, this velocity changes with a constant gradient $g_0 = -0.05$ s^{-1}. Below this depth, the gradient is $g_1 = +0.017$ s^{-1}. A transmitter is located at a depth of 100 m. This point source transmits an acoustic signal with an initial direction $\theta = 0°$.

We are now able to compute the following quantities

At transmitter's depth of 100 m

Speed of sound $c(100) = c(0) - 0.05 \cdot 100 = 1500 - 5 = 1495$ m/s

Curvature $g_0 \cdot \cos\theta(100)/c(100) = -0.05 \cdot 1/1495 = -3.34 \cdot 10^{-5}$

Radius $|1/\text{curvature}| = 29900$ m

At depth of 750 m

Speed of sound $c(750) = c(0) - 0.05 \cdot 750 = 1500 - 37.5 = 1462.5$ m/s

$\cos\theta(750) = \cos\theta(100) \cdot c(750)/c(100) \Rightarrow \theta(750) = 11.97°$

$x(750) - x(100) = |R \cdot \{\sin\theta(750) - \sin\theta(100)\}| = 29900 \cdot \sin(11.97°) = 6201$ m

Below depth of 750 m

Curvature $g_1 \cdot \cos\theta(750)/c(750) = 0.017 \cdot \cos(11.97°)/1462.5 = 1.14 \cdot 10^{-5}$

Radius $|1/\text{curvature}| = 87941$ m

Maximum depth $z_v - 750 = |87941\{\cos 0° - \cos 11.97°\}| = 1912$ m $\Rightarrow z_v = 2662$ m

$x(2662) - x(750) = |R \cdot \{\sin 0° - \sin 11.97°\}| = 18237$ m $\Rightarrow x(2662) = 24438$ m

Table 6.1: Analogy between electrical circuits and acoustics.

Electrical circuits	Acoustics
Potential difference V	Force $F = pA$
Current I	Particle velocity u
Impedance Z	Acoustic impedance $\rho_0 cA$
Ohm's law $V = IZ$	"Ohm's law" $F = \rho_0 cuA$
Power $P = ZI_{rms}^2$	Power $P = \rho_0 cu_{rms}^2 A$
$I_{rms} = \frac{1}{2}\sqrt{2}I_{max}$	$u_{rms} = \frac{1}{2}\sqrt{2}u_{max}$

6.2.4 Acoustic impedance, intensity and power

The quantity $\rho_0 c$, which is the ratio between acoustic pressure and particle velocity, see (6.18), is known as the *characteristic acoustic impedance* (the acoustic impedance per unit area). This terminology stems from the analogy that can be drawn between electrical and acoustic systems, see Table 6.1.

A measure for the power, transported by an acoustic wave, is the intensity I (in W/m^2). For a plane wave the intensity is defined as the average flow of power P per unit area A, perpendicular to the direction of propagation of the wave. The intensity of the wave (6.17) can be shown to be

$$I = P/A = \frac{1}{2}\frac{\hat{p}_e^2}{\rho_0 c}$$
(6.44)

At a large distance r from the transmitter, a spherical wavefront can locally be considered plane. The intensity then becomes

$$I = \frac{1}{2}\frac{\hat{p}_e^2}{r^2 \rho_0 c}$$
(6.45)

From this expression it can be concluded that for spherical waves, the intensity is inversely proportional to r^2. Since the area of a sphere equals $4\pi r^2$, the total power P (in Watt) transmitted by the source follows from the relationship between intensity, power and area as

$$P = I \cdot A = \frac{1}{2}\frac{4\pi\hat{p}_e^2}{\rho_0 c}$$
(6.46)

If the medium in which the wave is transmitted is bounded by two parallel surfaces a distance h apart, we are no longer dealing with a spherical wave, but with a

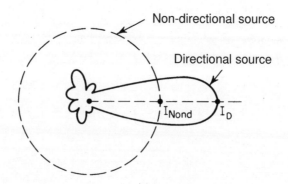

Figure 6.5: Directivity.

cylindrical wave. Then at a distance r of the source, the area of the cylinder is equal to $2\pi rh$ and the intensity of the wave is

$$I = \frac{P}{2\pi rh} \qquad (6.47)$$

For cylindrical waves the intensity is inversely proportional to r rather than r^2 and decreases less rapidly than for unbounded spherical waves.

Audible intensities are in the range $10^{-12}...10^1$ W/m^2. A logarithmic scale is introduced to compress this wide range of numbers. The most commonly used logarithmic scale to describe sound levels is the *decibel scale* (*dB*). The *intensity level IL* of a sound of intensity I is defined as

$$IL = 10\log(I/I_{ref}) \qquad (6.48)$$

where I_{ref} is a *reference intensity*. The reference intensity normally used for airborne sound is 10^{-12} W/m^2, which is the lower limit of human audibility. It should be stressed that the decibel is a comparison of intensities. The reference intensity should therefore always be mentioned, e.g., "20 dB re the intensity of a plane wave pressure equal to 1 μPa". However, this statement is often loosely formulated as "20 dB re 1 μPa".

So far non-directional sources were assumed. In practice, however, often devices are used that transmit mainly into one direction. This direction is called the *axis* of the transmitter. Thus, if the power transmitted by such a source is the same as the power by an non-directional source, the intensity along the transmitter's axis will be larger than the intensity in other directions, see Figure 6.5. This increase in intensity is called the directivity d and defined as

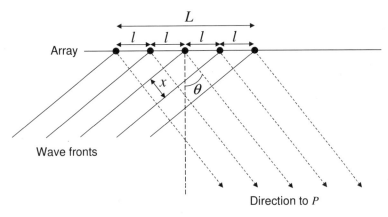

Figure 6.6: Array of omnidirectional transmitters.

$$d = \frac{I_{Directional}}{I_{Non-directional}} \qquad (6.49)$$

The intensities are measured at some reference distance, for example, one metre. For a transmitter with an area A, the directivity can be approximated by $d = 4\pi A / \lambda^2$ provided the square of the wavelength λ of the acoustic signal is much smaller than A.

A directional transmitter can also be constructed from an *array* of omnidirectional transmitters. Consider the array, consisting of n sources (transmitters), at distances l of each other, as shown in Figure 6.6. The length L of the array is $(n-1)l$. Assuming all sources have the same amplitude and phase, the total acoustic pressure at a point P far away from the array, is given by (using (6.27))

$$p_e(P,t) = \frac{\hat{p}_e}{r} \exp(j(\omega t - kr))[1 + \exp(jkl\sin\theta) + \ldots + \exp(jk(n-1)l\sin\theta)]$$

$$= \frac{\hat{p}_e}{r} \exp(j(\omega t - kr))[1 + \exp(jkl\sin\theta) + \ldots + (\exp(jkl\sin\theta))^{(n-1)}] \qquad (6.50)$$

whre k is again $2\pi / \lambda$. Since

$$1 + x + \ldots + x^{n-1} = \frac{1 - x^n}{1 - x}$$

expression (6.50) can be rewritten as

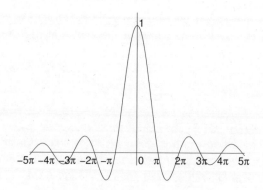

Figure 6.7: Directional factor as function of $\frac{1}{2}knl\sin\theta$.

$$p_e(P,t) = \frac{\hat{p}_e}{r}\exp(j(\omega t - kr))\frac{1-\exp(jknl\sin\theta)}{1-\exp(jkl\sin\theta)}$$

$$= \frac{\hat{p}_e}{r}\exp(j(\omega t - kr + \tfrac{1}{2}knl\sin\theta))$$

$$\cdot\frac{\exp(-j\tfrac{1}{2}knl\sin\theta)-\exp(j\tfrac{1}{2}knl\sin\theta)}{1-\exp(jkl\sin\theta)}\cdot\frac{\exp(-j\tfrac{1}{2}kl\sin\theta)}{\exp(-j\tfrac{1}{2}kl\sin\theta)} \qquad (6.51)$$

$$= \frac{\hat{p}_e}{r}\exp(j(\omega t - k(r-\tfrac{1}{2}(n-1)l\sin\theta)))\frac{\sin(\tfrac{1}{2}nkl\sin\theta)}{\sin(\tfrac{1}{2}kl\sin\theta)}$$

Defining p_0 as

$$p_0 = \frac{\hat{p}_e}{r}\exp(j(\omega t - k(r-\tfrac{1}{2}(n-1)l\sin\theta)))$$

which corresponds to the field of a single source in the centre of the array $((n-1)l/2 = L/2)$, and the *directional factor* $H(\theta)$ as

$$H(\theta) = \frac{\sin(\tfrac{1}{2}knl\sin\theta)}{n\sin(\tfrac{1}{2}kl\sin\theta)} \qquad (6.52)$$

(6.51) can be written as

$$p_e(P,t) = np_0H(\theta) \qquad (6.53)$$

In Figure 6.7 the directional factor is shown as a function of $\frac{1}{2}knl\sin\theta$. The directions in which no energy is transmitted follow from

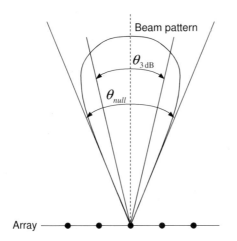

Figure 6.8: Beam pattern and beamwidth θ_{null}.

$$\sin \theta = \pm \frac{2\pi}{nkl}, \pm \frac{4\pi}{nkl}, \ldots$$

The denominator of $H(\theta)$ becomes zero if

$$\frac{kl}{2}\sin \theta = m\pi$$

where m is an integer. In that case the numerator is zero as well and the directional factor becomes one. Thus, apart from the one at $m=0$, there may be additional major lobes. These lobes are called *grating lobes*.

The *beamwidth* θ_{null}, see Figure 6.8, is defined as

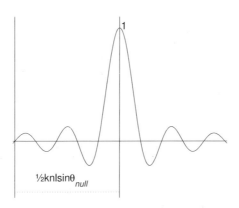

Figure 6.9: Directional factor of an array after rotation over an angle θ_0.

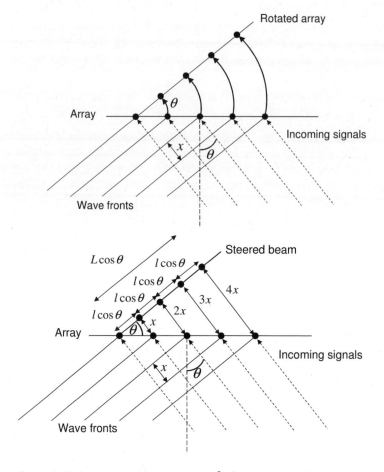

Figure 6.10: Array, rotated over an angle θ_0 (top) and a beam, steered electronically over the same angle.

$$\sin \theta_{null} = \frac{4\pi}{nkl} = \frac{2\lambda}{nl} \tag{6.54}$$

Instead of θ_{null} sometimes also the angle $\theta_{3\,dB}$, at which the intensity is 3 dB lower than the maximum value, is used to define the beamwidth. For small angles θ_{null} the above expression can be approximated by

$$\theta_{null} \approx \frac{2\lambda}{nl} \approx \frac{2\lambda}{(n-1)l} = \frac{2\lambda}{L} \approx 2\theta_{3\,dB} \tag{6.55}$$

What is said here about transmitting arrays, is equally valid for receiving arrays as well. Receiving arrays in particular need to be *steered* in order to receive signals from a particular direction, e.g., when mapping the seafloor, see Chapter 11. For narrow beamwidths, the arrays may be rather large, see (6.55). As a result, it is not practical (or feasible) to physically steer the beam (by rotating the array). Instead, *beam steering* is done by delaying the signals from each element m of the array by an amount $mkl\sin\theta_0$. The directional factor (6.52) becomes

$$H(\theta) = \frac{\sin(\frac{1}{2}knl(\sin\theta - \sin\theta_0))}{n\sin(\frac{1}{2}kl(\sin\theta - \sin\theta_0))} \qquad (6.56)$$

This function is shown in Figure 6.9. As can be seen from this figure, the directional factor is shifted by an amount $\frac{1}{2}knl\sin\theta_0$. The major lobe now points into the direction θ_0. However, this type of beam steering is not completely equivalent to physically rotating the array about the same angle, see Figure 6.10. Due to the steering of the beam, the length of the array will decrease to $L\cos\theta_0$, see again Figure 6.10, and the beamwidth, according to (6.55), will increase to

$$\theta_{null} \approx \frac{\lambda}{L\cos\theta_0}$$

Thus, the larger the angle θ_0, the larger the beamwidth.
The occurrence of grating lobes is a nuisance, since it may result in ambiguous acoustic measurements. They can be avoided if the equation

$$\tfrac{1}{2}kl(\sin\theta - \sin\theta_0) = m\pi$$

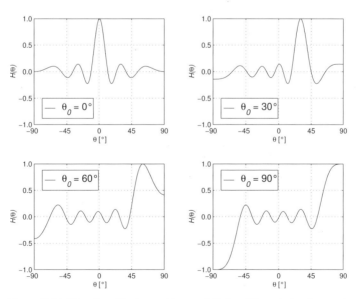

Figure 6.11: Directional factor and beamwidth for different steering angles θ_0 (n=10, $l = \lambda/2$).

has a solution only for $m=0$. This is the case if $l \le \lambda/2$. Shown in Figure 6.11 are the directional factors for a transmitter with $n=10$ and $l = \lambda/2$ for different angles θ_0. Only when the beam is steered towards 90°, there is a grating lobe, but this occurs at -90°, i.e., opposite to the steering direction.

The maximum amount of acoustic power is required to achieve the maximum range with active sonars. An active sonar is a system that purposely generates sound by one of its components, the *projector*. This generated sound is received by a listening device, the *hydrophone*. A passive sonar consists of a listening device only. *Cavitation*, which is a propagation property of the sound wave through the fluid medium, limits the power applied to a transmitter. Cavitation occurs when the instantaneous value of acoustic pressure exceeds static pressure. The resultant pressure becomes negative and small voids or cavities (bubbles caused by the rupture of the water) result in a gradual deterioration of the transmitter's performance.

When the acoustic pressure equals the static pressure in a fluid, the *cavitation threshold*, which is expressed in W/cm^2, occurs. Equality between hydrostatic and acoustic pressures occurs at the sea surface when the acoustic intensity (cavitation threshold) I_C is 0.3 W/cm^2. The cavitation threshold may be raised and more acoustic power may be radiated by

- decreasing the length of the transmitted acoustic pulse
- increasing the acoustic frequency, or
- increasing the depth (hydrostatic pressure) of the projector.

Variations in the cavitation threshold for five sonar transmitter frequencies measured in open water are shown in Figure 6.12 as a function of pulse length.

The cavitation limit increases with the shortening of the pulse length below 5 ms. Increased depth also causes an increase of the cavitation threshold by the amount of the hydrostatic pressure (each 10 m of water depth increases pressure by 1 atmosphere or about 10^5 Pa). The variation of the cavitation threshold of freshwater

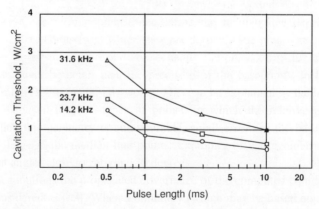

Figure 6.12: Cavitation threshold as a function of acoustic pulse length.

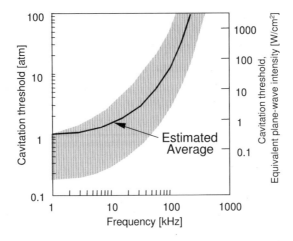

Figure 6.13: Cavitation threshold versus frequency for freshwater.

as a function of frequency is shown in Figure 6.13. The shaded area indicates the range of observed values. The solid line is an estimated average curve.

6.3   Sonar parameters

The *sonar parameters* represent the diverse effects in underwater sound propagation which are conveniently and logically grouped together quantitatively in a small number of units.

Parameters determined by the *equipment*
    Projector source Level   *SL*
    Self-Noise Level   *NL*
    Directivity Index   *DI*
    Detection Threshold   *DT*
Parameters determined by the *medium*
    Transmission Loss   *TL*
    Reverberation Level   *RL*
    Ambient Noise Level   *NL*
Parameters determined by the *target*
    Target Strength   *TS*
    Target Source Level   *SL*

Ambient noise and equipment self-noise are given the same symbol because they are indistinguishable from each other. Due to the wide range of intensities the sonar parameters (levels) are referred to a logarithmic scale and expressed in units of dB relative to an arbitrary but standard reference, i.e., reference intensity (pressure of 10^{-6} Pa plane wave) at 1 yard (or 1 m). The definitions of the different sonar parameters and standard reference locations are given in Table 6.2.

Table 6.2: Sonar parameters.

Sonar parameter		Reference	Definition
Source Level	SL	1 yard or 1 m from source on its acoustic axis	$10\log \dfrac{\text{Intensity of source}}{\text{Reference intensity}^*}$
Transmission Loss	TL	1 yard or 1 m from source and at target or receiver	$10\log \dfrac{\text{Signal intensity at reference distance}}{\text{Signal intensity at target or receiver}}$
Target Strength	TS	1 yard or 1 m from acoustic centre of target	$10\log \dfrac{\text{Echo intensity at reference distance from target}}{\text{Incident intensity}}$
Noise Level	NL	At hydrophone location	$10\log \dfrac{\text{Noise intensity}}{\text{Reference intensity}^*}$
Directivity Index	DI	At hydrophone terminals	$10\log \dfrac{\text{Noise power generated by an actual hydrophone}}{\text{Noise power generated by equivalent non-directional hydrophone}}$
Reverberation Level	RL	At hydrophone terminals	$10\log \dfrac{\text{Reverberation power at hydrophone terminal}}{\text{Power generated by signal of reference intensity}^*}$
Detection Threshold	DT	At hydrophone terminals	$10\log \dfrac{\text{Signal power to just perform a certain function}}{\text{Noise power at hydrophone terminals}}$

* The reference intensity is that of a plane wave of rms pressure 10^{-6} Pa (10^{-6} N/m^2).

Directivity Index (DI). The directivity index is a measure of the amount by which a *transducer* (an integrated projector and hydrophone) discriminates against noise in favour of the signal by concentrating its transmitting/receiving power along a directional axis of transmission/reception, as shown in Figure 6.5. The (transmitting) directivity index is given as (see also (6.49))

$$DI = 10\log d = 10\log(I_{Directional} / I_{Non-directional}) \tag{6.57}$$

Source Level (SL). The source level of a transmitter is related to the acoustic power that it radiates and to its directivity index. It can be interpreted as the intensity of radiated acoustic sound (relative to the reference intensity of a plane wave corresponding to a pressure of 10^{-6} N/m^2) at a point 1 yard (or 1 m) from the acoustic centre of the transmitter in the direction of the target.

In the case of a non-directional transmitter, the intensity I of the sound at a large distance r is given by the plane-wave expression, which follows from (6.45) and (6.46) and substitution of $\rho \approx 1000$ kg/m^3 and $c \approx 1500$ m/s

$$I = \tfrac{1}{2}\frac{\hat{p}_e^2}{r^2 \rho_0 c} = \frac{\hat{p}_{rms,e}^2}{1.5 \cdot 10^6 r^2} = \frac{P}{4\pi r^2} \tag{6.58}$$

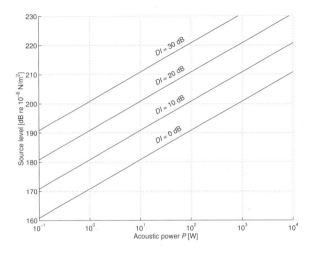

Figure 6.14: Acoustic power and source level.

If instead of a non-directional transmitter a directional transmitter is used, the intensity I should be multiplied by the directivity d, see (6.49). For a reference pressure of 10^{-6} N/m^2, we get at a distance of 1 m for the ratio I/I_{ref}

$$\frac{I}{I_{ref}} \cdot d = \frac{P/4\pi}{(10^{-6})^2 / 1.5 \cdot 10^6} \cdot d$$

The source level SL follows as the decibel value of the above expression and using (6.57)

$$SL = 10\log P + DI + 170.8 \tag{6.59}$$

This is the source level "re the intensity of a plane wave pressure equal to 10^{-6} N/m^2 at a reference distance of 1 m". Very often the source level is expressed re 10^{-6} N/m^2, at a reference distance of 1 yard (0.9144 m). In that case the source level becomes

$$SL = 10\log\{\frac{P/(4\pi \cdot 0.9144^2)}{(10^{-6})^2 / 1.5 \cdot 10^6} \cdot d\} = 10\log P + DI + 171.5 \tag{6.60}$$

The source level SL as a function of acoustic power output P and directivity index DI is shown in Figure 6.14.

In the above expressions, the quantity P is the total acoustic power radiated by the transmitter. In the case of an *electro-acoustic* transmitter, $P < P_{el}$, with P_{el} the acoustic power fed into the transmitter. The efficiency of the electro-acoustic transmitter is defined as

$$E = P / P_{el}$$

In such a case, the source level (6.59) should be written as

$$SL = 10 \log P_{el} + 10 \log E + DI + 170.8$$

Detection Threshold (DT). Before any other function is performed, the sonar system must first detect the presence of the signal reflected from the target. A certain level of the signal-to-noise ratio is required for making the decision whether the target has been detected or not. A signal-to-noise ratio at such a pre-assigned level is called a detection threshold. It is the term in the sonar equation, to be discussed in the next section, which satisfies the equation when the signal is just being detected. The detection threshold *DT* is defined as

$$DT = 10 \log \frac{S}{N} \qquad\qquad\qquad (6.61)$$

where S is the signal power in the receiver bandwidth and N is the noise power in a 1 Hz bandwidth.

Self-Noise (NL). Self-noise, which is not to be confused with radiated noise, is one of many different kinds of undesired noise in sonar. It depends strongly on the directivity of the transmitter (or receiver), its mounting, and its location on the ship. Self-noise is typically caused by propulsion machinery, propeller noise, and hydrodynamic noise. At higher speed, propeller noise due to cavitation becomes a major source of self-noise. Self-noise is defined in dB, referred to 10^{-6} Pa in a 1 Hz bandwidth. An example of *NL* (self-noise) versus ship speed at various frequencies is

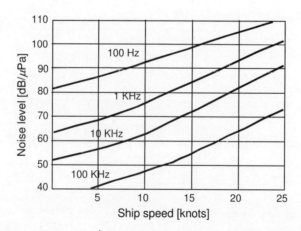

Figure 6.15: Self-noise as a function of ship speed for various frequencies.

shown in Figure 6.15.

Knowledge of the various noise sources and their noise levels is extremely important in designing systems. There is no point in designing an ultra sensitive system if the noise field is high.

Ambient Noise (NL). Ambient noise can be considered as the background noise of the sea. It is the residual noise after all identifiable noise sources are accounted for. The ambient noise level is the intensity (in dB) of ambient background noise measured with a non-directional transmitter referred to 10^{-6} Pa and reduced to 1 Hz bandwidth. There is a variety of natural and man-made sources of ambient noise.

Deep water noise
   Tides and hydrostatic effects of waves
   Seismic disturbances
   Oceanic turbulence
   Nonlinear wave interactions
   Ship traffic
   Surface waves
   Thermal noise

Shallow water noise
   Shipping and industrial noise
   Wind noise
   Biological noise

Intermittent sources of ambient noise
   Biological sounds
   Rain
   Explosions
   Seaquakes and volcanoes

Ambient noise is indistinguishable from self-noise. Under an ice cover, the ambient noise is different in character and level from the noise under ice-free conditions. Under an ice-pack, the ambient noise is 5 to 10 dB higher than that measured at the

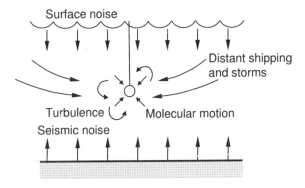

Figure 6.16: Ambient noise sources.

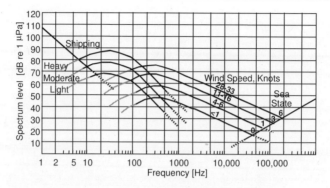

Figure 6.17: Average deep-water ambient noise spectra.

same state in ice-free waters. Some of the ambient noise sources in deep water are shown in Figure 6.16. The average deep-water ambient noise spectra for different wind speeds are shown in Figure 6.17.

Transmission Loss (TL). An underwater sound signal becomes delayed, distorted and weakened when travelling through the water. This results in the transmission loss which is one of the many phenomena associated with sound propagation in the sea. Transmission loss can be separated into two components. *Spreading loss* is a geometrical effect representing the regular weakening of a sound signal as it spreads outward from the source, *attenuation loss* includes absorption, scattering, and leakage out of sound channels.

Transmission loss is defined as

$$TL = 10\log\frac{P_{ref}}{P} = 10\log\frac{I}{I_{ref}} \tag{6.62}$$

The last term of this definition follows from the relationship between power P and intensity I. In (6.62) P_{ref} and I_{ref} are the acoustic power and intensity at a horizontal distance of one yard or one metre from the source. P and I are the same quantities at a distance of r yards or metres.

TL (geometric spreading). Consider an acoustic wave transmitted spherically from a source point at distances r_1 and r_2. The areas of spheres with radii r_1 and r_2 are $4\pi r_1^2$ and $4\pi r_2^2$. Assuming no loss due to the medium, the power P crossing these concentric spheres must be the same. Since $P = I \cdot A$, we have

$$P_1 = 4\pi r_1^2 I_1 = 4\pi r_2^2 I_2 = P_2$$

The spreading loss will be

$$TL(spreading) = 10\log\frac{I_1}{I_2}$$

which after insertion of the preceding expression gives

$$TL(spreading) = 10\log\frac{r_2^2}{r_1^2}$$

For $r_1 = 1$, we get for the transmission loss due to geometric spreading that it is equal to $20\log r_2$. In general, for an arbitrary distance r, we get

$$TL(spreading) = 20\log r \tag{6.63}$$

The spreading loss for spherical waves is independent of frequency and increases as r^2, as already shown in equation (6.45). For cylindrical waves, it can be derived in much the same way that the spreading loss is equal to $10\log r$, i.e., it increases as r.

TL (attenuation due to propagation medium). Attenuation is a loss of acoustic energy from a sound beam. It gradually increases with an increase of frequency. *Absorption* involves a process of conversion of the acoustic energy into thermal energy (heat). It represents the true loss of acoustic energy to the medium during propagation. Absorption is usually the most significant parameter. *Scattering* is a re-radiation of sound due to inhomogeneities (dust particles, air bubbles, schools of fish, sea bottom, etc.) in the water. This results in unwanted signals competing with the echo from the desired target.

Leakage out of sound channels is caused by the scattering and diffusion of sound.

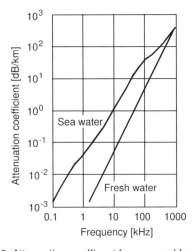

Figure 6.18: Attenuation coefficent for sea- and freshwater.

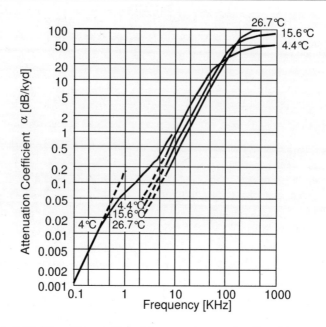

Figure 6.19: Attenuation coefficient for seawater as a function of frequency.

Sound leaks out of the channel at a rate given by a leakage coefficient that expresses the attenuation in dB per unit distance of sound trapped in the channel.

There is more absorption in seawater, due to salinity, than in freshwater. At frequencies between 5 kHz and 50 kHz, the absorption in seawater is 30 times larger than that in distilled water. The comparison of absorption in seawater and in freshwater is shown in Figure 6.18 for a temperature of 5°C and a salinity of 35 ppt.

The total propagation loss for a spherical wave can be written as

$$TL = 20\log r + \alpha \cdot r \cdot 10^{-3} \tag{6.64}$$

where r is the horizontal distance, and α is the attenuation coefficient in dB/km (or dB/kyard). The attenuation coefficient in seawater as a function of frequency is shown in Figure 6.19.

Reverberation is the sum of all scattering contributions from all the scatters. It decreases with increasing range. There are three classes of reverberation-producing scatters in the sea. *Volume reverberation* is produced by marine life and inanimate matter within the sea (schools of fish could prevent a clear definition of the bottom, but on the other hand, acoustics is used to detect schools of fish). *Sea surface reverberation* is produced by scatters near the sea surface. Finally, *sea bottom reverberation* is produced by scatters near the sea bottom.

Table 6.3 - Nominal values of target strength.

Target	Aspect	TS [dB]
Submarines	Beam	25
	Bow-stern	10
	Intermediate	15
Surface ships	Beam	25 (highly uncertain)
	Off-Beam	15 (highly uncertain)
Mines	Beam	10
	Off-Beam	10 to -25
Torpedoes	Bow	-20
Fish of length L (inches)	Dorsal view	19 log L - 54 (approx.)
Swimmers	Any	-15
Seamounts	Any	30 to 60

Target Strength (*TS*). In active sonar this parameter refers to the echo returned by the underwater target. It reflects the ability of the target to reflect a portion of the acoustic energy which ensonifies it. Target strength is defined as

$$TS = 10\log\frac{I_{ref}}{I_i} \qquad\qquad (6.65)$$

where I_i is the incident intensity and I_{ref} is the intensity of return at one yard (metre) from the target. Nominal TS values for selected objects are listed in Table 6.3.

TS may be positive because the reference distance of one yard (metre) from the acoustic centre of the target is relatively short. Such positive values should not be interpreted as the result of more sound coming back from the target than the incident sound upon it. They should rather be considered as a consequence of the arbitrary reference distance.

6.4   Sonar equations

The relationship between sonar parameters, i.e., the relationship between effects of medium, equipment and target, is described by the *sonar equations*. The functions of the sonar equations are:

- Prediction of performance of sonar equipment.
- Sonar equipment design.

A transducer echo-ranges the target, i.e., it produces a source level that reaches the target and returns to the transducer after being reflected (echoed). If *SL* is produced by the transducer source level at unit distance on its axis, then

- *SL - TL*   will be the source level once it reaches the target, i.e., the source level reduced by the transmission loss *TL*.

- *SL - TL + TS*   will be the source level after reflection from the target, i.e., the source level reduced by the transmission loss *TL* and reflected by the target.

- $SL - TL + TS - TL$ will be the echo level which returns to the transducer, i.e., the source level reduced by the transmission loss TL, reflected by the target and reduced again by the transmission loss TL.

Thus the echo level at the transducer is $SL - 2TL + TS$. The echo level will be further affected by the background effect. It can be considered as noise or reverberation. In the case of noise:

- NL is isotropic noise.
- $NL - DI$ is isotropic noise reduced by the directivity index (directivity gain) DI of the transducer acting as the receiver.

In the case of reverberation, $NL - DI$ will be replaced by an equivalent plane-wave reverberation level RL. At the transducer terminals, the echo-to-noise ratio is thus $(SL - 2TL + TS) - (NL - DI)$.

The detection threshold DT equals the signal-to-noise ratio when the target is just being detected, i.e.,

$$(SL - 2TL + TS) - (NL - DI) = DT$$

The above equation is called the *active-sonar equation*. Another form of the active-sonar equation with a more convenient arrangement is

$$SL - 2TL + TS = NL - DI + DT$$

Table 6.4 - Terminology of various combinations of sonar parameters.

Name	Parameters	Remarks
Echo level	$SL - 2TL + TS$	The intensity of the echo as measured in the water at the hydrophone.
Noise masking level	$NL - DI + DT$	Another name for these two combinations is *minimum detectable echo level*.
Reverberation masking level	$RL + DT$	
Echo excess	$(SL - 2TL + TS) -$ $(NL - DI + DT)$	Detection just occurs, under the probability conditions implied in the term DT, when the echo excess is zero.
Performance	$SL - (NL - DI)$	Difference between the source level and the noise level measured at the hydrophone terminals.
Figure of merit	$SL - (NL - DI + DT)$	Equals the maximum allowable one-way transmission loss in passive sonars or the maximum two-way loss for $TS=0$ dB in active sonars.

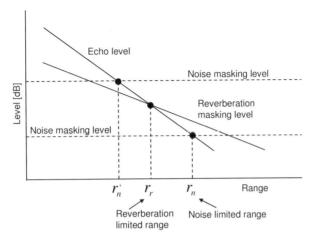

Figure 6.20: Noise and reverberation limitations.

The left-hand side of this expression is called the *echo level*, the right-hand side the *noise masking background level*. The above equation is valid for a transducer when the transmitter and receiver are coincident (monostatic case).

It is convenient to have separate names for different combinations of the parameters in the sonar equations. Table 6.4 lists the names and the combination of terms that each represents.

The sonar equations represent an equality between the *desired* portion of the acoustic field called the signal (echo or noise from a target), and an *undesired* portion of the acoustic signal called the background noise or reverberation.

A sonar system may be limited by the ambient noise level or by reverberation as shown in Figure 6.20. The curves of echo level, noise-masking level, and reverberation are shown. The masking levels are shown as a function of range.

The echo from the desired target and reverberation falls off with increasing range from target but the noise remains constant. The echo-level curve usually falls off more rapidly with range than the reverberation-masking curve.

The range will be limited either by
- reverberation r_r when noise (r_n) is low ($r_r < r_n$) (the range will be said to be *reverberation-limited*), or
- noise (r_n') when it is higher than reverberation ($r_n' < r_r$) (the range will be said to be *noise-limited*).

The knowledge of whether a sonar will be noise- or reverberation-limited is used to design or select the type of transducer required for a specific application.

6.5 Sound in water

The speed of sound in seawater c can be expressed as a function of temperature T, pressure p (or depth D) and salinity S. These parameters affect the bulk properties of the medium. Other parameters such as air bubbles and biological organisms can also

Table 6.5: Expressions for speed of sound c in m/s, in terms of temperature T (°C), depth D (m) and salinity S (ppt).

Expression	Limits
$c = 1492.9 + 3 \cdot (T - 10) - 6 \cdot 10^{-3} \cdot (T - 10)^2$ $- 4 \cdot 10^{-2} \cdot (T - 18)^2 + 1.2 \cdot (S - 35)$ $- 10^{-2} \cdot (T - 18) \cdot (S - 35) + 1.6 \cdot 10^{-2} \cdot D$	$-2 \leq T \leq 24.5$ $0 \leq D \leq 1000$ $30 \leq S \leq 42$
$c = 1449.2 + 4.6 \cdot T - 5.5 \cdot 10^{-2} \cdot T^2$ $+ 2.9 \cdot 10^{-4} \cdot T^3 + (1.34 - 10^{-2} \cdot T) \cdot (S - 35)$ $+ 1.6 \cdot 10^{-2} \cdot D$	$0 \leq T \leq 35$ $0 \leq D \leq 1000$ $0 \leq S \leq 45$
$c = 1448.96 + 4.591 \cdot T - 5.304 \cdot 10^{-2} \cdot T^2$ $+ 2.374 \cdot 10^{-4} \cdot T^3 + 1.340 \cdot (S - 35)$ $+ 1.630 \cdot 10^{-2} \cdot D + 1.675 \cdot 10^{-7} \cdot D^2$ $- 1.025 \cdot 10^{-2} \cdot T \cdot (S - 35) - 7.139 \cdot 10^{-1} \cdot T \cdot D^3$	$0 \leq T \leq 30$ $0 \leq D \leq 8000$ $30 \leq S \leq 40$

affect the speed of sound. The speed of sound is usually modelled using *empirical formulae* of the general form

$$c = f(T, p, S) = f(T, D, S)$$

Typical empirical formulae are shown in Table 6.5. The speed of sound increases with increasing temperature, salinity and depth. From these expressions, it can be concluded that the speed of sound is most sensitive to variations in temperature.

Two instruments are commonly used to determine the velocity of sound in the sea. A *bathythermograph* is a simple and generally inexpensive instrument. It is lowered into the sea to measure temperature T as a function of depth. The expendable bathythermograph is capable of providing the temperature profile without having to retrieve the sensing unit afterward. The bathythermograph converts the temperature-depth trace to sound speed. It is assumed that salinity gradients are known or non-existent. For above reason, the bathythermograph is accurate in deep waters far from shores.

A *velocimeter* measures directly the travel time between a transmitter and a receiver fixed to a small platform. This instrument is accurate under any conditions, including along shorelines and melting ice caps where salinity variations are significant.

The average speed of sound $\bar{c}$ in a water column of height $z - z_0$ is given by

$$\bar{c} = (z - z_0) [\int_{z_0}^{z} \frac{dz}{c(z)}]^{-1} \tag{6.66}$$

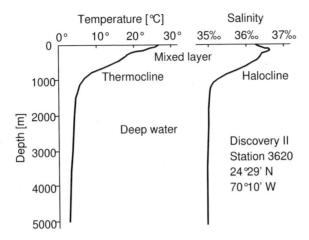

Figure 6.21: Thermocline and halocline.

The integral is the time required for the acoustic signal to travel the distance $z - z_0$. If the speed of sound is measured or computed at a discrete number of depths z_i, $i = 1, \ldots, n$, the integral should be replaced by a summation. Assuming constant velocity in each layer $z_i - z_{i-1}$, we get

$$\bar{c} = (z - z_0)[\sum_{i=1}^{n} \frac{z_i - z_{i-1}}{c_i}]^{-1} \tag{6.67}$$

If the velocity in a layer is not constant but has a constant gradient g_i, defined as $g_i = (c_i - c_{i-1})/(z_i - z_{i-1})$, the travel time t_i in the layer $z_i - z_{i-1}$ is

$$t_i = \int_{z_{i-1}}^{z_i} \frac{dz}{c(z)} = \int_{z_{i-1}}^{z_i} \frac{dz}{c_{i-1} + g_i \cdot (z - z_{i-1})} = \frac{1}{g_i} \ln \frac{c_i}{c_{i-1}} \tag{6.68}$$

The average velocity now becomes

$$\bar{c} = (z - z_0)[\sum_{i=1}^{n} \frac{1}{g_i} \ln \frac{c_i}{c_{i-1}}]^{-1} \tag{6.69}$$

A sound velocity profile represents the variation of sound velocity with depth. Typical temperature (*thermocline*) and salinity (*halocline*) profiles are shown in Figure 6.21. A typical sound velocity profile for the deep ocean at mid-latitude regions is given in Figure 6.22.

There are distinguishable variations (gradient changes) due to mixed surface layers, seasonal thermocline, and main thermocline. Below 1,000 m the speed of sound increases fairly uniformly as a function of depth. The total variation is 30 to 50 m/s, i.e., $\Delta c < 5\%$, since c is approximately 1500 m/s. It can become critical for certain

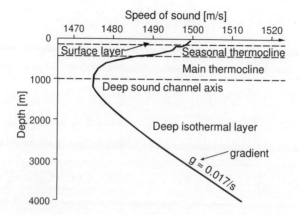

Figure 6.22: Sound velocity profile as a function of depth for mid-latitude regions.

bathymetric surveys. Deep-sea velocity profile variations for different latitudes are shown in Figure 6.23.

In shallow waters and coastal regions the speed of sound profile is irregular and unpredictable. This is due to significant surface heating and cooling, frequent salinity changes (nearby freshwater, e.g., in a river delta) and occurrence of water currents. In freshwater, the sound velocity is lower, e.g., 1402 m/s (0°C) to 1529 m/s (40°C).

Wave motion causes a mixing of water in the surface layer, resulting in a so-called *mixed layer*. This layer extends to a depth of about 200 m. It is also referred to as *isothermal layer*, since the mixing causes temperature to be constant. Variations in speed of sound occur mainly due to change in pressure with increasing depths. The velocity gradient is positive and amounts to 0.017 s^{-1}. Below the mixed layer, temperature decreases in the *seasonal* and *main* thermoclines, resulting in a negative gradient. In the *deep isothermal layer*, finally, temperature increases again with depth

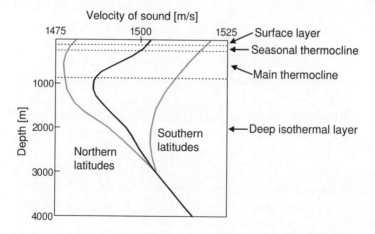

Figure 6.23: Sound velocity profile variations for northern and southern latitudes.

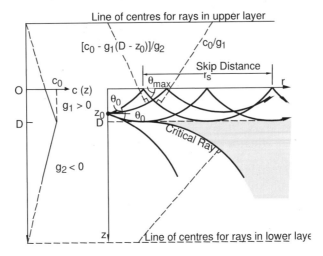

Figure 6.24: Critical ray and shadow zone.

and this, together with increasing pressure, results in a positive gradient for the speed of sound.

Using (6.40) and the simplified velocity profile shown in Figure 6.24, it is possible to compute the curvature of an acoustic ray when travelling through the medium. A ray travelling upward reflects from the surface, whereas a ray travelling downward may either be reflected upward by the layer at which velocity is minimal or cross this boundary, depending upon the angle θ_0 with which the ray leaves the source. The rays that either graze the boundary or just cross it are called *limiting* (or *critical*) *rays*. They determine the *shadow zone*, in which no acoustic signals can penetrate from the source.

When a non-directional signal is transmitted from a source, it will initially spread spherically. However, as soon as it becomes trapped in the mixed layer, it will have the characteristics of a cylindrical wave. As a result, the geometric transmission loss will be inversely proportional to the distance from the source rather than to the square of it, allowing the signal to travel long distances.

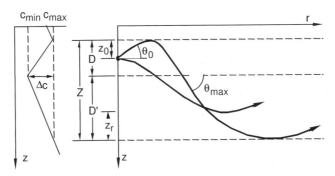

Figure 6.25: Deep sound channel.

The *deep sound channel* axis is the depth at which the speed of sound in the oceans reaches its minimum. All rays originating near this axis and making small angles with the horizontal, will return to it without reaching the bottom or the surface. They will remain trapped in the deep sound channel, as shown in Figure 6.25. Deep sound channels are found in many parts of the ocean at a depth of around 1000 m. The signals in these channels may propagate over thousands of kilometres. The *SOFAR* (SOund Fixing And Ranging) technique uses this property. A person in distress detonates a small charge of explosive in the deep sound channel. From the differences in times of arrival at three or more listening stations, it is possible to determine the location of the explosion using hyperbolic positioning techniques.

6.6 Major references

Caruthers, J.W.: *Fundamentals of marine acoustics*. Elsevier, Amsterdam, 1977.

Kinsler, L.E., A.R. Frey, A.B. Coppens, J.V. Sanders: *Fundamentals of acoustics*. John Wiley & Sons, Inc., New York, 4th edition, 2000.

National Defense Research Committee: *Physics of sound in the sea*. Peninsula Publishing, Los Altos, reprint, originally published in 1945.

Stephens, R.W.B. (ed.): *Underwater acoustics*. Wiley Interscience, London, 1970.

Tucker, D.G., B.K. Gazey: *Applied underwater acoustics*. Pergamon Press, Oxford, 1966.

Urick, R.J.: *Principles of underwater sound*. Peninsula Publishing, Los Altos, 3rd edition, 1983.

Urick, R.J.: *Sound propagation in the sea*. Peninsula Publishing, Los Altos, 1982.

7 Law of the Sea

7.1 History

The basis for the law of the sea has been laid by the Dutch jurist Hugo de Groot (Hugo Grotius). In his work *Mare Liberum*, published in 1609, the freedom of Sea is advocated. The underlying principle of Hugo de Groot was: "Nations are free to use the seas for whichever purpose, provided it does not interfere with another nation's use of the sea". The work of Hugo de Groot was primarily meant to support the claim of the Dutch East India Company to trade in the Far East, which was considered by the Portuguese and Spanish to be their sole right. Hugo de Groot had a specific (commercial) reason to write his *Mare Liberum*.

In the same period several attempts were undertaken to govern fishing areas and access to natural off-shore resources; the international community also realised that a coastal nation should have control over the ocean adjacent to its coast. So there were various reasons in the 17th century for the international community to look at establishing some sort of "Law of the Sea".

The coastal area was initially defined "within a cannon's shot", but around the beginning of the 19th century it became common amongst coastal nations to proclaim an area at sea of about three nautical miles (nM) from the coast. Within this area, complete sovereignty of the coastal state was claimed. Outside this area of three nautical miles, the freedom of sea applied. This concept was for a long time respected by most of the world, but never officially ratified.

After World War II, there was a need for regulated international Law of the Sea. In 1958 the first United Nations Convention on Law of the Sea (UNCLOS) was held in Geneva, Switzerland. Most of the 86 participating countries had at that time divided their waters into three or four main parts, with different rights and duties. On the basis of these claims, which were considered general customary law, four conventions were drafted during the UNCLOS conference. They discussed, respectively:

- the territorial seas and contiguous zone;

- the high seas;
- the continental shelf and fisheries;
- the conservation of biological resources of the high seas.

It was agreed that a coastal state could have sovereignty in a near-shore area, the territorial sea. There was, however, no agreement during the conference on the extent of these waters.

The continental shelf was defined as the area outside inland waters or territorial sea to a depth of 200 metres. However, if the seabed or subsoil beyond the 200 metres depth contour could be exploited by the coastal state, the continental shelf was not limited to the 200 metres depth contour, and could be extended. The conference did also not result in an agreement on the exact limits of such an extended continental shelf.

Although the above mentioned issues remained unresolved, there was agreement about the definition of the so-called *baseline*. The baseline is where the width of the territorial sea and other off-shore areas of UNCLOS are to be measured from. These baselines are normally the low-water lines along the coasts. They can be found on large-scale nautical charts officially recognised by the coastal state. Further there was consensus during the first UNCLOS meeting about the fact that there is such an entity as "high sea": off-shore areas where no state can claim control.

At the second UNCLOS meeting in 1960, an attempt was made to resolve some of the open issues, but again, no agreement about the width of the territorial sea and the continental shelf was reached. Different countries claimed different areas as their territorial sea at that time, varying between 3, 12 and even 200 nM from the baseline.

Because of new technical possibilities to further exploit the sea, new customary law and the non-solved aspects of the first two conventions, there was a need for a third Convention on Law of the Sea. Also the deep seabed exploitation by the rich industrial states gave concern to the world, especially to those countries that were not able to join the exploitation, and needed to be discussed. In the 1960's the world developed the idea of "the common heritage of mankind". This concept would mean that all rights and resources of the high sea, its seabed and its subsoil should be for the benefit of all and should not be appropriated by any one state. These developments and ideas necessitated a third UNCLOS convention.

The third convention, UNCLOSIII, started in 1973. Because of the decolonisation process that had taken place, the number of participants had increased to 165. Among the results of the conference was an agreement about the maximum width of the different maritime zones, including the territorial sea and the continental shelf (Section 7.3).

Furthermore, agreement about the *Exclusive Economic Zone* (EEZ) was established. The text on the delimitation of the EEZ and continental shelf between states was highly influenced by a judgement of the International Court of Justice in the North Sea Continental Shelf Cases of 1969, because in this judgement for the first time the principle of equitability was used.

After nine years, in 1982, UNCLOSIII was signed in Montego Bay, Jamaica. UNCLOSIII also contained articles dealing with the deep seabed, although not all states agreed unanimously with those articles. Especially the industrialised countries, since they saw their monopoly to use the deep seabed resources significantly reduced, had objections.

UNCLOSIII came into operation on November 16th 1994 (21 years after the start of the convention), because only at that time the minimum number of 60 states had ratified the convention. In April 2002, 138 states had signed the convention. Some articles of UNCLOSIII have become state practice, and thus become customary law.

7.2 Baselines

All the outer limits of the zones mentioned in UNCLOS are defined from the baseline (except the article 76 Continental Shelf, see Subsection 7.3.4). There are two types of baselines: *normal* baselines (Subsection 7.2.1) and *straight* baselines (Subsection 7.2.2), see Figure 7.1. Both normal and straight baselines consist of interconnected *basepoints*.

7.2.1 Normal baseline

The normal baseline is the low water line along the coast as marked   on   large-scale nautical charts officially recognised by the coastal state (Article 5 of UNCLOS). A large-scale chart is according to the International Hydrographic Organisation (IHO) a chart of scale 1:50,000 to 1:150,000. Nautical charts may be overlapping in their area of coverage. In that case the baselines have to be taken from the most recent large-scale chart.

The baseline of a state includes the low-water line around islands and the outer limits of permanent harbour works. A low-tide elevation (e.g., sand bars, drying banks

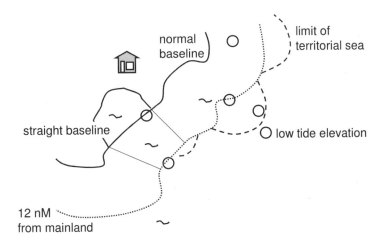

Figure 7.1: Normal and straight baselines and the territorial sea.

often indicated as green areas on nautical charts) may also form part of the normal baseline if all or a part of this low-tide elevation lies within the area of the territorial sea measured from the low-water line of the mainland or an island, see Figure 7.1. The low water line corresponds to the depth contour of zero metre, referred to as the Chart Datum. There are about 100-200 different vertical (chart) datums in the world. In areas affected by tide, the Chart Datum is nearly always some kind of low water level, see Chapter 4. The fact that there are different realisations of vertical datum means that adjacent or opposite states may use different levels to establish their baselines. This means consequently that for instance a low-tide elevation could appear on one chart and not on another (which uses a different Chart Datum).

Just like horizontal datums, several international organisations try to adopt one reference system to refer heights (or depths) to, worldwide. The IHO and IMO (International Maritime Organisation) already stated in the early 1980's that the world should consider adopting LAT as standard reference level for Chart Datums. A consequence of the transition from a locally used Chart Datum to LAT is that the low-water line along the coast will change, and thus, the baseline. Especially when the sea floor near the coastline is not steep, the change may be considerable.

Since the low water line regularly changes due to the dynamics of the water, the coastline and low tide elevations may also change. So at every new edition of a chart, there is a possibility that the legal baseline has changed. Apart from natural causes, the baseline may also change because of human activities, for instance as the result of land reclamation or the building of extensions to harbours.

If the real-life situation has been changed, but the chart has not been updated, the legal baseline that is used to define the maritime zones is still the one that is visualised on the chart (changes in a baseline on a nautical chart may also be announced through a Notice to Mariners (NtM)). When old charts or otherwise "unreliable" charts are used for a delimitation case (simply because there are no new charts available), the states involved could agree on using additional measurements to define the baseline. Aerial photogrammetry, new hydrographic surveys or precise GPS measurements of the coastline may be used to get a better understanding of the position of the low water line.

If two states have already agreed on a maritime boundary (a ratified treaty) and the situation changes, this has no effect anymore on the agreed maritime boundary. But it has effect on the unilateral limits of a state (the zones that are discussed in Section 7.3).

7.2.2 Straight baseline

In addition to normal baselines, also straight baselines exist. A straight baseline is a straight line joining specified basepoints on the low water line, not necessarily following the coastline exactly (straight baselines can, however, not deviate too much from the general direction of the coastline).

Straight baselines may be used when the coastline is "deeply indented", or when there is a fringe of islands along the coast's "immediate vicinity". Due to the general way it is formulated, Article 7 of UNCLOSIII, which deals with straight baselines, is open for discussion. For instance, Article 7 does not give an explanation on how "deeply indented" the coastline may be or what is still defined as "immediate vicinity". The United States have refined these general rules for their own purposes, but most countries use the UNCLOSIII convention as it is.

Also the presence of a delta, or other natural conditions, may cause the coastline to be irregular and may make the use of a straight baseline possible. Furthermore, straight lines can be drawn across the mouth of a river, i.e., between points on the low water line on its banks. It is also possible to define a bay-closing line, which may be used as a straight baseline. The bay must fulfil a number of characteristics when a bay-closing line is drawn (Article 10 of UNCLOSIII). These characteristics include, but are not limited to, the condition that an indentation is only considered to be a bay when its area is smaller than that of the semi-circle whose diameter is a line drawn across the mouth of that indentation. Also a bay-closing line may not exceed 24 nM. A bay closed by an Article 10 bay-closing line is called a "juridical bay".

Besides the juridical bay, also for "historic" bays (e.g., Fortune Bay in Canada or the Varanger Fjord in Norway) it is possible to define a bay-closing line, even when it does not fulfil the Article 10 conditions. For a "historic" bay no definition is given in UNCLOSIII.

A special kind of straight baseline is the so-called *archipelagic* baseline. In Article 47 of UNCLOSIII one finds a description of the conditions a system of archipelagic baselines must meet, see also Subsection 7.3.6.

For the exact use of straight baselines, one should define what kind of "straight lines" are meant, e.g., loxodromes or geodesics. Especially when long distances are covered with straight baselines, it is important to define the type. This is not always done, resulting in an ambiguously defined line. Especially when a straight baseline has an East-West direction at a higher latitude, the variation between the different types can be in the order of several hundreds of metres.

A state may use a combination of normal and straight baselines as their baseline system. For example for the Netherlands nine straight baselines are defined by law in 1985, between the Frisian Islands in the northern part of the country, between seaport constructions and in the mouth of the Scheldt river.

7.2.3 Precision of basepoints

Baselines consist of basepoints. When determining the limits of a maritime zone it is often only necessary to use a selection of relevant basepoints. Geographical coordinates of basepoints are usually given to the nearest second in latitude and longitude. They are in most cases digitised from nautical charts and a higher resolution is therefore not possible. As a result, their resolution is of the order of 30-50 metres, depending on the latitude. So irrespective of the accuracy of the survey of the low water line, the fact that basepoints are only expressed to the full second makes differences between the position of the low water line and the basepoints of several tens of metres possible.

The accuracy of charts (and thus of the low-water line) depends on the accuracy of the surveys that were conducted to make the chart and the accuracy of the charting. Some of the recently published nautical charts are still (partly) based on very old surveys (the survey date can be checked at the source diagram in the chart). Although this data may not be very accurate, the legal basepoints are still the ones that are selected from the chart.

Sometimes a sort of artificial illusion of precision is introduced, created by the large number of digits in which the coordinates of the basepoints are presented. In such cases, the actual number of significant digits is usually much smaller than the number of digits given.

In numerous cases even the geodetic datum used in the chart is unknown, which makes coordinating the base points again more difficult. Additional inaccuracy can also be introduced when transforming coordinates from one datum (if it is known) into another. Although the transformation can mathematically be performed without errors, in many cases the transformation parameters are of such quality or defined for such a large area that the precision of the transformed coordinates degrades significantly.

The above should make it clear that the delimitation of the different maritime zones is by no means a matter of centimetres.

7.3   Maritime zones

In UNCLOSIII several *zones* are defined in which different rights and duties are in force. For an overview of the zones, see Figure 7.2. The outer limits of the maritime zones are not drawn as lines parallel to the baseline, but are arcs around the relevant, most seaward lying basepoints, see Figure 7.1. Before the computer age the boundaries were graphically constructed on a paper chart. Now, they can be computed accurately using geodetic calculations on the ellipsoid.

7.3.1 Internal waters

The internal waters comprise all waters, with a connection to the sea, landward of the baseline. Most internal waters are bays, estuaries, ports and waters enclosed by straight baselines. Lakes are not internal waters, as they do not have an open connection to the sea. Internal waters are part of the territory of the coastal state. A state exercises complete sovereignty over its internal waters with the exception that a right of innocent passage exists for foreign vessels in areas that had not been considered as internal waters prior to the establishment of a system of straight baselines.

7.3.2 Territorial sea

According to UNCLOSIII, coastal states are allowed to establish a territorial zone of at most 12 nM from the baseline, in which the state has full sovereignty. The sovereignty is valid for the seabed, subsoil, water and airspace. There is the right of innocent passage and transit passage for all foreign vessels. Roadsteads that are normally used for loading, unloading and anchoring of ships, and which would be situated wholly or partly outside the territorial sea, are also included in the territorial sea.

7.3.3 Contiguous zone

The contiguous zone is the area seaward of the territorial zone up to a limit of 24 nM from the baseline. The coastal state may exercise the control in this zone necessary to prevent infringement of its customs, fiscal, immigration or sanitary laws and regulations that are in effect within the state's territory or territorial sea. The contiguous zone comprises international waters in, and over which the ships and aircraft (including warships and military aircraft) of all nations enjoy the high seas freedoms of navigation and overflight.

The contiguous zone is not something a nation automatically possesses on the basis of UNCLOS regulations, but it needs to be claimed. The Netherlands for instance, have no contiguous zone because the Dutch government never claimed one.

7.3.4 Continental shelf

The outer limit of the juridical continental shelf is 200 nM, or more if there is a larger natural continental margin (the natural continental margin consists of the shelf, the slope and the rise, see Figure 7.2). In the first two UNCLOS conventions, the juridical continental shelf was only defined by the natural continental margin. Some countries had a major advantage with this definition, because their natural continental

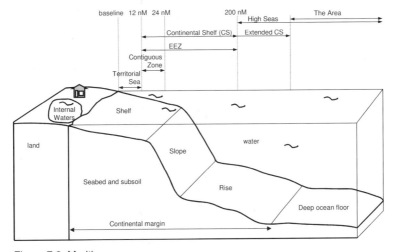

Figure 7.2: Maritime zones.

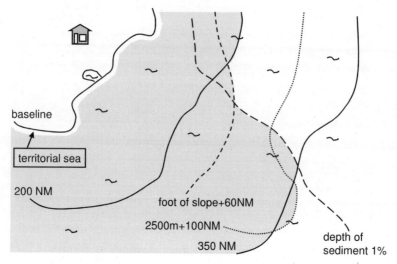

Figure 7.3: Continental shelf.

margin stretched far more into the sea than the continental margin of other countries. Therefore, during the third UNCLOS convention the distance criterion was established. The continental shelf can also have a smaller distance than 200 nM from the baseline, namely when baselines of opposite states are within 400 nM from each other. In that case the outer limit of the continental shelf stretches up to the agreed maritime boundary between those two countries.

The continental shelf contains the seabed and subsoil of the submarine areas that extend beyond the territorial sea. It excludes waters above it, as well as the fish in these waters. The coastal state has sovereign rights for exploration and exploitation of the natural resources of the seabed and subsoil, including mineral and other   non-living resources and living organisms belonging to sedentary species. Other states may lay submarine cables and pipelines on the continental shelf. The coastal state has the right to delineate the course of such cables and pipelines.

The continental shelf can extend beyond 200 nM in case the natural margin is more than 200 nM from the baseline. Article 76 of UNCLOS sets out the conditions under which a coastal state may be entitled to claim an extended continental shelf beyond 200 nM from the baseline. In the most complex situations, the outer limits of the extended continental shelf can be defined by a combination of lines, which are derived from geophysical, hydrographic and geomorphologic data, see Figure 7.3. The extended continental shelf is subject to a number of limitations:

- It cannot go beyond the line where sediment thickness is 1% of the distance of that point to the foot of the slope.
- It cannot go beyond 60 nM from the foot of the continental slope (point of maximum change of gradient at the base of the slope).
- It cannot go beyond 100 nM from the 2500 m isobath (depth contour).
- It cannot go beyond 350 nM from the baseline.

More than 30 states possibly meet the requirements for an extended continental shelf.

A coastal state that wishes to claim an extended continental shelf must put its claim down with supporting scientific and technical data at the United Nations Commission on the Limits of the Continental Shelf (CLCS) (www.un.org/Depts/los/clcs_news/-clcs_home.htm) within ten years of the Convention entering into force for that state. In May 2001, however, it was decided that the ten-year period should commence on 13 May 1999 for all states that signed the Convention before that date.

The CLCS examines all submissions for extended continental shelfs, and makes recommendations to the coastal state. Next, the boundaries will be established by the coastal state, based on the recommendations of the CLCS, and they become final and binding from that time. Should the coastal state disagree with the recommendations of CLCS, UNCLOS provides for it to make a revised or new submission to the CLCS within a reasonable time. The CLCS can also give scientific and technical advice upon request of a coastal state when they are preparing a submission. The Russian Federation was the first to submit a claim for an extended continental shelf in the Barents Sea, the Bering Sea, the Sea of Okhotsk and the Arctic Sea to the commission on 20 December 2001. In the beginning of July 2002 the CLCS returned their recommendations to the Russian Federation.

Currently a lot of countries are surveying their continental margins to gather the data that is needed to support a claim for a continental shelf beyond 200 nM. Special software packages have been developed to do automated interpretation of surveys and measurements and assist in the claim.

The coastal state shall make payments, or contributions in kind, in respect of the exploitation of the non-living resources of the continental shelf beyond 200 nM from the baseline. The payments or contributions will be distributed to Parties to UNCLOS on the basis of equitable sharing criteria. This way also states with a smaller continental shelf benefit from the extended continental shelves of other states.

7.3.5 Exclusive Economic Zone

The Exclusive Economic Zone (EEZ) is a zone adjacent to the territorial sea. The outer limit of the EEZ is at maximum 200 nM from the baseline, i.e., it has a maximum width of 188 nM.

In an EEZ the coastal state has sovereign rights for the purpose of exploration and exploitation (including hydrographic surveying) and conservation and management of living and non-living resources of the waters superadjacent to the sea-bed and of the sea-bed and its subsoil. Furthermore it has jurisdiction with regard to the establishment and use of artificial islands, installations and structures, marine scientific research and the protection and preservation of the marine environment. The coastal state may establish safety zones, not exceeding 500 metres, around such artificial islands, installations and structures, except where interference may be caused to the use of recognised sea lanes essential for international navigation. The rights enjoyed by all states in the EEZ of another state comprise navigation and overflight as well as the laying of submarine cables and pipelines.

The EEZ is overlapping with the continental shelf. The continental shelf belongs automatically to the coastal state, the EEZ has to be announced (claimed) similar to the contiguous zone. The EEZ contains the seabed, the subsoil and the waters above it, where the continental shelf only encompasses the seabed and subsoil.

The outer limits of the EEZ are to be shown on charts of a scale adequate for ascertaining their position. Where appropriate, lists of geographical coordinates of points, including details of the geodetic datum, may be used.

Where islands can have an EEZ and continental shelf of their own, rocks, which cannot sustain human habitation or economic life of their own shall have no EEZ or continental shelf (Article 121).

7.3.6 Archipelagic waters

An archipelago is defined as a group of islands, including parts of islands, inter-connecting waters and other natural features which are so closely interrelated that such islands, water and other natural features form an intrinsic geographical, economic and political entity, or which historically have been regarded as such. An archipelagic state is entitled to draw straight archipelagic baselines around the outermost islands of the archipelago, and to measure its territorial sea seaward from those baselines. Archipelagic waters are the waters enclosed by the archipelagic baselines. The archipelago has sovereignty over those waters. Through archipelagos, archipelagic sea lanes (and the air routes above) can be defined. Foreign vessels and aircraft have a right of innocent passage within such sea lanes and air routes through or over archipelagic waters. If an archipelagic state does not designate sea lanes or air routes, the right of archipelagic sea lane passage may be exercised through the routes normally used for international navigation.

7.3.7 Fishery zone

A lot of states have a fishery zone claimed (amongst them the Netherlands in 1977). The fishery zone is not included in UNCLOSIII, but customary law makes such claims valid. One could look at the fishery zone as a predecessor of the EEZ, where economic rights are established in relation to fishery only. Since the EEZ also includes fishery rights, a fishery zone is not needed anymore once an EEZ is claimed, but still they exist next to each other. The outer limits of fishery zones are generally 200 nM from the baseline (same as the EEZ).

7.3.8 High sea

The waters beyond the EEZ are called high sea (possibly partially overlapping with an extended continental shelf). In the high seas the principle of freedom of sea counts. This comprises freedom of navigation, freedom of overflight, freedom to lay submarine cables and pipelines, freedom to construct artificial islands and other installations, freedom of fishing, freedom of scientific research. There is no sovereignty by states over the high sea. Two thirds of all off-shore waters are defined as high seas. The waters above the (extended) continental shelf (unless there is an EEZ) fall under the high sea as well, since the continental shelf only applies to the seabed and subsoil of the submarine areas. The flag state of ships sailing through the high seas has special duties to ensure safety at high sea. There is also the duty to render assistance to any person or ship in danger. Concerning fishing in the high sea, states should cooperate in the conservation and management of living resources.

The term "high sea" has a feel of huge areas of open water, but in some cases it only consists of a small part of the sea. Examples can be found between Russia and the USA in the Bering Sea or between the USA and Mexico in the Gulf of Mexico. It is not unthinkable that the seabed of these small-enclosed high sea areas in the near future will be claimed as an extended continental shelf.

7.3.9 The Area

The "Area" is defined as the seabed and ocean floor and subsoil thereof, beyond the limits of national jurisdiction. It is part of the "common heritage of mankind". All states manage jointly the resources of the Area through the International Seabed Authority (ISBA). ISBA conducts its own mining operations through its organ "Enterprise" and contracts with private and state ventures by granting them mining rights in the Area. The seat of ISBA is based in Jamaica and established by UNCLOS.

High sea and the Area largely cover the same parts of the sea. The high seas concern the waters, where the Area consists of the seabed, ocean floor and subsoil. High sea may be overlapping with an extended continental shelf or the Area.

7.4 Boundaries between states

States with neighbouring seas have to agree upon the delimitation of the above mentioned areas. Settlement of the boundaries is especially important for the off-shore and fishing industry, and for pipelines and cables. When a boundary is not determined, often provisional, practical regulations are in use. In the case of the territorial sea, the *median line* is kept as the provisional boundary between states. Pending agreement on delimitation of the EEZ or the continental shelf, the states concerned are to make every effort to enter into provisional arrangements of a practical nature and, during this transitional period, not to jeopardize or hamper the reaching of the final agreement. Such arrangements are without prejudice to the final delimitation of the EEZ or the continental shelf.

The negotiations about the maritime boundary are generally done by a small team, of which the Ministry of Foreign affairs has the leadership, added with several experts (e.g., a legal, political and technical expert). When an agreement has been reached, the result (including the coordinates of the boundary) is laid down in a boundary treaty. The boundary is officially in use when both countries have ratified the treaty.

In UNCLOS the basis for delimitation of the territorial sea is laid at the equidistance line. The existence of an historic title or other special circumstances may be reason to deviate from that basis. Ultimately, the delimitation of the continental shelf and the EEZ should be done in such a way that an equitable solution is reached, on the basis of international law.

7.4.1 Equidistance line

An *equidistance line* or median line is defined as "a line where every point has equal distances to the nearest points of the baselines of the states concerned". It consists of a number of sections. The positions that define these sections are known as *turning points*. A turning point has equal distances to three basepoints on the two baselines involved. Two of the three basepoints belong to the baseline of one state and the third to the other. The next turning point has equal distances to two of the three basepoints that were used in the previous turning point plus a new basepoint. This principle is illustrated in Figure 7.4. An end point of an equidistance line could be a tripoint: a turning point with equal distances to basepoints of three different states. A method for computing an equidistance line is described in (Carrera, 1987).

There are several ways to connect turning points of a maritime boundary. Especially when the distance between two points is large, the method chosen is of importance. A geodesic, a loxodrome or great circle could join the points. In earlier times the way

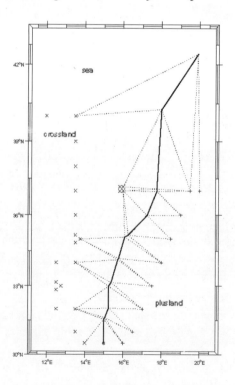

Figure 7.4: Determination of equidistance line.

to connect the turning points was by drawing a straight line on a nautical chart, which generally uses the Mercator projection. In those days the turning points were therefore connected by loxodromes (straight lines on Mercator projections result in loxodromes). Nowadays computarized solutions exist to connect the turning points by geodetic lines (geodesics) on the ellipsoid. If in a treaty a line is called a "straight line", the boundary is not unambiguously defined, simply because there is no mathematical realisation of a "straight line" on a curved surface. Another example of boundaries not being sharply defined, is when different "calculation surfaces" are mixed up in one treaty. In the North Sea for instance, many boundaries are defined using parts of great circles on a sphere, while the horizontal datum is defined on an ellipsoid. It also happens that limits that use the same turning points, such as those of a continental shelf and an EEZ, differ because the connections between the turning points are defined in a different way for the two zones. In the past, it has happened that boundaries were connected by non-defined straight lines, or by lines on a small-scale chart, which not necessarily used the Mercator projection. For some maritime boundaries the geodetic datum of the coordinates is even unknown.

The charts of the two states involved in the process of determining a boundary can be of a different geodetic datum (horizontal) and Chart Datum (vertical). Therefore the states need to reach an agreement about the use of the datums. Transformation between two different horizontal datums may be necessary. With GPS becoming available, today the boundary calculations are often performed in the global WGS84 datum.

There is a potential total of 434 maritime boundaries between states in the world, of which around 180 have been agreed upon and ratified. Most of the boundaries were delimited in the 1970's and 1980's, mainly in areas where oil and gas reserves were expected to be found, like the North Sea and the Persian Gulf.

7.4.2 Deviations from strict equidistance

The negotiations concerning a maritime boundary can take a very long time, especially when it is expected that economic benefits will be high in the area concerned. In most cases, negotiations start with the computation of the equidistance line. It is determined whether the equidistance line is an equitable solution or whether the existence of an historic title or other special circumstances may be reason to deviate from equidistance. In the second stage, deviations from the equidistance line are negotiated.

When it is agreed that the boundary should be an equidistance line, the final boundary is usually a simplified equidistance line, because a strict equidistance line would make it very irregular. This is due to the fact that the normal baseline (the low water line) is usually very irregular as well. Since an irregular maritime boundary is difficult to control, often a simplified equidistance line is defined as the final boundary. For this purpose equal areas are exchanged between the two nations involved. The resulting sum of areas lost and gained should be zero.

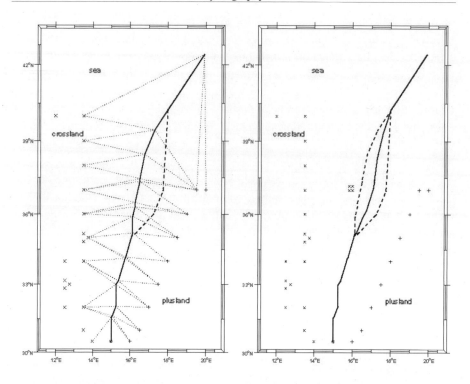

Figure 7.5: Null effect line in relation to full effect line.

Figure 7.6: Half effect line as angle bisector of full and null effect line.

States can agree that some features, which have a disproportional effect on the "true median line", are given only a partial effect (e.g., half effect). The very small size of a specific feature may for instance be a reason to give it only a partial effect. There are various computation methods for achieving half effect:

- The half effect line is computed as the angle bisector of the full effect line and the null effect line, see Figures 7.5 and 7.6.
- An imaginary basepoint is made halfway the shortest distance from the feature giving the half effect and the mainland, see Figure 7.7.
- The area between no effect line and full effect line is divided into two equal areas (there are several possibilities for such a solution).

The different options give different results, depending on the geographical situation. The first option is the most commonly used method.

A remarkable situation in maritime boundary delimitation is that of enclaving islands. Enclaving islands are given no effect in the determination of the boundary and because of this are falling in an area belonging to the other state. Around the islands generally a zone of jurisdiction is defined with the width of the territorial sea. If these zones connect to one of the maritime zones of the state to where the island belongs to, one speaks of *partial enclaving*. When this is not the case it is called *full enclaving*. Figures 7.8 and 7.9 give examples.

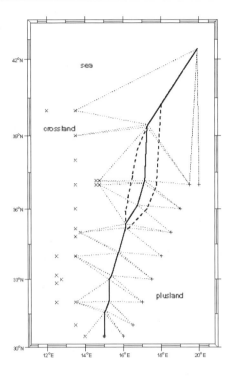

Figure 7.7: Using imaginary basepoints to construct the half effect line.

Full enclaving was first done at the Channel Islands in the English Channel. These islands are enclaves in French waters. The English Channel Islands were given a zone of 12 nM to the north and west and a smaller zone to their east, south and southwest. This because otherwise the zone of jurisdiction around the islands would become too large in relation to the French territorial sea.

An example of partial enclaving are the four Italian islands Pantelleria, Linosa, Lampione and Lampedusa in the Mediterranean Sea, which are partial enclaves in relation to the boundary with Tunisia.

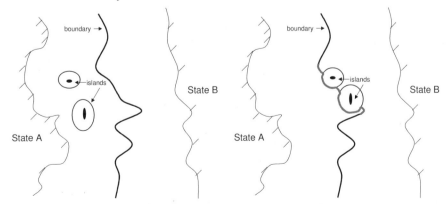

Figure 7.8: Full enclaving.   Figure 7.9: Partial enclaving.

For reasons of practicality sometimes meridians of longitude and parallels of latitude
are used as maritime boundaries. This is for instance the case between several states
in South America.

Special circumstances form an important aspect in finding an equitable solution
when determining a boundary. Both terms can be interpreted in many ways, and a lot
of aspects can play a role in defining something as a special circumstance. One could
consider for example the form of the coastline, the proportionality test, social-
economic circumstances, historic title, non-party states (involvement of states, which
were initially no party to the bilateral negotiations).

A test of proportionality is sometimes performed to see if the proposed maritime
boundary is an equitable solution. For this purpose the ratio of the lengths of the
coasts is compared to the (off-shore) area ratio of the two states, to see if they are
similar. Especially when the coast is very irregular, it is not possible to compute this
ratio very precisely. Such tests are known to have been computed in state
negotiations as well as in juridically obtained maritime boundaries. It is not
mentioned in UNCLOS, but it is state practice.

Instead of a maritime boundary, another possibility is to agree for a *joint development
arrangement*. Such an arrangement can be temporary in a disputed area or (part of) a
final agreement. In summer 2002 there were 22 joint development arrangements, for
example between Iceland and Norway, near Jan Mayen Island, and the arrangement
between Bahrain and Saudi Arabia with respect to the Faasht Bu Saafa oilfield. There
are different regimes possible within such a joint development arrangement. It is
important to have a clear agreement on how decisions are to be taken for the joint
development area, and how the revenues from such an area have to be divided.

7.4.3 Precision of maritime boundaries

There is a great diversity in the number of significant digits used in coordinates to
describe locations in boundary treaties. Nowadays they are usually given to a full
second or two digits of a minute of arc, but earlier boundaries were sometimes only
defined in a graphical way. From the 1970's onwards, the boundaries are computed.
The precision of the turning points that define the median line depends on the
precision of the basepoints from which they are derived. The precision of the points
that define an equidistance line, and consequently the precision of the equidistance
line itself, can never be better than the precision of the basepoints. In fact, it may
even be several orders of magnitude worse. This can be explained by the linear(-ized)
relationships between the two types of points, in which the relative geometry is
included. When this geometry is unfavourable, small errors in the basepoints may
become very large in the median line points. Examples of bad geometries are lines
intersecting at angles close to zero or 180 degrees.

During the negotiations the propagated covariance of the computed equidistance line
should be considered as well. When a boundary (which may be based on a computed

equidistance line) is fixed by means of a treaty, a boundary is permanent and the coordinates are absolute, and the resolution does not matter anymore.

7.5 Third party settlement

Part XV of UNCLOS requires Parties to the Convention to settle any dispute between them concerning the interpretation or application of the Convention by peaceful means. A person, another non-directly involved state or an organisation can do third party settlement. Where no settlement can be reached, article 286 of the Convention stipulates that the dispute is submitted at the request of any party to the dispute to a court or tribunal having jurisdiction in this regard. Article 287 of the Convention defines those courts or tribunals as:

- The International Tribunal for the Law of the Sea, including the Seabed Disputes Chamber.
- The International Court of Justice.
- An arbitral tribunal constituted in accordance with Annex VII of the UNCLOS Convention.
- A special arbitral tribunal constituted in accordance with Annex VIII of the UNCLOS convention. A special arbitral tribunal can only arbitrate in disputes concerning fisheries, protection and preservation of the marine environment, marine scientific research or navigation, including pollution from vessels and dumping.

7.5.1 ITLOS

The International Tribunal for the Law of the Sea (ITLOS) (www.itlos.org) is an independent judicial body established by UNCLOS to adjudicate disputes arising out of the interpretation and application of the UNCLOS Convention. ITLOS is based in Hamburg, Germany, but may sit and exercise its functions elsewhere whenever it considers this desirable. It provides for limits of maritime areas, access to the sea, navigation, protection and preservation of the marine environment, fisheries, scientific research, seabed mining and the settlement of disputes. Until mid 2002, 10 cases were handled by ITLOS.

The jurisdiction of the Tribunal comprises all disputes and all applications submitted to it in accordance with UNCLOS and all matters specifically provided for in any other agreement, which confers jurisdiction on the Tribunal. The Tribunal has exclusive jurisdiction, through its Seabed Disputes Chamber, with respect to disputes relating to activities in the international seabed Area.

ITLOS does not have authority to deal with sovereignty issues. Delimitation issues in the first instance often relate to questions concerning sovereignty. None of the cases handled up to now were cases where maritime delimitation was involved.

The Tribunal consists of 21 independent members of recognised competence in the field of the law of the sea. The first members were elected and inaugurated in 1996. They are elected for varying terms from three to nine years. Decisions of the Tribunal are final and shall be complied with by all the parties to the dispute. Other parties are not bounded by the decision of the Tribunal.

7.5.2 International Court of Justice

The International Court of Justice (ICJ) (www.icj-cij.org), which domiciles in the Peace Palace in The Hague, the Netherlands, acts as a world court. It decides in accordance with international law, disputes of a legal nature submitted to it by states, whilst in addition certain international organs and agencies are entitled to call upon it for advisory opinions. It was set up in 1945 under the Charter of the United Nations to be the principal judicial organ of the Organization, and its basic instrument, the Statue of the Court, forms an integral part of the Charter. Its predecessor was the Permanent Court of International Justice, which had functioned since 1922.

The Court consists of 15 judges. There is also a provision for parties to appoint two ad hoc judges, so a total of 17 judges may sit on a case. It may not include more than one judge per nationality. The judgement of the ICJ is final and without appeal.

It is also possible that a Chamber of the Court hears the case. A Chamber should be comprised of at least three judges. The Chamber may be made up of permanent members of the Court and ad hoc judges.

Cases may be brought to the ICJ by agreement of the Parties. They may also be brought unilaterally to the Court when the other party has accepted the jurisdiction of the Court.

Up to now, there have been several cases for the ICJ (see its website). With the ICJ the parties to a dispute are not free to choose the members of the Court and are not dependent on the willingness of the parties to agree and participate as is with arbitration (see Subsection 7.5.3). Until 2002, the ICJ has ruled in about 13 cases involving a maritime boundary with several cases pending.

The United Nations pay for the Court, its administration and the judges, but the costs involved for the Parties may still be considerable (legal advisors, technical experts, pleading for all the judges). The judgement is final and binding. The time for the whole procedure and before a judgement is made, may take a number of years, depending on the number of cases on which the ICJ is working simultaneously (for example, the case between Bahrain and Qatar took about nine years).

The first major dispute resulting from conflicting views on the legal determination of common seabed boundaries occurred in the second half of the 1960's. Germany, Denmark and the Netherlands asked the ICJ to indicate what relevant rules and principles of international law governed their bilateral relations in this respect. Germany found that, due to its concaved-shaped coastline, an equidistance solution of the boundary was not equitable. The judgement decided that "delimitation is to be effected by agreement in accordance with equitable principles." This decision was of great influence and was adopted in UNCLOSIII for the delimitations of the EEZ and the continental shelf.

7.5.3 Other arbitration

An arbitration tribunal may be appointed to settle maritime boundary cases if the parties choose to go to arbitration. One of the arbitration tribunals, which may decide in a case concerning UNCLOS, is the Permanent Court of Arbitration (PCA) (www.pca-cpa.org). The PCA was founded in 1899 and began operating in 1902. It also has residence in the Peace Palace in The Hague, just like the ICJ, but is independent with a registry of its own. The PCA exists independently of all international organisations (i.e., also independent of the UN) and its participating parties now count 80.

Very often cases for an arbitration tribunal last shorter in time than cases brought for the ICJ. The parties have the choice to decide if the hearings are closed to the public, for instance when they are of a delicate character.

The parties have to a certain extent control over the number of arbitrators (an arbitration consists of a minimum of five arbitrators), the arbitrators themselves (the UN maintains a list of arbitrators that have been nominated by state parties; each party may nominate up to four arbitrators and may appoint one member from this list, unless otherwise agreed), the place and also the rules of procedures. The costs can however be higher than for the ICJ, since the arbitration needs to be financed by the parties themselves, besides the costs of the pleadings and the experts.

There have been several cases at the PCA where a maritime delimitation was involved, of which the most recent was between Eritrea and Yemen. Examples of other arbitration tribunals are the case between the UK and France, in which the Channel Islands were involved, and the case between Guinea-Bissau and Senegal (at first instance).

7.6 Major references

Beazley P.B.: *Half-effect applied to equidistance lines.* International Hydrographic Review, Monaco, LVI (1), January 1979.

Beazley P.B.: *Technical Aspects of Maritime Boundary Delimitation.* Maritime Briefing vol. 1, number 2, IBRU, Durham, 1994.

Carrera G.: *A method for the delimitation of an equidistant boundary between coastal states on the surface of a geodetic ellipsoid.* International Hydrographic Review, Monaco, LXIV(1), January 1987, pp 147-159.

Carleton C., C. Schofield: *Developments in the Technical Determination of Maritime Space: Charts, Datums, Baselines, Maritime Zones and Limits.* Maritime Briefing vol. 3, number 3, IBRU, Durham, 2001.

Carleton C., C. Schofield: *Developments in the Technical Determination of Maritime Space: Delimitation, Dispute Resolution, Geographical Information Systems and The Role of the Technical Expert.* Maritime Briefing vol. 3, number 4, IBRU, Durham, 2002.

Charney J.I., L.M. Alexander (editors): *International Maritime Boundaries.* vol. 1, Martinus Nijhoff publishers, Dordrecht, 1993.

Churchill R.R, A.V. Lowe: *The Law of the Sea.* 2nd edition, 1988, Manchester University Press.

Cook P.J, C.M. Carleton (editors): *Continental Shelf Limits, The Scientific and Legal Interface.* Oxford University Press, 2000.

Guy N.R.: *The relevance of non-legal technical and scientific concepts in the interpretation and application of the law of the sea.* Reprint No. 20, IHO, November 2000.

IBRU (International Boundary Research Unit): *Course on Maritime Boundary Delimitation.* Durham, 2000.

IHO: *Manual on Technical Aspects of the United Nations Convention on Law of the Sea - 1982.* Special Publication No. 51, 3rd edition, July 1993, Monaco.

IHO: *Chart Specifications of the IHO and regulations of the IHO for international Charts.* 750-VI-1988.

Roach J.A., R.W. Smith: *United States responses to excessive maritime claims.* 2nd edition, Martinus Nijhoff Publishers, The Hague, 1996.

United Nations: *SPLOS/91.* 13 June 2002, New York.

8 Concepts of marine positioning

8.1 Geometry of positioning

Lines of position

Every navigation system defines its system of lines of position (LOP). The position of the user is located at the intersection of two or more such lines (or surfaces in 3D) of position. A line of position is the locus of points on the Earth's surface having a constant measurement by a radiopositioning system of:

1) *Distances* (or ranges) from the reference stations, which result in a set of concentric circles, see Figure 8.1. Each circle corresponds to a range measurement to an unknown point. This approach is called the circular mode and its use is widespread with the availability of electronic measurement systems. At least two ranges are needed to obtain a unique position. It is assumed that no timing bias exists at either the transmitter or the receiver. This can be difficult to achieve in the case of a passive system where signals are transmitted one way (transmitters to the receiver) and the transmitters and receivers are assumed to be in the same time frame in order to measure the time of propagation of the signal.

If the user does not know on which side of the line A-B (baseline) he is located (see Figure 8.1), a third range is required to resolve this ambiguity. In the case of shipborne positioning where the transmitters are installed along the shore (or inland in the case of long range systems like Loran-C), one of the two possible positions is usually on the inland side and is thereby eliminated, in which case a minimum of two ranges is sufficient. This is, however, not an ideal situation since no redundant measurement is available to verify the reliability of the solution. For instance, if least squares is used to obtain the horizontal position using two ranges, the residuals will be zero, regardless of the accuracy of the two ranges.

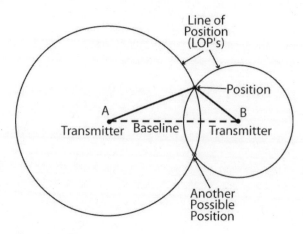

Figure 8.1: Distance (circular) mode.

2) *Angles* based on known reference shore-based stations, which result in a set of eccentric circles. Each circle corresponds to an angle measurement from an unknown point to two known points. This system was widely implemented in the past using a sextant. The user on the ship would measure horizontal angles with the sextant to two fixed references (e.g., two lighthouses). A minimum of two angles was needed to obtain a unique horizontal position for the ship.

3) *Azimuths* of the reference stations, which result in a set of straight lines. Each line corresponds to a direction measurement between a known and an unknown point. An example would be the measurement of a direction to a lighthouse from the ship using a sextant. A celestial body, e.g., the North star, could be used to provide an absolute direction. A gyrocompass may also be used to make azimuth measurements. A minimum of two azimuths is required for a unique solution.

4) *Range differences* are measured or formed to deal with time bias at the receiver. This occurs with one-way transmission (passive) systems when the transmitter and receiver time bases are different (a unique time base is very difficult to achieve as it requires a primary clock at the receiver). The receiver time bias is the same for all *pseudoranges* (range + bias) if the measurements are made simultaneously or nearly simultaneously. By differencing between two pseudoranges, the receiver time bias is cancelled and the range difference remains (instead of a pseudorange difference).

Range differences (or time differences × velocity of light corrected for propagation delays, e.g., PF, SF and ASF) reflect the change in distances from the reference stations, which result in a set of hyperbolae. Each hyperbola corresponds to a distance difference measured at an unknown point from two known points, usually, but not always, transmitters. This approach is called the *hyperbolic* mode and its use is widespread with the availability of passive radionavigation systems.

Mathematically, hyperbolic positioning is the same as *pseudorange positioning* (ranging with a receiver time or range bias) as shall be demonstrated by numerical

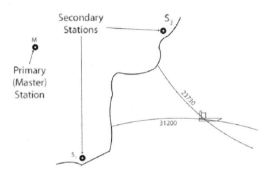

Figure 8.2: Hyperbolic mode (range or time differences).

examples later in this chapter. Single point GPS positioning using pseudoranges is a form of hyperbolic positioning in three dimensions.

A minimum of two hyperbolae is required to obtain a unique position. As in the case of the circular mode, the user needs to know at which side of the S_1-S_2 baseline he is located, see Figure 8.2. This ambiguity is usually trivial in the case of a long-range shore-based system used for ship positioning, because the transmitters are deep inland and the second solution (on the other side of the baseline) would be inland. An application where this is not the case, however, is cellular telephone positioning where the distances between the cell stations are short (Klukas et al., 1996). In such a case, a third hyperbola is needed to resolve the ambiguity.

The closer the intersection angle of the hyperbolae to 90°, the better the accuracy of positioning (e.g., better DOP), as shown in Figure 8.3. The solution will be best where the hyperbolic lines are dense and nearly perpendicular to each other. If either

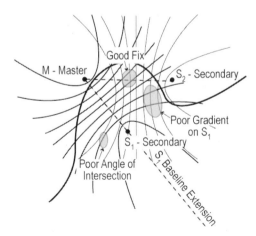

Figure 8.3: Hyperbolic positioning - LOP intersections and geometry.

characteristic weakens, the DOP will become larger and the solution less accurate.

When two hyperbolae are needed, these can be formed from signals coming from three or four stations. In the former case, one of the three stations is used twice to form range differences. If three hyperbolae are needed, a minimum of four stations is required.

5) *Combinations* of any of the other systems: e.g., distance plus azimuth, which is sometimes referred to as a rho-theta system.

8.1.1 Hyperbolic positioning mode - general

In hyperbolic positioning, at least three ground-based transmission stations are required (one master or primary station and two secondary stations). Distance or time differences (TD's) between

- user - primary station range, and
- user - secondary station range

are measured using various methods (e.g., phase comparison in the case of Omega, pulsed signals in the case of Loran-C).

Lines of constant distance differences (or time differences) from two known stations (*A* and *B* in Figure 8.4) form a set of hyperbolae, each hyperbola representing a specific range or time difference. For example, Figure 8.4 shows loci for 13 separate time differences equally spaced in increments of 1,000 µs. If the user vehicle *i* moves in such a way that the distance differences A_i-B_i are kept constant, the trajectory of the vehicle will coincide with a hyperbola.

In Figure 8.4, the distance *AB* is 1,800 km, which corresponds to a one-way transmission delay of 6,000 µs (Δt_{AB}). *A* is selected as the primary station and *B* as the secondary. Station *A* transmits at $t_{t,A}$ and station *B* at $t_{t,B}$ (where the subscript *t* denotes the time of transmission, as opposed to time of arrival - in which case the subscript *a* is used). If both *A* and *B* were transmitting at the same time, the half-way

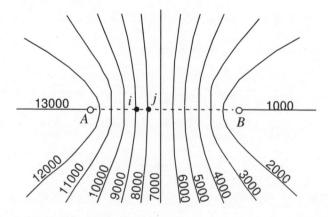

Figure 8.4: Hyperbolic lines of positions - two transmitters (*A* and *B*).

hyberbola (7,000 μs in Figure 8.4) would be zero. On each side of the half-way hyperbola there would be symmetric hyberbolae with the same delays. This would create an ambiguity.

This ambiguity is avoided by having B transmit only after it has received the signal from transmitter A. This also helps with the clock synchronization of B with respect to A. In the above example, the delay between A and B would therefore be 6,000 μs (transmission delays due to the various phase lags are neglected in this simple example). If this were the only delay implemented, another problem would occur, however. The 1,000 μs hyperbola in Figure 8.4 would be 0 μs. For any location on this 0 μs hyperbola a simple one-channel receiver could not distinguish between the signals arriving from A and B. Signals from A and B would, in the simple case, have the same frequency and modulation - discrimination between the signals at the receiver is through time delays in most cases. To avoid this problem, an additional delay Δt_c is added to the time of arrival of the signal from A at B. The delay Δt_c is called the *coding delay*. The relationship between $t_{t,A}$ and $t_{t,B}$ is therefore

$$t_{t,B} = t_{t,A} + \Delta t_{AB} + t_c \qquad\qquad\qquad (8.1)$$

In Figure 8.4, Δt_c is 1,000 μs.

The distance (lanewidth L'_w) between two successive 1,000 μs hyperbola on the baseline AB in Figure 8.4 is 150 km, which corresponds to a one-way transmission delay of 500 μs. There are twelve intervals of 150 km = 1,800 km.

Example 8.1: Hyperbolic positioning.
Consider the following case in Figure 8.4:

$$\Delta t(i) = t_{a,i}(A) - t_{a,i}(B) = 30,000 \ s - 21,000 \ s = 9,000 \ s$$

where $t_{a,i}(A)$ and $t_{a,i}(B)$ are the times of arrival of the signals at point i from A and B, respectively. Point i is 600 km away from A. The signal from A therefore takes 2,000 μs to travel to i. If a time of 21,000 μs is measured on A at i, the signal left A 2,000 μs previously, i.e., at 19,000 μs. The signal from A continues to travel from i to B. The distance is 1,200 km or 4,000 μs. The signal reaches B at (21,000 + 4,000) μs. A coding delay of 1,000 μs is added and the signal is retransmitted from B at 26,000 μs. It takes another 4,000 μs to reach i. The signal from B therefore arrives at i at 30,000 μs.

Lane and lanewidth

The interval between two adjusted hyperbolae for the same baseline (same secondary station) is called the *lane*. The lane corresponds to: 1) the greatest possible phase difference between two signals (180°) in the case of phase comparison; or 2) to the difference between two lines of constant time differences for the Δt intervals selected, e.g., 1000 µs in Figure 8.4.

The *lanewidth* L'_w on the baseline primary-secondary is

$$L'_w = c \cdot \frac{t}{2} \qquad\qquad (8.2)$$

for a *pulsed system*, e.g., Loran-C, where Δt is the two-way time difference (in Figure 8.4, the Δt between i and j is 1,000 µs - in practice Δt is selected to be much smaller); c is the speed of light.

The lanewidth is

$$L'_w = \frac{\lambda}{2} \qquad\qquad (8.3)$$

for a *phase comparison system*, where λ is the wavelength of the comparison frequency. Note that the lanewidth changes due to the divergence of hyperbolae, as shown in Figure 8.5. The above formulae are only valid for points on the baseline joining the two transmitters.

Let M be the primary station, S_1 and S_2 secondary stations, and P the moving vehicle to be positioned. The width of the lane L_w at point P is

$$L_w = L'_w \, \mathrm{cosec} \frac{\rho}{2} \qquad\qquad (8.4)$$

for the M-S_2 pair (baseline), and

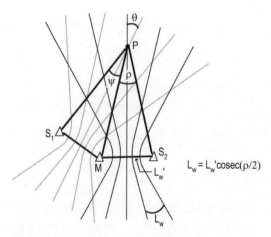

Figure 8.5: Geometry of hyperbolic lines of position.

$$L_w = L'_w \cosec\frac{\psi}{2} \tag{8.5}$$

for the M-S_1 pair (baseline). The term

$$\cosec\frac{\psi}{2}$$

is sometimes called the *lane expansion factor*; ρ and ψ are the angles at the unknown point P subtended by the baselines joining the primary and the secondary stations. The angle θ between the intersecting hyperbolae at point P is obtained as

$$\theta = \frac{\rho + \psi}{2} \tag{8.6}$$

Two-dimensional hyperbolic positioning solution

Least-squares estimation is used to derive the positioning solution (e.g., estimates of two horizontal components – such as x and y, or northing N and easting E, or latitude ϕ and longitude λ). The coordinate corrections vector $\hat{\underline{x}}$ to the initial approximate horizontal position values is derived as

$$\hat{\underline{x}} = (A^T Q_y^{-1} A)^{-1} A^T Q_y^{-1} \underline{y} \tag{8.7}$$

where A is the design matrix (matrix of coefficients of linearized observation equations), $\underline{y}$ are the observation residuals (difference between actual and computed observations, where the observations could, e.g., consist of time or range differences) and Q_y is the covariance matrix of the observations.

Accuracy estimates

The covariance matrix $Q_{\hat{x}}$ of $\hat{\underline{x}}$ is

$$Q_{\hat{x}} = (A^T Q_y^{-1} A)^{-1} \tag{8.8}$$

If the range differences are assumed to be uncorrelated and to have the same accuracy, then $Q_y = \sigma_0^2 I$. Accuracy measures such as DRMS and/or HDOP (DRMS/σ_0), can be calculated directly using the covariance matrix $Q_{\hat{x}}$.

This estimation can be done for any hyperbolic configuration, e.g., 1 Primary + 2 Secondaries, 1 Primary + 3 Secondaries, etc. A typical error propagation pattern for an isotropic chain of 1 Primary + 3 Secondaries is shown in Figure 8.6.

The covariance matrix Q_y depends on
- The timing accuracy between the transmitters.

- Multipath.
- The magnitude of the primary (PF), secondary (SF) and additional secondary (ASF) phase lags.
- The resolution accuracy of the receiver used.

Many of the above characteristics are affected by the RF frequency of the system and the propagation conditions (e.g., multipath). The total standard deviation of a measurement (σ_0), which is the same as the UERE (User Equivalent Range Error), is the square root of the quadratic sum of the above errors. Measurements are usually correlated due to the nature of the above error sources. This physical correlation is difficult to quantify and is often neglected.

A mathematical or serial correlation is also introduced in the case of range differences when these differences are derived using common transmitter(s). Assume that the three pseudoranges from transmitter stations M, S_1 and S_2 in Figure 8.5 are used to form two range differences (quasi-observables)

$$\delta \underline{y} = B \underline{y} \tag{8.9}$$

where $\underline{y}$ is a 3-vector consisting of the three pseudoranges, $\delta \underline{y}$ is a 2-vector consisting of the two range differences, and B is the 2×3 design matrix

$$B = \begin{pmatrix} 1 & -1 & 0 \\ 1 & 0 & -1 \end{pmatrix} \tag{8.10}$$

The covariance matrix $Q_{\delta y}$ of $\delta \underline{y}$ is, according to error propagation theory

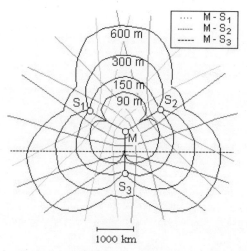

Figure 8.6: Hyperbolic chain DRMS error propagation.

$$Q_{\delta y} = BQ_y B^T \tag{8.11}$$

Even if errors in $\underline{y}$ are uncorrelated (e.g., $Q_y = \sigma_0^2 I$), $Q_{\delta y}$ is serially correlated due to the common use of one pseudorange from M to derive the two range differences.

Example 8.2: Error estimation.

In Figure 8.6, what is the σ_0 implied?

Measure the approximate horizontal coordinates of the four transmitters in an arbitrary 2D coordinate system, select a point on one of the error curves, measure its coordinates, form the design matrix A in range difference mode, derive the cofactor matrix $C_{\hat{x}} = (A^T C_{\delta y}^{-1} A)^{-1}$ with $C_{\delta y} = BB^T$ (in which case $Q_{\hat{x}} = \sigma_0^2 (A^T (BB^T)^{-1} A)^{-1}$), and calculate the HDOP for the point selected. Then derive $\sigma_0 = \text{DRMS/HDOP}$.

8.1.2 Positioning solutions

In Figure 8.7, coordinates of point P are determined using two range differences, namely ΔR_{ki} and ΔR_{kj}. These can be derived from the three pseudoranges R_i, R_j and R_k. Let us assume that the accuracy of a measured pseudorange is $15\sqrt{2}$ m. What are the HDOP and DRMS of point P?

Case 1: Hyperbolic mode, no correlation between range differences

In this case, $Q_{\delta y} = \sigma_0^2 I$ with $\sigma_0 = \sqrt{2} \cdot (15\sqrt{2}) = 30$ m. Therefore

$$Q_{\hat{x}} = \sigma_0^2 (A^T A)^{-1} = \sigma_0^2 C_{\hat{x}} \tag{8.12}$$

The approximate coordinates of P can be set as $x_P = y_P = u$, in which case the design matrix A can be written as

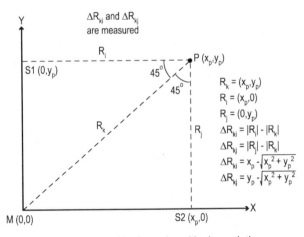

Figure 8.7: Geometry of horizontal positioning solution.

$$A = \begin{pmatrix} \dfrac{\partial \Delta R_{kj}}{\partial x} & \dfrac{\partial \Delta R_{kj}}{\partial y} \\ \dfrac{\partial \Delta R_{ki}}{\partial x} & \dfrac{\partial \Delta R_{ki}}{\partial y} \end{pmatrix} = \begin{pmatrix} -0.7071 & 0.2929 \\ 0.2929 & -0.7071 \end{pmatrix} \qquad (8.13)$$

and

$$C_{\hat{x}} = (A^T A)^{-1} = \begin{pmatrix} 3.4138 & 2.4138 \\ 2.4138 & 3.4138 \end{pmatrix} \qquad (8.14)$$

The HDOP is derived as

$$\mathrm{HDOP} = \sqrt{3.4138 + 3.4138} = 2.613 \qquad (8.15)$$

The covariance matrix $Q_{\hat{x}}$ is

$$Q_{\hat{x}} = (30\,\mathrm{m})^2 C_{\hat{x}} = \begin{pmatrix} \sigma_x^2 & \sigma_{xy} \\ \sigma_{xy} & \sigma_y^2 \end{pmatrix} = \begin{pmatrix} (55.43\,\mathrm{m})^2 & 2172.42\,\mathrm{m}^2 \\ 2172.42\,\mathrm{m}^2 & (55.43\,\mathrm{m})^2 \end{pmatrix} \qquad (8.16)$$

The DRMS can be calculated as

$$\mathrm{DRMS} = \sqrt{(55.43\,\mathrm{m})^2 + (55.43\,\mathrm{m})^2} = \mathrm{HDOP} \times \sigma_0 = 78.39\,\mathrm{m} \qquad (8.17)$$

Case 2: Hyperbolic mode, correlation between range differences

In this case, $Q_{\delta y} = \sigma_0^2 B B^T = \sigma_0^2 C_{\delta y}$ where B is the 2×3-matrix

$$B = \begin{pmatrix} 1 & -1 & 0 \\ 1 & 0 & -1 \end{pmatrix} \qquad (8.18)$$

$$Q_{\delta y} = (15\sqrt{2}\,\mathrm{m})^2 \begin{pmatrix} 2 & 1 \\ 1 & 2 \end{pmatrix} \qquad (8.19)$$

A is the same as for Case 1 and $Q_{\hat{x}}$ is

$$Q_{\hat{x}} = \sigma_0^2 (A^T A)^{-1} = \sigma_0^2 C_{\hat{x}} \qquad (8.20)$$

$$C_{\hat{x}} = (A^T C_{\delta y}^{-1} A)^{-1} = \begin{pmatrix} 9.2426 & 8.2426 \\ 8.2426 & 9.2426 \end{pmatrix} \tag{8.21}$$

$$\text{HDOP} = \sqrt{9.2426 + 9.2426} = 4.2995 \tag{8.22}$$

$$Q_{\hat{x}} = (15\sqrt{2}\ \text{m})^2 C_{\hat{x}} = \begin{pmatrix} \sigma_x^2 & \sigma_{xy} \\ \sigma_{yx} & \sigma_y^2 \end{pmatrix} = \begin{pmatrix} (64.49\ \text{m})^2 & 3709.17\ \text{m}^2 \\ 3709.17\ \text{m}^2 & (64.49\ \text{m})^2 \end{pmatrix} \tag{8.23}$$

$$\text{DRMS} = \sqrt{(64.49\ \text{m})^2 + (64.49\ \text{m})^2} = \text{HDOP} \times \sigma_0 = 91.20\ \text{m} \tag{8.24}$$

Case 2 shows that the HDOP and DRMS increase significantly when the mathematical correlation is (correctly) taken into account. As stated earlier, the physical correlation can also be high, depending on the system characteristics. If it is neglected (since it is difficult to estimate), accuracy estimates might be too *optimistic*.

Case 3: Pseudoranging mode

This case will show numerically that the use of the pseudoranging mode yields the same results as the hyperbolic mode. In this case there are three unknowns, namely x, y and the receiver range bias cdt. The three observables are the pseudoranges R_i, R_j and R_k. Observation equations have the form

$$R_i = \sqrt{(x_P - x_{S,i})^2 + (y_P - y_{S,i})^2} + cdt + \varepsilon \tag{8.25}$$

where R_i is the observed pseudorange, $x_{S,i}$ and $y_{S,i}$ are the known coordinates of the transmitting station, x_P and y_P are the unknown coordinates of P, cdt is the unknown receiver range bias, and ε is the pseudorange error. The least-squares estimators for the unknowns $\hat{x}$ (i.e., corrections to the approximate coordinates of P and bias value cdt) and their covariance matrix are

$$\hat{\underline{x}} = (A^T C_y^{-1} A)^{-1} A^T C_y^{-1} \underline{y} \tag{8.26}$$

$$Q_{\hat{x}} = \sigma_0^2 (A^T C_y^{-1} A)^{-1} = \sigma_0^2 C_{\hat{x}} \tag{8.27}$$

where A is the 3×3 design matrix (matrix of coefficients of linearized observation equations), $\underline{y}$ is the 3-vector of observation residuals (difference between observed and computed pseudoranges) and C_y is the cofactor matrix of the pseudoranges $\underline{y}$.

To be consistent with Cases 1 and 2, we define the covariance matrix of the observations Q_y as $Q_y = \sigma_0^2 C_y = \sigma_0^2 I$, with $\sigma_0 = 15\sqrt{2}$ m. The design matrix A can be written as

$$A = \begin{pmatrix} \dfrac{\partial R_i}{\partial x} & \dfrac{\partial R_i}{\partial y} & \dfrac{\partial R_i}{\partial cdt} \\[2mm] \dfrac{\partial R_j}{\partial x} & \dfrac{\partial R_j}{\partial y} & \dfrac{\partial R_j}{\partial cdt} \\[2mm] \dfrac{\partial R_k}{\partial x} & \dfrac{\partial R_k}{\partial y} & \dfrac{\partial R_k}{\partial cdt} \end{pmatrix} = \begin{pmatrix} 1.0000 & 0.0000 & 1.0000 \\ 0.0000 & 1.0000 & 1.0000 \\ 0.7071 & 0.7071 & 1.0000 \end{pmatrix} \qquad (8.28)$$

$$C_{\hat{x}} = (A^T A)^{-1} = \begin{pmatrix} 9.2426 & 8.2426 & 9.9497 \\ 8.2426 & 9.2426 & 9.9497 \\ 9.9497 & 9.9497 & 11.6569 \end{pmatrix} \qquad (8.29)$$

$$\text{HDOP} = \sqrt{9.2426 + 9.2426} = 4.2995 \qquad (8.30)$$

Accuracy estimates are determined as follows

$$Q_{\hat{x}} = (15\sqrt{2}\text{ m})^2 C_{\hat{x}} = \begin{pmatrix} \sigma_x^2 & \sigma_{xy} & \sigma_{xcdt} \\ \sigma_{yx} & \sigma_y^2 & \sigma_{ycdt} \\ \sigma_{cdtx} & \sigma_{cdty} & \sigma_{cdt}^2 \end{pmatrix}$$

$$= \begin{pmatrix} (64.49\text{ m})^2 & 3709.17\text{ m}^2 & 4477.36\text{ m}^2 \\ 3709.17\text{ m}^2 & (64.49\text{ m})^2 & 4477.36\text{ m}^2 \\ 4477.36\text{ m}^2 & 4477.36\text{ m}^2 & (72.43\text{ m})^2 \end{pmatrix} \qquad (8.31)$$

$$\text{DRMS} = \sqrt{(64.49\text{ m})^2 + (64.49\text{ m})^2} = \text{HDOP} \times \sigma_0 = 91.20\text{ m} \qquad (8.32)$$

These results are identical to those for Case 2 - where the mathematical correlation was taken into account using the hyperbolic mode.

Which method is the best to use, hyperbolic positioning or pseudoranging? The estimated unknowns are identical in both cases. From an analysis aspect, the pseudoranging method is generally better because one can analyse the correlation between the estimated receiver clock bias and coordinates. If there are redundant observations, the residuals, in the case of the pseudoranging method, are given for each pseudorange as opposed to a range difference - allowing for a more thorough

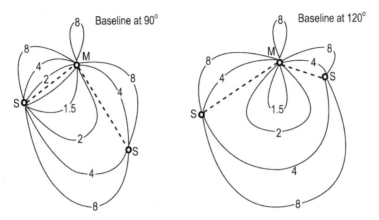

Figure 8.8: HDOP values for 90° and 120° angles between baselines.

analysis. It is not always possible, however, to use the pseudoranging method due to certain biases which are only eliminated in differencing mode.

It should be noted that there are no redundant observations for any of the three cases studied above. This means that the estimated residuals obtained from the least-squares estimators will be zero. No error detection based on residual analysis is possible in these cases.

Advantages/disadvantages of the hyperbolic/pseudoranging mode

There are numerous advantages of the hyperbolic/pseudoranging approach, namely
- Unlimited number of users.
- User equipment is relatively inexpensive (there is no need to have an expensive user's clock - a relatively low cost quartz clock is sufficient).

The major disadvantages are that more transmitters are required and that there is a relatively rapid geometry (HDOP) degradation. Figures 8.8 and 8.9 show HDOP values for different transmitter configurations. Note the relatively more rapid HDOP degradation on the back of the chains. Chains are always designed facing the

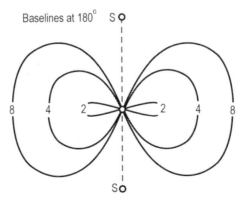

Figure 8.9: HDOP values for 180° angle between baselines.

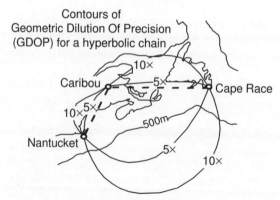

Figure 8.10: Configuration for partial Loran-C Canadian
East Coast Chain (after EMR, 1982).

coverage area required. This is especially noticable for Loran-C, which was initially deployed for coastal marine coverage - see Figure 8.10 (EMR, 1982). Note that *singularities* (no solution) exist on the baseline extensions when no redundant measurements are available.

Circular mode

The *circular mode* is based on the concept of simultaneous observation of distances from two or more known stations to determine the location of the unknown point. Ranges are measured directly with no timing bias errors. The pseudoranging method is occasionally classified as a circular mode. This is a misnomer since pseudoranging is equivalent to the hyperbolic mode, as shown previously. The circular mode is herein reserved only for the case when range observations are available.

In the circular mode, two intersecting circles (LOPs) are sufficient for a 2D solution if the user knows the side of the baseline *AB* he is on. The geometry in the circular

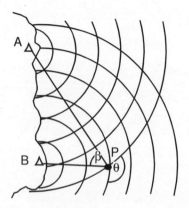

Figure 8.11: Circular positioning mode – lines of position.

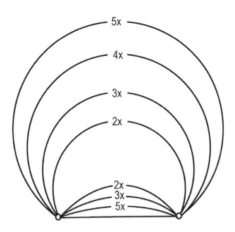

Figure 8.12: HDOP - circular mode with two transmitters.

approach is better than in the hyperbolic approach since the LOP intersection angles are generally closer to 90°. There is also no lane expansion in the circular approach. Typical HDOP values for a two-transmitter configuration are shown in Figure 8.12. The HDOP (and DRMS) contours are circles subtending a constant angle at the baseline. Note that the HDOP increases rapidly close to the *AB* baseline - this is caused by poor geometry.

There are two circular modes of operation:

1) *Range-range mode*: Signals from a transmitter carried onboard the vessel are received at two or more transponders on shore, and retransmitted to a receiver on the vessel, as shown in Figure 8.13. No accurate clock is required on the ship. This is, however, an active system with a limited number of users.

2) *Rho-rho mode*: A passive system is used. The ship is equipped with an accurate clock (e.g., cesium FTS), which is synchronized prior to departure or using the shore-based transmitters if more than two transmitters are used. In the latter case,

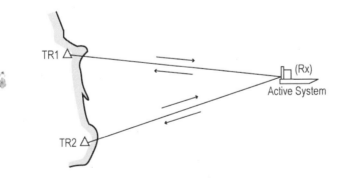

Figure 8.13: Circular range-range mode.

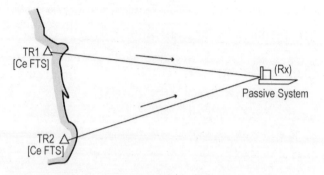

Figure 8.14: Circular rho-rho mode.

depending on the operating procedures, the mode can become a mix between circular and pseudoranging.

In *rho-theta mode*, ranges and azimuths are measured from one shore station. Ranges are obtained by interrogation from the ship (the same way as in range-range mode). The azimuth can be determined from the shore using radio direction finding (RDF) and transmitted to the ship.

Case 4: (Circular) ranging mode

Consider again the transmitter geometry in Figure 8.7. In this case, there are two unknowns, namely x and y. The three observables are the ranges R_i, R_j, and R_k. Observation equations have the form

$$R_i = \sqrt{(x_P - x_{Si})^2 + (y_P - y_{Si})^2} + \varepsilon \tag{8.33}$$

To be consistent with the previous cases, we define we define $Q_y = \sigma_0^2 I$, with $\sigma_0 = 15\sqrt{2}$ m. The 3×2 design matrix A can be written as

$$A = \begin{pmatrix} \dfrac{\partial R_i}{\partial x} & \dfrac{\partial R_i}{\partial y} \\[1mm] \dfrac{\partial R_j}{\partial x} & \dfrac{\partial R_j}{\partial y} \\[1mm] \dfrac{\partial R_k}{\partial x} & \dfrac{\partial R_k}{\partial y} \end{pmatrix} = \begin{pmatrix} 1.0000 & 0.0000 \\ 0.0000 & 1.0000 \\ 0.7071 & 0.7071 \end{pmatrix} \tag{8.34}$$

$$C_{\hat{x}} = (A^T A)^{-1} = \begin{pmatrix} 0.75 & -0.25 \\ -0.25 & 0.75 \end{pmatrix} \tag{8.35}$$

$$\text{HDOP} = \sqrt{0.75 + 0.75} = 1.225 \tag{8.36}$$

$$Q_{\hat{x}} = (15\sqrt{2}\ \text{m})^2\, C_{\hat{x}} = \begin{pmatrix} \sigma_x^2 & \sigma_{xy} \\ \sigma_{yx} & \sigma_y^2 \end{pmatrix} = \begin{pmatrix} (18.37\ \text{m})^2 & -112.50\ \text{m}^2 \\ -112.50\ \text{m}^2 & (18.37\ \text{m})^2 \end{pmatrix} \qquad (8.37)$$

$$\text{DRMS} = \sqrt{(18.37\ \text{m})^2 + (18.37\ \text{m})^2} = \text{HDOP} \times \sigma_0 = 25.98\ \text{m} \qquad (8.38)$$

Note that the HDOP and DRMS are much smaller than for any of the previous cases. In addition, there is one redundant observation which allows some error detection using the residuals.

Sample question: Circular ranging mode using two ranges.
Two ranges are measured at point P from points A and B with an accuracy of $15\sqrt{2}$ m. The geometry is in the figure below. What are the HDOP and DRMS accuracy of point P?

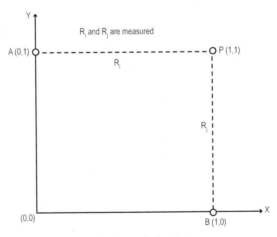

Geometry of positioning solution for two ranges.

Answer: HDOP = 1.414 and DRMS = 30 m.

HDOP examples – hyperbolic and circular modes

Figures 8.15-8.18 illustrate HDOP values computed for hyperbolic and circular positioning modes. Figure 8.16 realistically represents the case where correlations between observations are correctly accounted for in the hyperbolic positioning solution. The HDOP values degrade more rapidly with distance from the transmitters, as compared with Figure 8.15, where the correlations are ignored. In circular mode the HDOP values are improved for a configuration of three, versus two, transmitters (Figures 8.17 and 8.18). Note that singularities exist on the baseline extension when there is no redundancy.

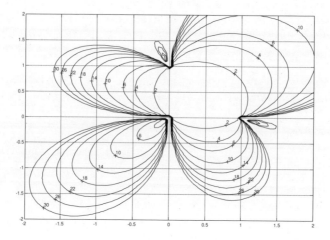

Figure 8.15: HDOP for three transmitters, hyperbolic mode with no correlation between range differences.

Limitations in hyperbolic positioning

Two major limitations exist with the use of hyperbolic positioning methods. Firstly, the solution of the user's position may diverge, thus providing no information. Secondly, the solution may converge to an alternate solution if it exists. Both of these problems arise from the fact that a least-squares position solution requires an initial estimate of the user's position to drive the least-squares algorithm for the case of a non-linear model. If the initial position error is sufficiently large, the above problems may result. These problems do not normally occur in marine applications. However, when baselines are very short, as in the case of cellular telephone positioning (Klukas

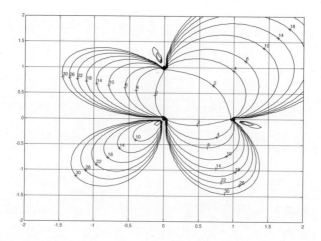

Figure 8.16: HDOP for three transmitters, hyperbolic mode with correlation between range differences (or pseudoranging mode).

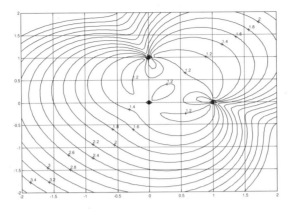

Figure 8.17: HDOP for three transmitters, circular mode (one redundant transmitter).

et al., 1996), these problems are frequent.

Figure 8.19 shows three "transmitter" stations (A,B,C) used to determine the user's position, which is at (0,0). However, a second possible solution exists north of the correct solution. A grid of 289 different initial estimates for the user's position is also shown. A simulation was run to determine the result of the least-squares algorithm using each of these initial estimates, and the results are shown in the Figure 8.19. The number of correct solutions (+) was 117, versus 63 second (•) solutions and 109 diverging solutions. These problems can also occur in the overdetermined case (e.g., four reference stations). There are mathematical techniques which can deal with these problems but their successful solution depends on many characteristics.

8.2 Classification of marine positioning systems

There are several major classes of marine positioning systems, e.g.

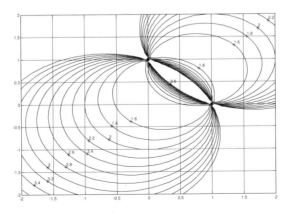

Figure 8.18: HDOP for two transmitters, circular mode.

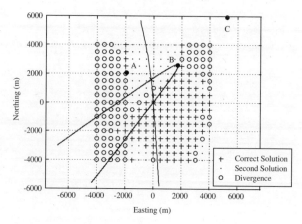

Figure 8.19: Hyperbolic mode – two possible solutions (x) and convergence/divergence problems.

Dead reckoning systems
- Inertial navigation systems
- Logs
- Gyroscopes

Underwater acoustic systems
- Using underwater propagation of acoustic waves

Electromagnetic systems
- Optical
- Laser
- RF

Integrated systems
- Integration of at least two systems within same or different classes

The electromagnetic systems are the most widespread and most commonly used for marine positioning. Examples of such EM systems are provided as follows:

Optical (directions and angles)
- Line of sight (LOS)
- Shore-based theodolites
- Sextants

Laser (ranging)
- Line of sight, but accurate
- Operating in circular mode with at least two shore-based stations (EDM units)
- Shore-based or shipborne reflectors

Optical/Laser
- Line of sight, good visibility

- Combination of theodolites and ranging
- One shore station with reflectors on ship
- Typical range: 5-10 km

RF - satellite-based
- UHF - line of sight
- Transit (1960's, lower part of UHF (450 MHz), polar orbits, intermittent 2D fixes)
- GPS, GLONASS (1.2-1.6 GHz, inclined orbits, instantaneous 3D positions)
- RDSS (radiolocation)

RF - shore-based

1) Short range
- Range less than 100 km
- 3-10 GHz, line of sight
- Circular (range-range, rho-rho) and rho-theta modes
- SHF

2) Medium range
- Range less than 500 to up to 800 km
- 1.6-1300 MHz, over horizon using ground wave
- Circular and hyperbolic
- UHF and MF

3) Long range
- Range between 1,000 and 10,000 km
- Less than a few hundred kHz
- Hyperbolic and circular
- LF (Loran-C and Decca) and VLF (Omega)

Tables 8.1-8.8 list twenty-four commercial systems belonging to one of the three *RF – shore-based* categories, with the following characteristics described:
- Principle
- Mode
- Number of mobiles (remotes, e.g., ships) allowed
- Frequency
- Resolution
- Accuracy
- Range
- Other characteristics

Most of the RF systems are now replaced by GPS operating in differential mode.

Table 8.1: Characteristics of 1980's commercial SHF systems (after Offshore Systems Ltd.).

SHF System	Principle	Mode	Mobiles	Reso-lution	Accuracy (Instrument)
MOTOROLA – Mini Ranger III	Pulse - Match	Range/Range	10 with time sharing	1 m	±2m range error
MOTOROLA – Mini Ranger IV	Pulse - Match	Range/Range	10 with time sharing	1 m	±2m range error
MOTOROLA – Mini Ranger Falcon IV	Pulse - Match	Range/Range	20 with time sharing	0.1 m	±2m error
MOTOROLA – Mini Ranger Falcon 484	Pulse - Match	Range/Range	20 with time sharing	0.1 m	±2m error
CUBIC Autotape DM-40A/DM-43	Phase Comparison	Range/Range	1	0.1 m	±0.5 m
TELLUROMETER – MRD1 (Plessey)	Phase Comparison	Range/Range	Up to 6	0.1 m	$1\ m \pm 3 \times 10^{-6}\ D$, where D is the distance measured
TELLUROMETER – Hydroflex (Plessey)	Phase Comparison	Range/Range	6	0.1 m	$1\ m \pm 3 \times 10^{-6}\ D$, where D is the distance measured
C.H.L. Artemis Mk III	Rho θ - pulse	Range/Bearing	1	0.1 m	0.5 m - 1.5 m Bearing 0.03 degree
ODOM – Aztrac	Rho θ - pulse	Range/Azimuth	1	0.01°	±1 m
SPC – Audister 8D-100		Range/Range	1		±0.1 m
MICROFIX – 100C	Phase Comparison	Range	1	1 mm	±15 mm - 3 ppm of distance measured (M.S.E.)
DEL NORTE – Trisponder	Pulse - Match	Range/Range	8 with time sharing	0.1 m	±1 meter, typical

Table 8.2: Characteristics of 1980's commercial SHF systems, continued (after Offshore Systems Ltd.).

SHF System	Propagation	Range	Characteristics
			Direction wave propagation, no reading ambiguity, low power, and small antennas
MOTOROLA – Mini Ranger III	5400-5600 MHz	37 km line of sight, 20 to 200 km options available	Output binary coded decimal TTL (+8421), RS232C, ASCII optional.
MOTOROLA – Mini Ranger IV	5400-5900 MHz	37 km or 74 km	Output RS232C, ASCII, built in selftest (BITE), a CRT which displays 4 ranges.
MOTOROLA – Mini Ranger Falcon IV	5400-5600 MHz	100 m to 37 km/74 km optional	Output RS232C, IEEE 488, BCD parallel, automatic switching between R/T 1 and R/T 2 to eliminate range holds.
MOTOROLA – Mini Ranger Falcon 484	5400-5600 MHz	100 m to 37 km/74 km optional	150 MHz real time clock, the processor has an erasable 120 kilobyte E Prom and Ram Velocity data vector along actual track, a selectable output format under CDU control, output RS232C or IEEE 488 optional.
CUBIC Autotape DM-40A/DM-43	2900-3100 MHz	100 m to 150 km	DM40A - DM43 - output BCD 8-4-2-1, low power, high stability, adjustable beam width.
TELLUROMETER – MRD1 (Plessey)	2920-3080 MHz 3200-3300 MHz	100 m to 100 km	Crystal controlled, readout: three six-digit displays, self test and keyboard for entering data, speech link between master and remotes.
TELLUROMETER – Hydroflex (Plessey)	2920-3080 MHz 3200-3300 MHz	40 km	RS232C output, 1 x 5 digit parallel BCD input and 1 incremental plotter output.
C.H.L. Artemis Mk III	9200-9300 MHz	10 m to 30 km	Output BCD (+8421) TTL parallel out, with data ready pulse, only 1 shore station required.
ODOM – Aztrac	460-470 MHz	5 km (20 km optional)	Output asynchronous ASC11 at RS232C or parallel, at a rate of 9600 baud, used in conjunction with separate ranging system such as microwave, only 1 shore station required.
SPC – Audister 8D-100	2900-3200 MHz	100 km	Transmitters controlled by crystal oscillators for high accuracy, output GPIB.
MICROFIX – 100C	16.25 GHz	20 m to 60 km	Measurement time update every 0.5 seconds, maximum rate of change of distance 100 m/s.
DEL NORTE - Trisponder	9320-9500 MHz 8800-9000 MHz	80 km	Output standard serial with BCD optional, the microprocessor automatically de-skews all ranges, and three are presented as if obtained simultaneously, 80 different remote codes available.

Table 8.3: Characteristics of 1980's commercial UHF systems (after Offshore Systems Ltd.).

UHF system	Principle	Mode	Mobiles	Reso-lution	Accuracy (Instrument)
SERCEL – Syledis MR3, SR3	Pulse - Match	Range/Range, hyperbolic, compound	Up to 4, unlimited, up to 3/unlimited	0.1 m	±1 m within LOS to 5 x 10^{-5} × distance (CEP) beyond LOS
THOMPSON-CSF – Trident III	Pulse - Match	Range/Range	50 max.	1 m	±3 m (absolute) ±1 m (relative)
MAXIRAN CORP. – Maxiran	Pulse - Match	Range/Range	6	1 m	±3 m to 350 km
DEL NORTE – UHF Trisponder	Pulse - Match	Range/Range	8	0.1 m	±2 m to 75 km

Table 8.4: Characteristics of 1980's commercial UHF systems, continued (after Offshore Systems Ltd.).

UHF system	Propagation	Range	Characteristics Direct wave plus diffraction and tropospheric scatter; characteristics between SHF and HF
SERCEL – Syledis MR3, SR3	406-450 MHz	10 m to 400 km	A long coded pulse of 2.5 msec and low power output provide the range. Power output: high power 20 W, low power 100 mW, peak power 13 W. Pulse length selectable: 266 - 5.33 or 10.66 ms. Number of slots: 4 to 30. Receiver band width: 2 MHz at 30 dB.
THOMPSON-CSF – Trident III	420-450 MHz 582-606 MHz 1215-1300 MHz	250 km	BCD for calculator or recorder.
MAXIRAN CORP. – Maxiran	420 to 450 MHz	370 km	Up to six base stations. 3 ranges displayed. Automatic or manual tracking. Two serial (TTY) and parallel BCD outputs (for 21 column line printer) at TTL logic levels - output data format.
DEL NORTE – UHF Trisponder	430 to 440 MHz	2 - 3 times line of sight	Data display VDU/CRT. Serial and parallel output variable baud rate. Power saver standard in T/Rs.

Table 8.5: Characteristics of 1980's commercial MF systems (after Offshore Systems Ltd.).

System	Principle	Mode	Mobiles	Reso-lution	Accuracy (Instrument)
ONI – Spot	Phase comparison	Range/Range	Unlimited	0.002 lane	±0.005 lane
ONI – Microphase	Phase comparison	Range/Range	Unlimited	0.001 lane	±0.005 lanes (1 m) per range
CUBIC Western – Argo DM 54	Phase comparison	Range/Range, hyperbolic, compound	7 to 12, unlimited, 6 to 11/ unlimited	0.01 lane	±5 to 10 m position accuracy field achievable
RACAL – Hyper-Fix	Phase comparison	Range/Range, hyperbolic, compound	6, unlimited, 5/unlimited	0.01 lane	Range/Range better than 1.5 m, hyperbolic better than ±1 m
SERCEL – Toran, P10, P100	Phase comparison	Hyperbolic	Unlimited	0.01 lane	one centilane under normal operation conditions
ODOM – Hydrotrac	Phase comparison	Range/Range, hyperbolic	1, unlimited	0.01 lane	±2 m at 300 km Range/Range
TELEDYNE HASTINGS – Raydist, DRS-H.T.	Phase comparison	Range/Range, hyperbolic, compound	Up to 4, unlimited, 3/unlimited	0.01 lane	approximately 2 to 3 m at ranges up to about 400 km

Table 8.6: Characteristics of 1980's commercial MF systems, continued (after Offshore Systems Ltd.).

System	Propagation	Range Day	Range Night	Characteristics Ground wave signals providing medium range and good accuracy
ONI –Spot	1.6-2.0 MHz	700 km	700 km	3 range display, featuring ground wave tracking only, advanced signal processing techniques, output: RS232, IEEE 488. Full range tracking 24 hours.
ONI – Microphase	1.6-2.0 MHz	700 km	300 km	Second order smoothing with operator selectable time constants. Operator selected ranges from 2, 3 or 4 ranges. Coordinates for 10 lines may be entered at one time, either separate segments or doglegged in the computer, includes complete navigation processor with logging displays, graphics, etc.
CUBIC Western – Argo DM 54	1.6-2.0 MHz	700 km	200-500 km	4 range digital display. Frequency is operator selectable from 16 preset frequencies. Selectable signal processing for long range applications. Two frequency lane identification.
RACAL – Hyper-Fix	1.6-3.4 MHz	700 km	300 km	Phase reference for each station can be controlled through a key-pad to provide maximum performance and coverage of the chain. Hyper-fix uses ground wave propagation. Output: RS232, IEEE 488 and RS 422. These figures represent long term and short term repeatability over sea water at the 65% probability level.
SERCEL – Toran, P10, P100	1.6-4.0 MHz	550 km	250 km	Two lines of position digitally displayed. May select up to 5 chains that are pretuned.
ODOM – Hydrotrac	1.6-4.0 MHz	300 km	200 km	Data output: digital/analogue, achieves maximum range of stability by using long sample periods, narrow bandwidth and limited rate of lane change.
TELEDYNE HASTINGS – Raydist, DRS-H.T.	1.65-3.3 MHz	400 km	250 km	Type DRS-H (Range-Range or Hyperbolic) and Type T (Hyperbolic). Type T system allows up to four independent lines of position to be determined simultaneously. Data output digital, analogue, RS232 or parallel BCD. Continuous position data.

Table 8.7: Characteristics of 1980's commercial LF Systems (after Offshore Systems Ltd.).

System	Principle	Mode	Mobiles	Reso-lution	Accuracy (Instrument)
LORAN-C	Pulse (time difference)	Rho-Rho, hyperbolic	Unlimited, unlimited	0.01 ms	±50 m ±300 m
Accufix and Pulse 8	Pulse (time difference)	Rho-Rho, hyperbolic	Unlimited, unlimited	10 ns	±50-100 m

Table 8.8: Characteristics of 1980's commercial LF Systems, Continued (after Offshore Systems Ltd.).

System	Propagation	Range	Characteristics
			Longest range of shore based radio positioning systems, Repeatability and accuracy reduced in comparison to higher frequency systems
LORAN-C	100 KHz	2000 km	Loran C chains are operated and maintained by the Coast Guard. The chains may be used with a variety of receivers including LC 404, LC 408, ONI 7000 and the Austron 5000, etc. All base stations have cesium standard atomic clocks for timing. Continuously available in areas covered.
Accufix and Pulse 8	100 kHz	500-800 km	Portable Accufix/Pulse 8 chains are similar to Coast Guard Loran C chains. The Pulse 8 Chains can use a variety of receivers.

8.3 Marine positioning requirements and standards for hydrographic surveys

8.3.1 Marine positioning requirements

The requirements for marine positioning are specified in terms of
- Accuracy, which includes:
  - *Predictable accuracy*, frequently understood as absolute accuracy, which defines the capability of locating a point relative to a reference point or a coordinate system.
  - *Relative accuracy* which corresponds to the capability of locating a point relative to another point being positioned.
  - *Repeatable accuracy*, which defines the capability of returning to the same point.

- Reliability, which expresses the probability that a specified level of performance is met under specified conditions for a given period of time.
- Integrity or accuracy assurance, which defines the ability of a system to provide timely warnings that the system does not meet accuracy or reliability requirements.
- Coverage, which defines the area in which the system is available.
- Availability, which specifies times when the system is available and its accessibility.
- Fix interval, which defines a minimum interval between two consecutive position fixes as obtained using a particular positioning system.
- Fix dimension, which specifies a dimension of a position fix, e.g., 2D or 3D, provided by a positioning system.
- Ambiguity, which defines the confidence level in percent for the positioning solution of a given point.

There are four classes of applications specified in the U.S. Federal Radionavigation Systems document (DoD/DoT, 2001):

- Ocean phase
- Coastal phase
- Harbour entrance and approach phase
- Inland waterway phase

Different accuracies are specified for each of these classes, and accuracy requirements are provided in Tables 8.9 through 8.12 (after DoD/DoT, 2001).

8.3.2 International Hydrographic Organisation standards for hydrographic surveys

These standards, which are to be interpreted as minimum standards, have been developed by the International Hydrographic Organisation (IHO, 1998) with the assistance of numerous national hydrographic offices. Hydrographic data collected using these standards should be sufficiently accurate, and their spatial uncertainty adequately quantified, to be safely used by mariners. The concepts of accuracy and accuracy estimates are therefore used in these standards. In developing these standards, it has been recognized that hydrographic surveys are no longer used only for the compilation of nautical charts but also for other diverse applications such as coastal zone management, environment monitoring, resource development, legal and jurisdictional issues, ocean and meteorological modelling, engineering and construction planning, etc.

Orders of hydrographic surveys

Four orders of hydrographic surveys are specified. *Special Order* hydrographic surveys are used in specific critical areas with minimum underkeel clearance and where bottom characteristics are potentially hazardous to vessels. These areas are designated by the agency responsible for survey quality. Examples are harbours, berthing areas, and associated critical channels. All error sources should be minimized. Special Order requires the use of closely spaced lines in conjunction with side scan sonar, multi-transducer arrays (sweep systems) or high-resolution multibeam echosounders (swath systems) to obtain 100% bottom search. It must be ensured that cubic features greater than 1 m (one side) can be discerned by the sounding equipment. The use of side scan sonar in conjunction with a multibeam echosounder may be necessary in areas where thin and dangerous obstacles may be encountered.

Table 8.9: Marine requirements and benefits – Ocean phase [1,2,3].

Require-ments	Measures of minimum performance criteria to meet requirements					
	Accuracy (2DRMS)		Coverage	Availability	Reliability	Fix interval
	Predict-able	Repeat-able				
Safety of navigation	2-4 nM minimum; 1-2 nM desirable	-	Worldwide	99% fix at least every 12 hours	**	15 minutes or less desired; 2 hours maximum

Benefits	Measures of minimum performance criteria to meet benefits					
	Accuracy (2DRMS)		Coverage	Availability	Reliability	Fix interval
	Predict-able	Repeat-able				
Large ships Maximum efficiency	0.1-0.25 nM*	-	Worldwide except Polar regions	99%	**	5 minutes
Resource Exploration	10-100 m*	10-100 m*	Worldwide	99%	**	1 minute
Search operations	0.1-0.25 nM	0.25 nM	National maritime SAR regions	99%	**	1 minute

1: 2D (Horizontal).
2: Unlimited capacity in terms of number of users.
3: Ambiguity resolvable with 99.9% confidence.
* Based on stated user need.
** Depends on mission time.
Note: nM – nautical mile, SAR – Search and rescue.

Table 8.10: Marine requirements and benefits - Coastal phase [1,2,3].

Require-ments	Measures of minimum performance criteria to meet requirements		Coverage	Availability	Reliability	Fix interval
	Accuracy (2DRMS)					
	Predict-able	Repeat-able				
Safety of navigation (all ships)	0.25 nM	-	U.S. coastal waters	99.7%	**	2 minutes
Safety of navigation (recreation boats & other smaller vessels)	0.25 nM-2 nM	-	U.S. coastal waters	99%	**	5 minutes

Benefits	Measures of minimum performance criteria to meet benefits		Coverage	Availability	Reliability	Fix interval
	Accuracy (2DRMS)					
	Predict-able	Repeat-able				
Commercial fishing (including commercial sport fishing)	0.25 nM (460 m)	50-600 ft (15-180 m)	U.S. coastal/ fisheries areas	99%	**	1 minute
Resource exploration	1.0-100 m*	1.0-100 m*	U.S. coastal areas	99%	**	1 second
Search operations, law enforcement	0.25 nM (460 m)	300-600 ft (90-180 m)	U.S. coastal/ fisheries areas	99.7%	**	1 minute
Recreation-al sports fishing	0.25 nM (460 m)	100-600 ft (30-180 m)	U.S. coastal areas	99%	**	5 minutes

1: 2D (Horizontal).
2: Unlimited capacity in terms of number of users.
3: Ambiguity resolvable with 99.9% confidence.
* Based on stated user need.
** Depends on mission time.

Table 8.11: Marine requirements and benefits – Harbour entrance and approach phase [1,2,3].

Require-ments	Measures of minimum performance criteria to meet requirements		Coverage	Availability	Reliability	Fix interval
	Accuracy (2DRMS)					
	Predict-able	Repeat-able				
Safety of navigation (large ships & tows)	8-20 m***	-	U.S. harbour entrance & approach	99.7%	**	6-10 seconds
Safety of navigation (smaller ships)	8-20 m	8-20 m	U.S. harbour entrance & approach	99.9%	**	***
Resource exploration	1-5 m*	1-5 m*	U.S. harbour entrance & approach	99%	**	1 second
Engineering & con-struction vessels (harbour phase)	0.1**** -5 m	0.1**** -5 m	Entrance channels, jetties, etc.	99%	**	1-2 seconds
Benefits	Measures of minimum performance criteria to meet benefits		Coverage	Availability	Reliability	Fix interval
	Accuracy (2DRMS)					
	Predict-able	Repeat-able				
Fishing, recreational and other small vessels	8-20 m	4-10 m	U.S. harbour entrance & approach	99.7%	**	***

1: 2D (Horizontal) except for Engineering & construction vessels which have a 3D requirement.
2: Unlimited capacity in terms of number of users.
3: Ambiguity resolvable with 99.9% confidence.
* Based on stated user need.
** Depends on mission time.
*** Varies from one harbour to another.
**** Vertical.

Table 8.12: Marine requirements for system planning and development – Inland waterway phase [1,2,3].

Require-ments	Accuracy (2DRMS)		Coverage	Availability	Reliability	Fix interval
	Predict-able	Repeat-able				
Safety of navigation (all ships & tows)	2-5 m	2-5 m	U.S. inland waterway systems	99.9 %	*	1-2 s
Safety of navigation (recrea-tional boats & smaller vessels)	5-10 m	5-10 m	U.S. inland waterway systems	99.9 %	*	5-10 s
River engineering & construction vessels	0.1**-5 m	0.1**-5 m	U.S. inland waterway systems	99 %	*	1-2 s

Measures of minimum performance criteria to meet requirements

1: 2D (Horizontal) except for river engineering & construction vessels which have a 3D requirement.
2: Unlimited capacity in terms of number of users.
3: Ambiguity resolvable with 99.9 % confidence.
* Depends on mission time.
** Vertical.

Order 1 hydrographic surveys are intended for harbours, harbour approach channels, recommended tracks, inland navigation channels, and coastal areas of high commercial traffic density where underkeel clearance is less critical and the geophysical properties of the seafloor are less hazardous to vessels (e.g., soft silt or sand bottom). Order 1 surveys should be limited to areas with less than 100 m water depth. Although the requirement for seafloor search is less stringent than for Special Order, full bottom search is required in selected areas where the bottom characteristics and the risks of obstructions are potentially hazardous to vessels. For these areas, it must be ensured that cubic features greater than 2 m in waters up to 40 m depth, or features with dimensions greater than 10% of the depth in waters deeper than 40 m, can be discerned by the sounding equipment.

Order 2 hydrographic surveys are intended for areas with water depths less than 200 m not covered by Special Order and Order 1, and where a general description of the bathymetry is sufficient to ensure there are no obstructions on the seafloor that will endanger the type of vessel expected to operate in the area. It is the criterion used for a variety of maritime uses in which higher order hydrographic surveys are not justified. Full bottom searches may be required in selected areas where the bottom characteristics and the risk of obstructions may be potentially hazardous to vessels.

Order 3 hydrographic surveys are intended for all areas not covered by the above Orders in water depths in excess of 200 m.

It is important to note that side scan sonar should not be used for depth determination, but to define areas requiring more detailed and accurate investigation. The standards for each Order are given in Table 8.13.

Positioning

The horizontal accuracy is defined as the accuracy at the position of a feature to be located within a geodetic reference frame, e.g., WGS84. If a local horizontal datum is used, it should be tied to a geocentric reference system. The contributions of all parameters to the total position error should be accounted for using a proper

Table 8.13: Summary of IHO Minimum Standards for Hydrographic Surveys (after IHO, 1998).

	Special Order	Order 1	Order 2	Order 3
Examples of typical areas	Harbours, berthing areas, and associated critical channels with minimum under-keel clearance	Harbours, harbour approach channels, recommended tracks and some coastal areas with depths up to 100 m	Areas not described in Special Order and Order 1, or areas up to 200 m water depth	Offshore areas not described in Special Order, Orders 1 and 2
Horizontal accuracy (95% confidence level)	2 m	5 m + 5% of depth	20 m + 5% of depth	150 m + 5% of depth
Depth accuracy for reduced depths (95% confidence level) [1]	a = 0.25 m b = 0.0075	a = 0.5 m b = 0.013	a = 1.0 m b = 0.023	Same as Order 2
100% bottom search	Compulsory[2]	Required in selected areas[2]	May be required in selected areas	Not applicable
System detection capability	Cubic features > 1 m	Cubic features > 2 m in depths up to 40 m; 10% of depth beyond 40 m[3]	Same as Order 1	Not applicable
Maximum line spacing[4]	Not applicable, as 100% search is compulsory	3 × average depth or 25 m, whichever is greater	3-4 × average depth or 200 m, whichever is greater	4 × average depth

1: The error limit for depth accuracy is calculated as $\pm (a^2 + (b \times d)^2)^{1/2}$ where a is the constant depth error, d the depth and $b \times d$ the depth dependent error.

2: For safety of navigation purposes, the use of an accurately specified mechanical sweep to guarantee a minimum safe clearance depth throughout an area may be considered sufficient for Special Order and Order 1 surveys.

3: The value of 40 m has been chosen considering the maximum expected draught of vessels.

4: Maximum line spacing is to be interpreted as "spacing of sounding lines for single beam echosounders" and "distance between the outer limits of swaths sounding systems". The line spacing can be expanded if procedures for ensuring an adequate sounding density are used.

Table 8.14: Summary of IHO Minimum Standards for Positioning of Navigation Aids and Important Features (after IHO,1998).

	Special Order Surveys	Order 1 Surveys	Order 2 and 3 Surveys
Fixed aids to navigation and features significant to navigation	2 m	2 m	5 m
Natural coastline	10 m	20 m	20 m
Mean position of floating aids to navigation	10 m	10 m	20 m
Topographical features	10 m	20 m	20 m

statistical method. The position error (95% confidence level) should be recorded with the other survey data. Redundant measurements should be used. Integrity monitoring for Special Order and Order 1 surveys is recommended.

Primary shore control points should be determined to a relative accuracy of 1 part in 100,000 if ground survey methods are used, or to an accuracy of 10 cm (95% confidence level) if satellite systems are used. The corresponding values for secondary stations are 1 part in 10,000 and 50 cm.

The accuracy of the position of a sounding is the accuracy at the position of the sounding on the bottom as located within a geodetic reference frame. The exceptions to this are Order 2 and Order 3 surveys using single beam echosounders, where it is the accuracy of the position of the sounding system sensor. In such cases, the agency responsible for the survey quality should determine the accuracy of the positions of soundings on the seafloor.

The horizontal positions of navigation aids and other important features should be determined to the accuracies stated in Table 8.14.

Depths

Depth accuracy is to be understood as the accuracy of the reduced depths. The sources of individual errors need to be quantified in determining the depth accuracy. These errors include measurement system and sound velocity errors, tidal measurement and modelling errors, and data processing errors. All anomalous features previously reported in the survey areas and those detected during the survey should be examined in greater detail and, if confirmed, their least depth should be determined.

Measured depths should be reduced to chart or survey datum, by the application of tidal or water level height. Tidal reductions should not be applied to depths greater than 200 m, except when tides contribute significantly to the total error budget.

In planning the density of soundings, both the nature of the seabed in the area and the requirements of users have to be taken into account to ensure adequate bottom search. No method, not even 100% search, which is desirable, guarantees by itself the reliability of a survey.

Table 8.15: Projected future accuracy requirements.

Activity	Accuracy (2DRMS)	Range	Lifetime
3D navigation in constricted channels[a]	≤ 0.1 m		
3D seismic (NRC,1983)	0.1 m	10 km	1 month
Radioactive waste disposal (NRC,1983)	10.0 m	10^4 km	1 month
Geodynamics[b] (NRC, 1983)	0.01 - 0.1 m	10 km	10^5 years
Geodynamics[c] (NRC, 1983)	0.01 - 0.1 m	10^3 km	10 years

a: E.g., navigation in the St. Lawrence navigation channel.
b: Spreading centres, transform faults, slump zones.
c: Subduction, interplate motion, interplate deformation.

Guidelines for quality control

To ensure that the required accuracies are achieved, it is necessary to check and monitor performance. Establishing quality control procedures should be a high priority. Quality control for positioning ideally involves observing redundant lines of position and/or monitor stations which are then to be analyzed to obtain error estimates.

In the case of depths, additional depth measurements are performed for quality control. Differences should be statistically tested to ensure compliance with the standards. All discrepancies should be resolved. Checklines crossing the principal sounding lines should always be run to confirm the accuracy of positioning, sounding and tidal reduction. Checklines should be spaced such that an efficient and comprehensive control of the principal sounding lines can be achieved. The interval between checklines should normally be no more than 15 times that of the selected sounding lines. Additional quality control procedures are included in (IHO, 1998).

Future requirements for emerging activities

Future requirements for emerging precise marine positioning activities can be expressed in terms of the accuracy, range and lifetime provided by the systems. Examples of projected accuracy requirements are shown in Table 8.15.

8.4 Major references

Beck, N. et al.: *Proceedings of the First GPS Canadian User and Supplier Workshop*. EMR/CCS, Ottawa, 1988.

Blankenburgh, J.C.: *High-Precision Marine Positioning Requirements, Limitations and Possible Problem Solutions*. Marine Geodesy, Vol. 7, No. 1-4, 1983.

Caissy, M. et al.: *CHS GPS Research and Development Program*. Proceedings of the Canadian Hydrographic Conference, Burlington, Ontario, 1987.

DoD/DoT: *U.S. Federal Radionavigation Systems*. U.S. Department of Defense/Department of Transport, 2001.

EMR: *Surveying Offshore Canada Lands for Mineral Resource Development*. 3rd edition, EMR Surveying and Mapping Branch Report No. M52-43/1983E, 1982.

IHO: *Positioning Systems Characteristics*. FIG Report WG 414b – IHO Reprint No. 8, 1981.

IHO: *IHO Standards for Hydrographic Surveys, Special Publication S-44*. 4th edition, International Hydrographic Organisation, Monaco, 1998.

Klukas, R., G. Lachapelle, M. Fattouche, A. Borsodi, M. Asteridge: *A System to Position Cellular Telephones Using GPS Time Synchronization*. Proceedings of the Third World Congress on Intelligent Transport Systems, ITS America, Orlando, Florida, October 14-18, 1996.

NRC: *Seafloor Referenced Positioning: Needs and Opportunities*. U.S. National Research Council, 1983.

9 Description of selected positioning systems

9.1 Optical and laser systems

The concept of an optical/laser system is similar to that of a total station, but more automated. With an optical/laser system the range is measured by infrared laser with a standard deviation of 3 to 30 cm and the azimuth with respect to a known direction can be obtained with a standard deviation of 0.01° to 0.1°.

An optical/laser system consists of a single measuring unit installed on shore and the reflectors mounted on the vessel. Once the system is initially set-up by the operator on shore, it automatically tracks moving reflectors. No shore operator assistance is required after initial set-up of the system.

The positions of the reflectors on the vessel are calculated in real-time and transmitted to the ship using a shore-to-ship telemetry link. Ranges up to 10 km can be measured. Line of sight and good visibility are required. The optical/laser system, due to the limited range, is mostly used for local surveys in sheltered areas such as harbours and rivers where waters are relatively calm for effective tracking of the ship mounted reflectors.

9.2 Omega

Omega was the first worldwide, long range, navigational system, originally intended for military use after World War II and deployed for civil use in the mid-1960s. Omega was terminated in September 1997. It used VLF unmodulated pulsed carrier waves. Unmodulated waves could be used because the wavelengths are very long.

Omega is based on phase difference measurements made on very low frequency (VLF) waves in the range of 10-14 kHz. Eight stations, distributed around the world, see Figure 9.1, transmit signals at four primary frequencies of 10.2, 11.05, 11.33, and 13.6 kHz. Secondary frequencies are used (1) to resolve the phase ambiguity with a

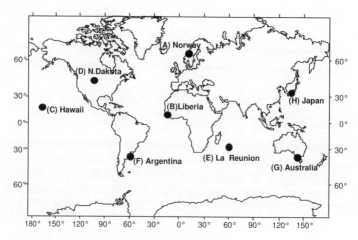

Figure 9.1: Omega transmitting stations.

widelane method and (2) for transmitter clock calibration purpose. The frequency of 10.2 kHz corresponds to a wavelength of 30,000 m.

Propagation of the signals is of the waveguide type. The Earth and lower layer of the ionosphere act as the wave guide. The user's position is determined by the intersection of hyperbolae or circles of constant relative phase obtained by phase comparison on unmodulated pulsed waves received quasi-simultaneously.

Omega is used primarily in hyperbolic mode. The circular (rho-rho) mode can be used if a precise clock is available at the receiver. The latter is mostly used in air and marine applications. The nominal accuracy of the Omega system is 1.5-3 nautical miles (2DRMS).

The wavelengths of the Omega VLF signal are of the same order of magnitude (30 km) as the distance between the D-region of the ionosphere and the Earth's surface (50-90 km). The waves are thus reflected between the Earth's surface and the lower layer of the ionosphere, D or E, which is a matter of diurnal variations. This results in a waveguide type propagation. Out of several existing waveguide modes, the most important ones in this case are the *transverse magnetic* (TM) modes. The two major TM propagation modes within the waveguide are called TM1 and TM2, as shown in Figure 9.2. TM1 is the one preferred because of its higher stability and accuracy.

The transmitting antenna must provide a high resolution frequency output and be able to simulate a short dipole (efficient simulation of a half-wavelength). There are two main types of the transmitting antennas used, namely

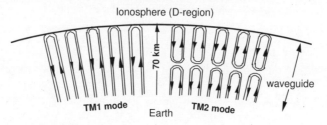

Figure 9.2: TM1 and TM2 transmission modes.

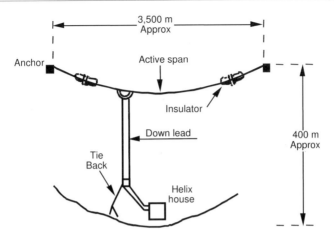

Figure 9.3: Valley span Omega transmitter antenna.

- Valley span antenna, as shown in Figure 9.3.
- Tower, i.e., top-loaded, vertical monopole (about 400 m high).

The transmitting antennas have the following common characteristics:

- Vertically polarized
- Several hundred metres in length
- 20% efficiency
- Radiated power of 10 kW

Near the transmitter, the TM2 propagation mode is stronger than TM1. TM1 equals TM2 for different distances from the transmitter, depending on the frequency, e.g.,

- At 10.2 kHz: TM1 = TM2 at 100 km (day) and 400 km (night),
- At 13.6 kHz, TM1 = TM2 at 400 km (day) and 1800 km (night).

Since the TM1 mode is preferred due to its superior stability, measurements within the above distances will be on TM2 and unusable.

Each transmission mode is affected by

- *Excitation factor*, which is the ratio of power of Omega waveguide to that projected into a flat waveguide with perfectly conducting boundaries for night and daytime height of the ionosphere.
- *Total attenuation* which is slightly higher at lower frequencies.
- *Phase velocity diurnal variations* of TM1, due to diurnal variations in the height of the ionosphere.

Due to the above effects and poor geometry, navigational errors may occur within several hundred kilometres from a transmitter (e.g., the Winnipeg Omega "hole" in Canada due to the proximity of the North Dakota transmitter and poor geometry). Lines of position (LOP's) are marked as dashed lines on Omega charts within 450 nM (nautical miles) from a transmitter to indicate the possibility of such errors. As already mentioned, Omega is in principle a worldwide system. The signal range is from 6,000 to 10,000 nM (11,000 to 18,500 km). In certain areas of the Earth, it is difficult to obtain an accuracy better than 5 nM (RMS). For example, for arctic paths,

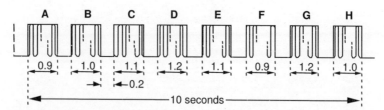

Figure 9.4: Omega signal format.

the higher attenuation over the freshwater ice cap, e.g., the Greenland shadow, causes large navigational errors.

There are eight Omega stations (A to H) transmitting with a radiated power of 10 kW, as shown in Figure 9.1. The transmitters are synchronized to a common atomic time scale using cesium clocks. Each station transmits for about one second, in turn, every 10 seconds at precisely the same frequency. In most locations the signals from four stations can be received. A minimum of three is required for the hyperbolic mode. The Omega system covers the whole Earth with a few exceptions like the Greenland shadow and areas near transmitters.

Each station transmits for approximately 1 s with a break of 0.2 s between each pulse (each segment of the signal format) and the repetition frequency of the signals is 0.1 Hz, as shown in Figure 9.4. The 0.2 s spaces between transmissions guarantee that each segment of the signal, which needs about 0.13 s to travel around the Earth, has time to decay before the start of the next segment.

The signals from different stations are not simultaneously received. Phase comparison is therefore made on asynchronous signals. Each pulse is different within a pulse train of 10 seconds. In order to measure the phase difference between signals from at least three stations for every position determination, a three-channel receiver has to select the best stations and synchronize its own signal segment generator with their signals.

Due to time sharing mode used by Omega, the receiver must be equipped with a

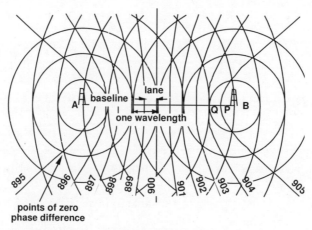

Figure 9.5: Omega hyperbolic pattern.

Frequency Time Standard (FTS) which is relatively stable over a period of time of several seconds (e.g., quartz FTS). Phase comparison between transmitter signals results in a hyperbolic pattern, as shown in Figure 9.5.

Points of zero phase difference (hyperbolic lines) occur at half wavelength, i.e., every 8 nM on the baseline (wavelength of 29.4 km which corresponds to 16 nM at 10.2 kHz). The line of position equidistant from the two transmitters is numbered 900, as shown in Figure 9.5. One lane corresponds to a full cycle difference, i.e. 360° of phase, and at 10.2 kHz equals 8 nM (15 km). One centilane equals to 0.01 lane, which corresponds to 3.6° of phase and at 10.2 kHz equals 150 m. The nominal ambiguity is half a lane, e.g., 4 nM or 7.5 km. Phase differences yield ambiguous measurements. The relative phase angle of the signals of each pair of stations defines the family of contours. Lane identification requires establishing the initial position of the observer by some external means. Lane ambiguity can be reduced by using more than one frequency.

Omega broadcasts on four primary frequencies, namely 10.2, 11.05, 11.33, and 13.6 kHz. The first frequency is the main frequency. The other three are used to resolve the ambiguity through widelaning. Other frequencies, namely 12.1, 12.0, 11.55, 13.1, 12.3, 12.9, 13.0, and 12.8 kHz, are unique for each station, and correspond to transmitters A to H, respectively. They are used only for control information between transmitting stations. The format of the multi-frequency signal is shown in Figure 9.6.

The differences between measurements on the above frequencies are used to widelane in order to resolve the ambiguity more easily, e.g.:

- Between 10.2 and 13.6 kHz: $\Delta f = 3.4$ kHz $= 1/3 \times 10.2$ kHz; 0.5 lanes (at 3.4 kHz) $= 3 \times 4$ nM $= 12$ nM.
- Between 10.2 and 11.33 kHz: $\Delta f = 1.13$ kHz $= 1/9 \times 10.2$ kHz; 0.5 lanes (at 1.13

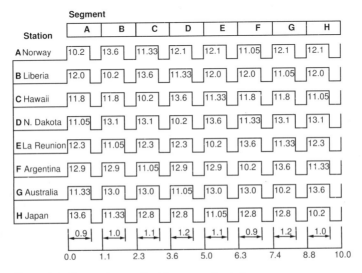

Figure 9.6: Omega transmitted frequency format.

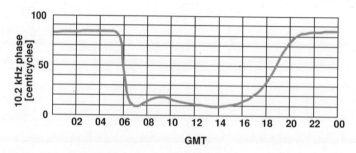

Figure 9.7: Omega diurnal propagation effect.

kHz) = 9 × 4 nM = 36 nM.
- Between 11.05 and 11.33 kHz: Δf = 0.28 kHz = 1/36 × 10.2 kHz; 0.5 lanes (at 0.28 kHz) = 36 × 4 nM = 144 nM.

Navigational errors are caused by the following sources:
- instrumental errors
- uncertainties in the knowledge of radio wave propagation
- diurnal propagation correction modeling
- operator errors

Errors due to propagation variations and propagation corrections are the major ones limiting accuracy. A limiting factor is the propagation diurnal effect due to the varying height of the ionosphere, as shown in Figure 9.7. The diurnal effect is systematic and can be obtained from correction tables. The effect of this error on the estimated position is σ = 5 cels (centilanes) = 750 m. Another error source is phase (i.e., frequency) stability at the transmitters (cesium FTS). The effect of phase stability error on the estimated position σ = 1-2 cels = 150-300 m. The effect of the receiver errors on the estimated position is σ = 1 cel = 150 m. For the hyperbolic positioning mode, a lane expansion factor of 1.6 has to be taken into account. The total error (under normal conditions) adds up to 1.3 km = 0.75 nM (2DRMS = 1.5 nM).

9.3   Loran-C

Loran-C is a low frequency (LF) navigation system that uses the difference in the time of arrival of signals broadcast by three or more transmitting stations. It has been developed from earlier military navigation systems Loran-A (invented in the United States during Word War II) and Cytac (automatic long-range bombing system deployed around 1950) and it has been in operation since 1957. In Canada and the U.S., Loran-C is being operated by the Canadian and U.S. Coast Guard, respectively. In Europe this is done by two organisations, NELS and SELS (Nortwest and South European Loran-C System), in which a number of countries participate. The Russian Chayka system is very similar to Loran-C and may be combined with NELS and SELS to expand coverage. Termination of the system in the USA in 2000 was initially decided upon, but this decision has been revised and Loran-C in the USA will likely continue until 2008. In Europe, the system may be terminated in 2004.

Loran-C operates at a frequency of 100 kHz, in the bandwidth 90 to 110 kHz, with amplitude modulation of the signal. The system is based on time (modulation envelope matching) as well as phase difference measurements. All transmitters use a single carrier frequency of 100 kHz and transmit pulses in time sharing mode. Loran-C is primarily a ground wave system. Since it is a pulsed system, the sky wave can be separated from the ground wave by using only the first 30 μs of each incoming pulse (the third cycle of the ground wave pulse). Although both ground wave and sky wave can be utilized for navigation, navigation normally is conducted using ground wave. However, at a distance of 1800 nM from the transmitters, the ground wave signal will gradually vanish, and only sky wave reception becomes possible. Sky wave is less accurate but results in longer range and therefore better coverage. Loran-C operates primarily in hyperbolic mode. It can also operate in circular mode using a synchronized clock at the receiver; only two transmitters are required in this case. The range of the system is a function of

• the power of the transmitter
• the ground conductivity
• the ambient noise (mostly atmospheric noise at 100 kHz)

The range is usually of the order of 1000-1500 nM at sea due to the high conductivity of sea water. It is considerably less on land. The accuracy is a function of geometry, receiver, conductivity and topography.

Predictable (absolute) accuracy is of the order of 460 m (0.25 nM) (2DRMS); 460 m is the minimum accuracy specified for Loran-C coverage for marine navigation. Repeatable accuracy is typically better than 50 m because the combined effect of primary, secondary and additional secondary factor, see Section 5.2, is nearly constant in time. Marine differential Loran-C accuracy is better than 20 m.

Loran-C is composed of a series of chains. A typical chain consists of one primary (master) station, and two to four secondary (slave) stations. Transmitting stations within a chain are separated by distances up to 2000 km. Coastal chains are layed out to maximize coverage at sea. Coverage is not universal. In Figure 9.8 the coverage in

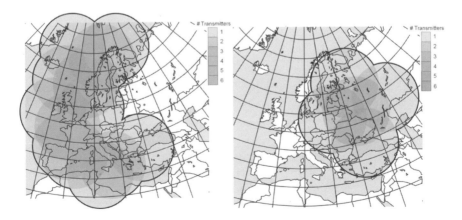

Figure 9.8: Coverage of Loran-C in Europe (NELS and SELS, left) and Chayka.

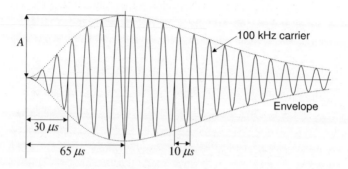

Figure 9.9: Loran-C amplitude modulated pulse.

Europe is shown for NELS and SELS and the Russian Chayka system.

The lower layer of the ionosphere, i.e., the D- or E-layer, depending on the time of day, acts as an almost perfect reflecting surface and two waves occur. The *ground wave* is primarily used for positioning due to its higher stability. The travel time of a ground wave along the Earth's surface can be precisely determined and is affected by refractivity, ground conductivity (and permittivity), and topography. Bending of the ground wave while travelling along the Earth's surface occurs due to diffraction and absorption into the ground (or water). The *sky wave*, which can be reflected off the ionosphere and the Earth's surface several times, can be used for lower accuracy positioning over longer ranges. The sky wave may interfere with the ground wave but, for short range, both waves can easily be separated. The intensity of the sky wave is greater at nighttime (due to D-layer of ionosphere).

Loran-C uses large transmitting antennas to ensure efficient transmission. A transmitter usually includes a 190 m vertical, top-loaded antenna with a synthetic groundplane with a radius of 300-500 m. The transmitted signal is vertically polarized (because man-made noise is also mostly vertically polarized).

The Loran-C amplitude modulated pulse $e(t)$, see Figure 9.9, is given by the expression

$$e(t) = A(\frac{t}{t_p})^2 \exp(2(1-\frac{t}{t_p}))\cos \omega t \qquad (9.1)$$

where A is a constant, t time in seconds, $t_p = 65 \cdot 10^{-6}$ s and $\omega = 2\pi \cdot 100$ kHz. With a carrier frequency of 100 kHz , we get

- A wavelength of 3,000 m.
- A period of a single cycle of $T_{cycle} = 1/f = 10$ μs.
- A period of a pulse T_{pulse} of 250 μs (one pulse corresponds to 25 cycles).

The pulse is quickly raising in amplitude to allow cycle measurement at the beginning of the ground wave pulse, before the sky wave pulse reaches the receiver and interferes with the ground wave pulse. A *coarse measurement* is made on the

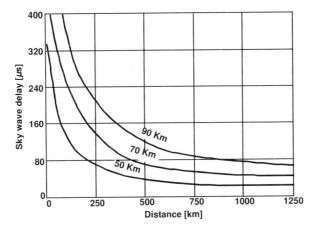

Figure 9.10: Sky wave delay as a function of the height of the ionosphere and distance from the transmitter.

pulse envelope with an accuracy of ±4 μs, which ensures automatic carrier phase ambiguity resolution. Cycle zero crossings are identified and tracked. *Cycle matching* on the third cycle (sixth zero crossing) of the carrier (30 μs from start of the pulse) is conducted in order to separate the delayed sky wave from the ground wave. To reduce sky wave contamination within each of the multi-pulse groups from the master and secondary stations, the phase of the carrier is changed systematically with respect to the pulse envelope from pulse to pulse. The final time difference is obtained by adding the fine cycle reading to the coarse envelope reading, i.e., the sum of envelope and cycle matching is equal to the total time difference (TD). The accuracy of cycle matching depends on the receiver and noise, and it is of the order of 0.01 to 0.1 μs, i.e., 0.01 μs = 0.001 cycle, since $T_{cycle} = 1/f = 10$ μs and 0.01 μs corresponds to 3 m.

The sky wave delay as a function of distance from the transmitter for various heights of the ionosphere is shown in Figure 9.10. The delay is caused by the longer path of

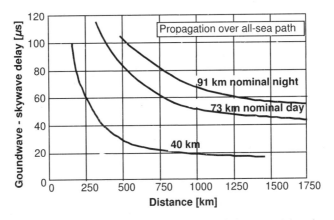

Figure 9.11: Differences between ground and sky wave delays for various heights of the ionosphere and distance from the transmitter.

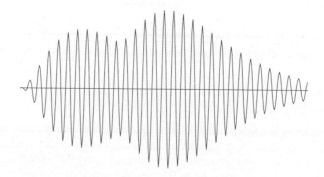

Figure 9.12: Interference between ground and sky waves.

the sky wave and can exceed 500 μs or 150 km.

With a low ionosphere and a large distance from the transmitter, the sky wave may arrive before the 30 μs point of the ground wave; Figure 9.11 shows that, for an exceptionally low ionosphere of 40 km, the 30 μs point occurs at about 500 km from the transmitter. This is likely to occur during periods of intense solar activity. The resulting interference (ground and sky wave pulses) is shown in Figure 9.12.

To get an accurate position using the ground wave, cycle matching is primarily made after the third cycle of the pulse, when more power is available. If the sky wave is used, cycle matching is made after the seventh cycle of the pulse.

The Loran-C pulse occupies a bandwidth of 20 kHz (within 90 to 110 kHz) and is subject to interference from other signals within this bandwidth, which can cause severe problems. The interference can be caused by the following sources:

- Sky wave interference.
- Interference from other transmitters of the same chain.
- Interference from other broadcasting transmitters.
- Ionospheric interference.

Notch filters are used to block out interference at specific frequencies within the 90 - 110 kHz bandwidth. The use of filters is, however, limited because, if too many filters are used, the pulse will be distorted which will result in lower accuracy. The signals transmitted by each transmitter contain groups of eight pulses, with a

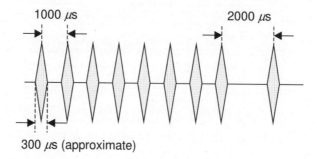

Figure 9.13: Pulse transmission structure.

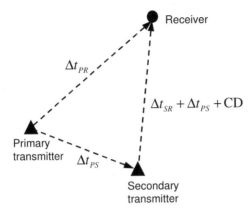

Figure 9.14: Loran-C observations.

separation of 1 ms (1000 μs) between each pulse. In addition, the master station transmits a ninth pulse, 2 ms after each group of eight pulses, see Figure 9.13. The eight pulses allow the receiver to make more measurements for a position fix. The ninth pulse transmitted from a master station can be switched on/off and is also used for user's warning, e.g., to transfer information on abnormal conditions in the signals to the secondary stations. The first two pulses can be used for the blinking service, which is a form of integrity check to warn Loran-C users if a signal is unreliable and should not be used for positioning.

Both primary (master) and secondary (slave) transmitters are precisely time and phase synchronized using cesium clocks. Secondary stations are transmitting after the master with unique delays for their identification. This delay is called *Emission Delay* (ED), which is the sum of the propagation time from primary to secondary station and a constant *Coding Delay* (CD). Each CD is sufficiently long to ensure that signals from all stations are received in the same sequence in the area of chain coverage. Coding Delays vary between 10,000 and 50,000 μs. Using the definitions, see also Figure 9.14

Δt_{PR} - transit time from primary transmitter to user receiver
Δt_{SR} - transit time from secondary transmitter to user receiver
Δt_{PS} - transit time from primary to secondary transmitter
the emission delay is given by

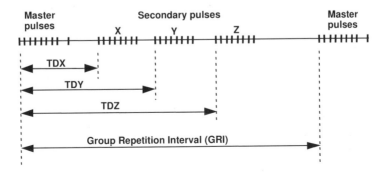

Figure 9.15: Loran-C chain group repetition interval (GRI).

Table 9.1: Conductivity versus distance for a 300 kW transmitter.

| Conductivity [S/m] | Distance from transmitter [nM] | | | | | |
	300	400	500	600	700	800
	Signal strength [dB above 1μV/m]					
5 (sea)	76.5	72	68	63.5	60	57
10^{-2} (good soil)	75	70	65.5	61	57	54
10^{-3} (poor soil)	67	60	53.5	46.5	40	35
5×10^{-4}	58	49	40	32	24	18
10^{-4}	39.5	27	16	5	-4	-12

$$ED = \Delta t_{PS} + CD \tag{9.2}$$

and the observed time difference at the receiver by

$$\Delta t = \Delta t_{PR} - (\Delta t_{SR} + ED) = \Delta t_{PR} - \Delta t_{SR} - \Delta t_{PS} - CD \tag{9.3}$$

Multiplication of this observed time difference by the speed of light and accounting for the known emission delay, results in the range difference between primary and secondary transmitter at the receiver location. Using two of these range differences, the receiver position can be computed as the intersection of two hyperbolas.

Each chain has its own unique period of pulse groups, called the *Group Repetition Interval* (GRI), as shown in Figure 9.15. There are 40 possible GRI's. The repetition rates of the pulse group of neighbouring chains have to be carefully chosen so that signals from different chains do not overlap and create interference between chains.

Table 9.2: Signal strength as a function of range and radiated power for a constant conductivity of 10^{-3} S/m (poor soil).

| Range [nM] | Radiated power [kW] | | | | | | | |
	200	280	300	400	500	700	1000	1125
	Signal strength [dB above 1μV/m]							
200	70.5	72	74.6	72.6	73.5	76	76	76.5
300	61.5	63	67	65	66	68	69	70
400	56	57	60	58	59.5	61.5	63	64
500	49.7	51.5	53	53	53.8	55	57	58
600	43	45	45.5	47	48	50	51	52
700	37	39	39.2	41	42	44.6	46	47
800	32	34	33	35	36	38	40	41

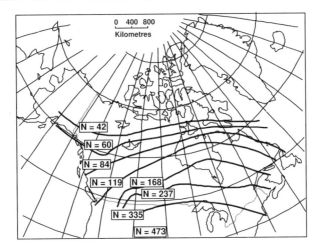

Figure 9.16: Estimated average atmospheric noise in the Loran-C band for Canada in μV/m.

A chain is designated by its GRI in μs divided by 10, e.g., the Canadian West Coast chain has a designation of 5990 and its GRI is 59,900 μs. The Norwegian Sea chain has a designation of 7,970 and the GRI is 79,700 μs. GRI's can vary between 4,000 and 99,990 μs. Stations may participate in different chains; they can be master in one chain and slave in another.

The radiated power of a Loran-C monopole antenna is normally about 200 - 400 kW, while in case of a multi-tower antenna system the radiated power can reach 1000 kW. The average predicted field intensity is about 400 kW. The actual signals may be undetectable in a designated coverage area if field noise is unusually high.

The signal strength (in dB above 1 μV/m) of Loran-C signals with a transmitter of 300 kW as a function of the distance from the transmitter (in nautical miles) is given in Table 9.1 for various conductivity values. Table 9.2 gives the corresponding signal strength for a radiated power of 200 to 1125 kW and a range of 200 to 800 nM for a constant conductivity of 10^{-3} S/m which is that of poor soil.

Atmospheric RF noise is caused by thunderstorms and lightning bursts. It can reach a very significant level for RF in the 90-110 kHz frequency band. Atmospheric RF noise is most substantial in the equatorial zone, and decreases with increasing latitude. The average estimated atmospheric noise in the Loran-C band in Canada is shown in Figure 9.16. The corresponding values in dB follow from the numbers in this figure as

$$\text{Noise}\,[\text{dB}] = 20\log\frac{1 \;\; \text{V/m}}{\text{Actual noise}} \tag{9.4}$$

Departures from yearly averages of noise can be represented in terms of:
- *Diurnal effects*: lowest noise in the morning, highest in the evening. The variation can exceed 20 dB.

Table 9.3: Estimated range capability by Canadian province considering atmospheric noise and terrain conductivity utilizing 500 kW transmitters.

Province	Atmospheric noise [dB]	Conductivity [S/m]	Theoretical distance at which -10 dB signal is observed [nM]
British Columbia			
South	41.5	0.003	1180
North	38.5	0.01	1450
Alberta	41.5	0.01	1350
Saskatchewan			
South	44.5	0.01	1240
North	41.5	0.0003	480
Manitoba			
Southwest	47.5	0.001	1180
Southeast	44.5	0.001	1280
North	41.5	0.0003	480
Ontario			
South	50.5	0.001	720
Mid	47.5	0.001	750
North	44.5	0.0003	450
Quebec-Maritimes	44.5	0.001	800
	47.5	0.001	750
Quebec-New Foundland	41.5	0.0003	480
	38.5	0.0001	385

- *Seasonal effects*: lowest noise in winter, highest in summer. The variation can exceed 20 dB.

The signal field strength and atmospheric noise values can be used to predict the maximum range at which Loran-C signals can be detected. Table 9.3 gives maximum ranges for various areas of Canada assuming that a signal strength of −10 dB (value most commonly used, given established receiver capability) above noise is required to measure the signals.

Since the Earth is not a perfect conductor, part of the electromagnetic energy is absorbed into the ground or water, resulting in a bending of a wave and an observable phase lag which increases with the distance from the transmitter and decreases with increasing conductivity and frequency. The three phase factors that should be taken into account are the primary, secondary and additional secondary factor (PF, SF and ASF) and were already discussed in Section 5.2. Also shown in that section was the combined effect of SF and ASF for a frequency of 100 kHz. Overland paths often occur when using Loran-C. In these cases, not only the ASF should be considered,

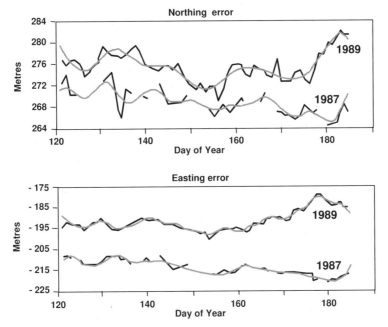

Figure 9.17: Comparison of Loran-C positions between 1987 and 1989 at Pemberton, B.C., Canada.

but also the effect of topography. This effect is large, but constant, and can be calibrated. The combined effect of ASF and topography results in permanent distortions (Loran-C Grid Distortions).

The repeatability of Loran-C can be illustrated by the following example. A point located in Pemberton, B.C., in a mountainous area of the Canadian West Coast chain (5990) was measured over a period of 60 days. The same experiment at exactly the same site and same time of the year was repeated two years later. No significant atmospheric variations occurred during both experiments. The differences in position between the two experiments in terms of north and east components are shown in Figure 9.17. The average differences were 5 m (north) and 25 m (east).

Eurofix is an integrated navigation system which combines Differential GPS (DGPS) and Loran-C. The Loran-C system is used to transmit messages which contain differential corrections and integrity information by additional modulation of the transmitted signals. Additionally, short messages for emergency operations may be included as well. DGPS, in turn, can be used to calibrate Loran-C to account for the combined effects of ASF and topography, such as shown in Figure 9.17.

Since Loran-C is a navigation system in itself, the transmission of the Eurofix messages should not affect the performance of Loran-C. When developing Eurofix in the 1990's, a number of restrictions were imposed on the Eurofix data channel:

• The Loran-C blinking service should be preserved, i.e., the first two pulses of a group could not be used for Eurofix modulation.

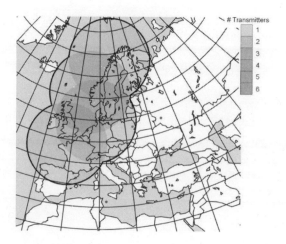

Figure 9.18: Eurofix coverage in 2002.

- The modulation should not induce tracking biases; this requires a balanced type of modulation.
- The modulation index should be kept small in order to minimise the loss in tracking signal power.

As a result, the Eurofix data channel consists of a 30 bps (bits per second) datalink, with a large overhead to ensure the robustness of the transmitted data. The degradation of the original Loran-C signal is only 0.79 dB, which is negligible. Loran-C receivers that have knowledge of the Eurofix signal, can easily compensate for the applied modulation to completely cancel the signal loss. Eurofix was originally tested using a single DGPS reference receiver installed at Sylt, off the German coast, which is part of NELS. Signals could be received for distances up to 1000 km and the resulting horizontal positioning precision was three metres during 95% of the time. Other tests were conducted in Russia, using Chayka for the Eurofix data channel to transmit both GPS and Glonass differential corrections.

In 2002 Eurofix was implemented on four European Loran-C stations (Bø and Værlandet in Norway, Lessay in France and Sylt) to test the concept in a regional network mode in order to improve accuracy to the one metre level. The coverage of this regional area system is given in Figure 9.18. Similar developments are going on in the USA and Canada, where the Loran-C signals will be used as data channel for the Wide Area Augmentation System (WAAS), in particular for high-latitudes, since at these locations the WAAS data transmitted by geostationary satellites above the equator cannot be received.

9.4 Satellite positioning systems

Each satellite positioning system consists of the following three segments:

- *Space segment* - a system of satellites transmitting RF signals of a certain structure designed for a particular positioning system, with high performance frequency and time standards.

- *Control segment* - a system of ground stations which monitor and control the satellite system and time, and predict the ephemeris and behaviour of the satellite clocks as well as update the navigation message for each satellite.
- *User segment* - observers equipped with receivers tracking the satellites to determine the position in a global coordinate system.

Tracking of the satellites provides

- *pseudoranging* on satellites, and/or
- observation of the *Doppler shift* over time.

These observables allow the user to model the distance from the receiver antenna to a satellite at the instant of observation. With the simultaneous observation of at least four satellites whose positions are known in the same global coordinate system, a position of the static or mobile receiver antenna can be uniquely determined.

Satellite positioning systems can be classified according to different criteria. In terms of inclination of the orbits, three systems can be distinguished. For systems with *inclined orbits*, satellites are in relative motion with respect to the Earth. This results in a constellation which changes with time. Satellite systems with inclined orbits provide global coverage, i.e., they make possible the determination of positions anywhere on the Earth. Moreover, the positions can be determined in a three-dimensional global coordinate system.

Examples of satellite systems with inclined orbits are

- Transit or NNSS (Navy Navigation Satellite System), with polar orbits (90° inclination).
- Tsikada (Soviet equivalent of Transit), with polar orbits.
- NAVSTAR GPS (Navigation System with Time and Ranging Global Positioning System) developed in the U.S., with orbits having a 55° inclination.
- GLONASS (Global Navigation Satellite System) developed in the former USSR, with orbits having a 64° inclination.

The satellites in systems with *geostationary orbits* are stationary with respect to the Earth's surface. The constellation of satellites visible from an individual observer remains constant. Satellite systems with geostationary orbits provides only partial coverage, i.e., they can only be used for positioning in certain latitude bands. Using such a system, only a two dimensional position in a global coordinate system can be determined. One such system was deployed in the mid 1980's in the U.S. and used until the early 1990's, namely Starfix by J.E. Chance & Associates (the current Starfix system, operated and owned by Fugro, uses GPS for positioning and geostationary satellites for transmitting integrity and correction data).

Mixed systems consist of satellites in *inclined* and *geostationary orbits*. The Inmarsat/WAAS geostationary satellites may be used to augment GPS (where the geostationary satellite signals provide additional ranging observations). Other possibilities include the potential combination of GPS with low-Earth orbit (LEO) satellites.

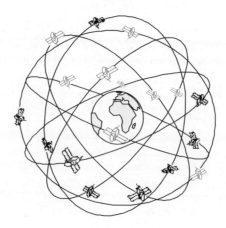

Figure 9.19: Global Positioning System (GPS) constellation.

9.4.1 Global Positioning System (GPS)

The nominal GPS constellation consists of 21 satellites plus three active spares, placed in six orbital, nearly circular, uniformly spaced planes, each inclined by 55° with respect to the equatorial plane, as shown in Figure 9.19.

The orbital period of each satellite is exactly 12 hours of sidereal time. The altitude of the satellites above the Earth's surface is 20,200 km. GPS has been designed as a worldwide system with continuous coverage, i.e., it can be used anywhere in the world at any time. It is also an all-weather system, but it requires line-of-sight visibility, i.e., the line of sight between the observer and the satellites being observed must be unobstructed.

GPS signal

The RF signals are both frequency and time synchronized by onboard cesium clocks that are frequently compared to and precisely synchronized with the GPS atomic time scale. The difference between UTC (USNO) and GPS time is known to a specified accuracy of 100 ns (10-30 ns in practice).

Each GPS satellite transmits signals on the following two carrier frequencies:

- L1 = 1575.42 MHz
- L2 = 1227.60 MHz

The carrier frequencies are modulated by two pseudo-random noise (PRN) codes which are used for pseudoranging:

- C/A (coarse acquisition) code on L1, and
- P (precise) code on L1 and L2

The signal structure will be enhanced early in the 21st century to improve performance. GPS modernization plans include adding a civil code on the L2 carrier and the addition of a third civil frequency L5 (1176.45 MHz). The additional coded

Table 9.4: GPS error sources (after NAPA, 1995).

Error source	Typical range error [m] (1σ)	
	SPS	PPS
Selective Availability (SA)	24.0	0.0
Ionospheric	7.0	0.01
Tropospheric	0.7	0.7
Clock and ephemeris error	3.6	3.6
Receiver noise	1.5	0.6
Multipath	1.2	1.8
Total (UERE) (1σ)	25.3	4.1

civil signals will provide many advantages, including improved signal redundancy and positioning accuracy (Shaw et al., 2000).

The continuous navigation message (supported by five ground-based monitor stations) is modulated on both carrier frequencies. Two basic GPS observables, code (pseudoranging) and carrier phase, are obtained with the following accuracies:

- pseudoranging : 0.1-1 m
- carrier phase (ambiguous): better than 1 cm

GPS user equivalent range error (UERE)

UERE is the square root of the quadratic sum of errors affecting the accuracies of the measured pseudoranges, namely satellite, propagation and receiver-related errors. The magnitude of the UERE depends on

- receiver type: L1 versus L1/ L2
- receiver noise and multipath rejection capability
- tropospheric model
- magnitude of satellite orbit errors
- magnitude of satellite clock errors
- effect of Selective Availability (SA) when it is activated

The UERE error components for both the Standard Positioning Service (SPS) and Precise Positioning Service (PPS) are given in Table 9.4. SPS is the service available to the public, PPS is reserved for U.S. (and NATO) military users. The SPS UERE was previously dominated by SA. SA was turned down to zero in May 2000, however, and the SPS UERE is now dominated by the ionospheric range error. With the introduction of a second civilian frequency to correct for the effect of the ionosphere, the SPS UERE would be similar to the current PPS UERE, namely a few metres. The accuracy of single point positioning with GPS would improve accordingly.

The accuracy of single point positioning is obtained by applying the following equation:

$$\text{Positioning accuracy} = \text{UERE} \times \text{DOP} \qquad (9.5)$$

Table 9.5: GPS single point positioning accuracies.

	DRMS (65-68%)			2DRMS (95%)		
	PPS	SPS (SA)	SPS (no SA)	PPS	SPS (SA)	SPS (no SA)
Position						
Horizontal	10.5	50	11	21	100	22
Vertical	14	70	16.5	28	140	33
Spherical	17.5	86	20	36	172	40
Veclocity						
Any axis		0.1 m/s			0.2 m/s	

For different types of DOPs, positioning accuracies are computed as
- UERE × PDOP = MRSE ($\approx$ 61 %) {mean radial spherical error}
- UERE × HDOP = DRMS ($\approx$ 66%)
- UERE × VDOP = 1σ (height) (68%)

The horizontal DOP, assuming an all-in-view satellite receiver and clear horizon, is in the range 1.5 to 2.0.

GPS single point positioning

GPS single point positioning refers to position determination using a single GPS receiver. Accuracies of single point positions that can be obtained by SPS and PPS users are given in Table 9.5. Ionospheric effects are included in the SPS error budget. With a second civilian frequency available, SPS accuracy would be similar to the current PPS accuracy.

Differential GPS (DGPS) positioning

In differential GPS (DGPS) positioning mode, two or more GPS receivers operate simultaneously, with at least one receiver serving as reference, usually in static mode. By differencing observations collected by at least two receivers, a number of substantial errors affecting GPS measurements are eliminated, or at least significantly reduced. The product of differential positioning is a relative position of one station with respect to the reference station expressed in terms of coordinate differences. The concept is illustrated in Figure 9.20.

The reference receiver need not be in a static mode. For instance, two receivers can

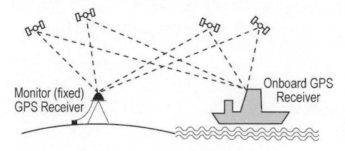

Figure 9.20: Differential GPS (DGPS) concept.

Table 9.6: DGPS positioning accuracies.

PDOP ≤ 3 [a]	Horizontal (DRMS in 2-D)	Vertical (RMS in 1-D)
Carrier phase smoothing of the code[1]	1-3 m	1-3 m
Carrier phase smoothing of the code[2]	0.5-1 m	0.5-1 m
Carrier phase – fixed ambiguities[3]	≤ 10 cm	≤ 10 cm
Carrier phase – float ambiguities	≤ 50 cm	≤ 50 cm

a: Single reference station - valid for inter-station distance less than about 100 km.
1: Standard (wide correlator spacing) C/A code receivers (code measuring accuracy ≈ 1 m).
2: Narrow correlator™ spacing C/A code receivers (code measuring accuracy ≈ 10 cm).
3: Carrier phase integer ambiguities resolved (baselines shorter than 20 to 30 km).

be installed on two different moving platforms. If the data is processed in differential mode, the relative accuracy between the two moving platforms will be similar to the DGPS case where the reference station is fixed.

There are several advantages achieved through differential positioning. The following errors are reduced/eliminated:

- orbital errors (reduction)
- ionospheric and tropospheric propagation errors (reduction)
- errors caused by Selective Availability (reduction/elimination)
- satellite and receiver clock errors (reduction/elimination)

Better quality control is also possible. The remaining errors after differential processing include

- receiver noise
- multipath
- ionospheric (with single frequency receiver) and tropospheric propagation errors
- residual orbital errors

The differential UERE (DUERE) is smaller than the UERE and the resulting DGPS positions are more accurate. Table 9.6 lists DGPS accuracies achieved for: 1) a good satellite geometry (DOP ≤ 3) when a single reference station is used; 2) the inter-receiver distance ℓ is less than 100 km; and 3) both code and carrier phase data are used.

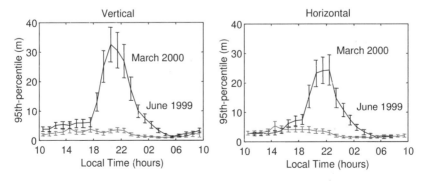

Figure 9.21: Differential positioning accuracies in the equatorial region for a 430 km baseline.

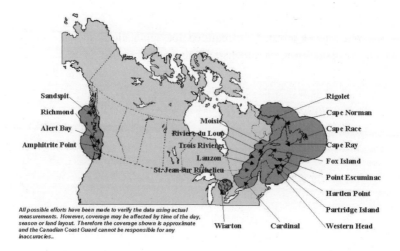

Figure 9.22: Canadian Coast Guard DGPS real-time system (Fisheries and Oceans Canada, 2001a; Fisheries and Oceans Canada, 2001b).

These accuracies may not be achieved under certain circumstances, e.g., for longer baselines in regions where large ionospheric gradients exist. Figure 9.21 shows an example of DGPS positioning accuracies for a 430 km baseline in the equatorial anomaly region. For the equinoctial months, during solar maximum, horizontal positioning accuracies are on the order of 25 m 2DRMS (95th-percentile) in the evening local time sector. This translates into 12.5 m DRMS.

Real-time DGPS

Real-time DGPS is used to obtain differential GPS positions in real-time. A reference station equipped with a GPS receiver collects GPS data and transmits it to users using a radio link. The remote receivers use the data transmitted from the reference station to correct their GPS observations for ranging errors which are correlated with those at the reference station, thereby improving substantially the DGPS positioning accuracy. The distance over which the corrections may be sent is a function of the data link frequency used. In practice, more than one reference receiver may be used to improve reliability.

In many parts of the world commercial (e.g., global Fugro and Thales systems) and public (Coast Guard) services of real-time DGPS are deployed and available for marine positioning. The Canadian Coast Guard (CCG) currently offers DGPS services along the Pacific and Atlantic coasts of Canada, in addition to the Great Lakes and St. Lawrence River regions (Fisheries and Oceans Canada, 2001a; Fisheries and Oceans Canada, 2001b). The CCG DGPS system uses marine radiobeacons (300 kHz range) to transmit the corrections in order to provide maritime coverage. The coverage is shown in Figure 9.22.

Water level profiling with GPS

Continuous water level profiles are required for applications such as precise tidal studies and the establishment of chart datums. Both spirit levelling as well as establishing and running tidal stations can be expensive. Shipborne carrier phase-based DGPS is fast, efficient and relatively inexpensive, and can provide sub-decimetre level accuracy, which is sufficient for most applications.

In this method, GPS carrier phase data is used, with ambiguity resolution on-the-fly. If VDOP values are in the range 2-3, and the standard deviation of the double difference carrier phase observations is 1 to 2 cm (due to receiver noise and multipath), the following accuracies should be achieved for water level determination, neglecting non-GPS error sources:

$$\sigma(\Delta h) \approx 2 - 6 \text{ cm} \tag{9.6}$$

Using a 13-m survey launch with dual frequency GPS receivers, a DGPS survey was conducted on the Fraser River in March 1993 to test the above concept (Lachapelle et al., 1994). Widelane observables ($\lambda = 86$ cm) were used to determine the carrier phase ambiguities on-the-fly. The DGPS-derived heights were transferred to benchmarks on shore to independently verify the accuracy of the DGPS heights. The accuracy $\sigma(\Delta h)$ of this procedure was estimated to be at ±2 cm.

The GPS observing sessions were conducted under adequate satellite coverage (PDOP < 5). Orthometric heights were calculated using a geoid solution provided by the Geodetic Survey Division of Canada (GSD). The consistency of the GSD geoid solution with the University of Calgary DGPS solution was 1-2 cm.

The RMS consistency of the GPS-derived heights between successive benchmark visits (intervals ranging from several hours to 3 days) was 5.5 cm, while the corresponding RMS agreement between GPS-derived and benchmark heights was 6.4 cm.

Wide Area Differential GPS

In *Wide Area Differential GPS* (WADGPS), a network of GPS reference stations is used to compute individual GPS error sources. By combining GPS observations from multiple reference stations, spatially correlated error sources are modelled over an extended area (i.e., North America). As a result, DGPS positioning accuracies do not degrade significantly with increasing distance from a given reference station. WADGPS systems allow consistent DGPS positioning accuracies within the network of reference stations. Typical positioning accuracies are at the metre level.

The DGPS corrections may be sent to users over a wide area via geostationary satellite downlink. Several commercial WADGPS services are currently available where users pay annual service fees (e.g., Fugro and Thales systems). The Wide Area Augmentation System (WAAS, see Figure 9.23) is currently under development by the U.S. Federal Aviation Administration (FAA) (FAA, 1999). This WADGPS

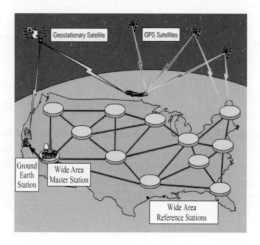

Figure 9.23: WAAS architecture (from CAASD: www.mitrecaasd.org).

system is intended primarily for aviation applications – enroute navigation and precision landing – but may be freely used by civil users for other applications such as marine navigation. In Europe a similar system, EGNOS (European Geostationary Navigation Overlay System) is being developed.

GLONASS and GLONASS-augmented GPS

The GLONASS (GLObal NAvigation Satellite System) was developed by Russia and has similar characteristics to the GPS, as described in Table 9.7. The satellites are, however, deployed on three orbital planes instead of six, as shown in Figure 9.24; the system also employs frequency division multiple access (FDMA) instead of the code

Table 9.7: GLONASS technical characteristics.

Satellite constellation	Satellites	21 satellites + 3 active spares; satellites broadcast signals autonomously
	Orbital characteristics	Three planes, eight satellites per plane; 64.8° inclination; 11 hr 15 min period; 19,100 km altitude
Signal structure	Frequencies	Dual L-band (L1: 1597-1617 MHz, L2: 1240-1260 MHz)
	Digital signal	Spread spectrum PRN @ 511 kHz chipping rate; continuous navigation message @ 50 Hz
	Other	FDMA signal separation: $f_j = f_1 + (j-1)\Delta f$, $\Delta f = 0.5625$ (L1) or 0.4375 (L2) MHz, j = 1,2,..., 24
Coverage		Worldwide
Accuracy	Position	30 m
	Velocity	0.15 m/s
	Time	1 microsecond

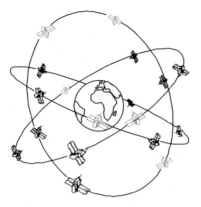

Figure 9.24: GLONASS constellation.

division multiple access (CDMA) used in GPS. Although the system is considered fully operational, the number of satellites available varies significantly and is well below the full twenty-four stated in the specifications.

GLONASS is most commonly used in conjunction with GPS (GLONASS-augmented GPS) and a number of GPS/GLONASS receivers are now commercially available. Significant improvements in availability and reliability can occur when using GPS/GLONASS, especially in constricted waterways and in charting areas with high obstruction mask angles such as fjords. Further augmentation with clock and height constraints can also be used to further improve availability and reliability (Ryan et al., 1998).

Pseudolite-augmented GPS

Pseudolites are pseudo-satellites that transmit PRN modulated signals similar to GPS signals. Pseudolites can therefore be used to augment GPS by installing them in critical locations such as along constricted waterways and in harbour entrances to improve accuracy, availability and reliability, as shown conceptually in Figure 9.25. Line-of-sight between the pseudolite and the GPS receiver is required. The pseudolite is assigned a C/A code not previously assigned to another satellite.

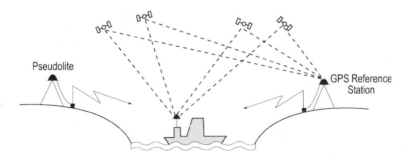

Figure 9.25: Pseudolite augmentation of GPS – marine case.

The concept of using pseudolites for marine applications was tested in (Morley and Lachapelle, 1997). One of the limitations is signal reflection (multipath) caused by the grazing signal propagation lines from the pseudolite to the receiver. Availability and reliability gains are, however, very significant under signal masking situations. The use of pseudolites is also advantageous in speeding up the carrier phase ambiguity resolution process in the shipborne environment (Morley and Lachapelle, 1998).

9.5   Speed determination

9.5.1   Doppler sonar speed log

A Doppler sonar provides an estimate of the speed of a vessel with respect to the sea bottom or an intermediate water layer. It can be used as part of a dead reckoning navigation system (where heading is also required from another system), i.e., a system in which the position of a vessel at any instant is estimated by updating the last estimated position using the vessel's course and the distance derived with the log measurements.

A Doppler sonar system is particularly suitable for

- Determining the velocity of vessels for general maritime navigation and for geophysical surveys.
- Anchoring and berthing of large vessels (to avoid damage).

In a Doppler sonar system, the transmitting/receiving transducer is obliquely mounted on the forward section of the vessel's hull. The transducer converts electric energy into an acoustic wave and vice-versa. The seabed acts as a reflector for the transmitted acoustic waves, as shown in Figure 9.26.

Due to the motion of the vessel relative to the sea bottom, the frequency of the received acoustic wave, as reflected from the seabed, differs from that of the transmitted wave (it is shifted with respect to the transmitted frequency). The difference between the two frequencies is an acoustic *Doppler shift*. The Doppler shift of the sonar beam is measured and converted into a speed measurement.

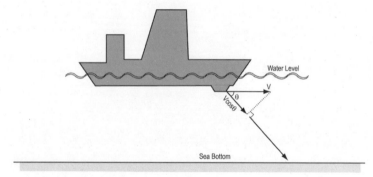

Figure 9.26: Principle of sonar speed log.

Assuming a simple motion with the transducer pointing in the direction of the component $v\cos\theta$ of the velocity vector v of the vessel, see again Figure 9.26, the observed frequency (Doppler) shift f_d is

$$f_d = f_0 - f_r \tag{9.7}$$

where f_0 is the transmitted frequency and f_r is the received frequency. The Doppler shift f_d can be expressed as

$$f_d = \frac{2vf_0\cos\theta}{c_{sw}} \tag{9.8}$$

where V is the magnitude of the horizontal velocity, θ is the angle between the sonar beam and the horizontal plane (the angle between the direction of motion and the transmitted acoustic signal), and c_{sw} is the acoustic wave propagation velocity in the medium. Thus, the horizontal velocity v of the vessel can be derived from the measured Doppler shift.

Derivation of Doppler shift

The Doppler equation, which expresses the relationship between the received frequency f_r and the transmitted frequency f_0, is

$$f_r = f_0 \frac{1 - \dfrac{v}{c_{sw}}}{\sqrt{1 - \dfrac{v^2}{c_{sw}^2}}} \tag{9.9}$$

where v is the velocity of the observer with respect to the reflector. The received frequency f_r can also be expressed as

$$f_r = f_0 \sqrt{\frac{c_{sw} - v}{c_{sw} + v}} \tag{9.10}$$

The frequency f_{rB} of the signal that reaches the sea bottom will be

$$f_{rB} = f_0 \sqrt{\frac{c_{sw} - v}{c_{sw} + v}} \tag{9.11}$$

This signal is then reflected from the sea bottom and returned to the ship. Consider the signal traveling from the sea bottom as having a transmitting frequency f_{rB}. This signal is then received by the transponder at frequency f_r

$$f_r = f_{rB}\sqrt{\frac{c_{sw}-v}{c_{sw}+v}} = f_0\sqrt{\frac{c_{sw}-v}{c_{sw}+v}}\sqrt{\frac{c_{sw}-v}{c_{sw}+v}} = f_0\frac{c_{sw}-v}{c_{sw}+v} \tag{9.12}$$

or, equivalently

$$f_r = f_0\frac{1-\dfrac{v}{c_{sw}}}{1+\dfrac{v}{c_{sw}}} \tag{9.13}$$

Using the series expansion

$$\frac{1}{1+x} = 1-x+x^2-x^3+\dots$$

f_r can be written as

$$f_r = f_0(1-\frac{v}{c_{sw}})(1-\frac{v}{c_{sw}}+\frac{v^2}{c_{sw}}--\dots) \tag{9.14}$$

Since $c_{sw}>>v$, the higher order terms can be neglected and

$$f_r = f_0(1-\frac{2v}{c_{sw}}) \tag{9.15}$$

Thus, the Doppler shift f_d is

$$f_d = f_0-f_r = 2v\frac{f_0}{c_{sw}} \tag{9.16}$$

The Doppler frequency f_d is measured by the sonar speed log. Since f_0 is known, v can be derived from (9.16).

Janus configuration

In lowering the beam from the horizontal plane in the forward direction (by the angle θ), the system becomes sensitive to vertical motion. The vessel's vertical motion (heave with no pitch or roll) will result in a vertical velocity component v_v. The resulting Doppler frequency shift error in the direction of the sonar beam will be

$$\frac{2v_v f_0 \sin\theta}{c_{sw}} \tag{9.17}$$

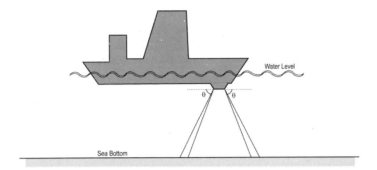

Figure 9.27: Janus configuration.

This problem is overcome using a *Janus* (Roman God with two faces to look into the past and future) configuration of transducers. A second transducer, transmitting at the same angle θ, and operating at the same frequency, is used with its beam pointing in the aft direction as shown in Figure 9.27. Assuming that there is no pitch (or roll) angle, the Doppler frequency shift $f_d(fore)$ observed at the forward transducer is

$$f_d(fore) = \frac{2vf_0\cos\theta}{c_{sw}} + \frac{2v_vf_0\sin\theta}{c_{sw}} \qquad (9.18)$$

The second term on the right-hand side represents the heave effect (error due to the vessel's vertical motion) on $f_d(fore)$. Similarly, the Doppler frequency shift $f_d(aft)$ observed by the aft transducer will be

$$f_d(aft) = -\frac{2vf_0\cos\theta}{c_{sw}} + \frac{2v_vf_0\sin\theta}{c_{sw}} \qquad (9.19)$$

The difference in frequency, obtained by heterodyning the returned energies, is

$$\Delta f_d(measured) = f_d(fore) - f_d(aft) = \frac{4vf_0\cos\theta}{c_{sw}} \qquad (9.20)$$

The term Δf_d is free from the heave effect, which cancels out with the Janus configuration. The vessel's horizontal velocity v is obtained, in the absence of pitch, from the measured difference frequency Δf_d as

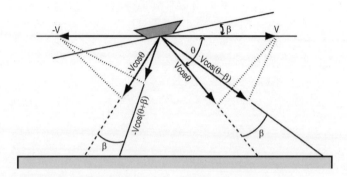

Figure 9.28: Effect of pitch on Janus configuration.

$$v = v_h = \frac{\Delta f_d c_{sw}}{4 f_0 \cos\theta}$$ (9.21)

Effect of pitch (or roll)

The Janus configuration does not totally compensate for the effect of pitch (or roll). Assume that β is the pitch angle (which may be determined separately by a pitch and roll sensor) as shown in Figure 9.28. The measured frequency difference is

$$\Delta f_d (measured) = f_d (fore) - f_d (aft)$$ (9.22)

which can be rewritten using the formulae derived previously as

$$\Delta f_d = \frac{2vf_0 \cos(\theta - \beta)}{c_{sw}} + \frac{2vf_0 \cos(\theta + \beta)}{c_{sw}}$$ (9.23)

This equation can be further rewritten as

$$\Delta f_d = \frac{2vf_0 (\cos(\theta - \beta) + \cos(\theta + \beta))}{c_{sw}}$$ (9.24)

$$\Delta f_d = \frac{4vf_0 (\frac{1}{2}\cos(\theta - \beta) + \frac{1}{2}\cos(\theta + \beta))}{c_{sw}}$$ (9.25)

Finally, the following expression for Δf_d is derived

$$\Delta f_d = \frac{4vf_0 \cos\theta \cos\beta}{c_{sw}}$$ (9.26)

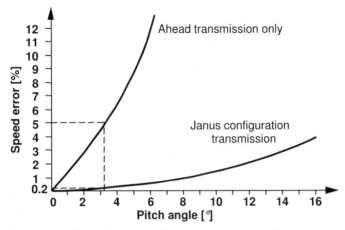

Figure 9.29: Effect of Janus configuration on pitch reduction.

and the horizontal velocity v, which still contains a residual pitch effect $(1/\cos\beta)$ is

$$v = \frac{\Delta f_d c_{sw}}{4 f_0 \cos\theta \cos\beta} = \frac{v_h}{\cos\beta} \qquad (9.27)$$

Although the Janus configuration does not eliminate the pitch effect from the derived horizontal velocity of the vessel, it substantially reduces it. The degree of compensation is a function of the pitch angle, as shown in Fig. 9.29.

Example 9.1: Pitch Effect.
The difference frequency Δf_d was measured on a vessel in the presence of a pitch angle β using a Janus system of two transducers with identical angles θ between the lowered sonar beams and the horizontal plane, with a transmitting frequency f_0. The numerical values of interest are

$$\theta = 60°, \ f_0 = 150 \text{ kHz}, \ c_{sw} = 1500 \text{ m/s}, \ \Delta f_d = 1 \text{ kHz, and } \beta = 10°$$

The horizontal velocity with a Janus configuration in the absence of pitch is

$$v = \frac{\Delta f_d c_{sw}}{4 f_0 \cos\theta}$$

i.e.,

$$v = \frac{1 \text{ kHz} \times 1500 \text{ m/s}}{4 \times 150 \text{ kHz} \times 0.5} = 4.92 \text{ m/s}$$

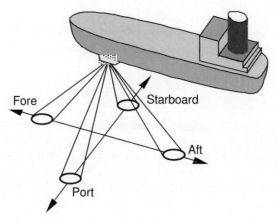

Figure 9.30: Two-axis Janus system.

The vessel's horizontal velocity when taking the pitch effect into account is
$v_h = v \cos \beta = 5.00 \, \text{m/s}$.

Two-axis Janus system to measure forward and athwart-ship speed

It has been shown that the effect of the pitch angle on the horizontal velocity derived from the observed Doppler shift can largely be compensated by using a Janus configuration mounted in the fore-aft direction. Similarly, a Janus configuration of transducers mounted in the port-starboard direction will result in compensation of the roll effect on the derived horizontal velocity, as shown in Figure 9.30. The effect of roll on the athwartship velocity is similar to that of pitch on the forward speed, and can be estimated if an independent instrument is available to measure the roll motion. Two Janus systems mounted at right angles will thus largely compensate for both pitch and roll effects. The incident angle θ of the sonar beam is usually approximately 60° to maximize both

- usable return signal (the larger θ, the stronger usable return signal), and
- usable component of horizontal velocity (the larger θ, the less accurately the horizontal velocity component is estimated).

Effect of beam geometry

The beam geometry of the acoustic signal may affect the estimation of the velocity of the vessel. If a side lobe of the beam dominates with respect to its main lobe, the velocity estimated will be in error, as shown in Figure 9.31. The Janus configuration cannot compensate for this effect. The best way to mitigate this effect is to use a transducer which will eliminate side lobe effects. However, even in such a case, the main beam width must be at least 3° to 6° in order to minimize bottom relief effects.

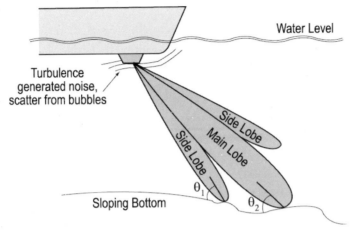

Figure 9.31: Beam geometry of acoustic signal.

Use of bottom reflections and reverberation

Typical transducers operate at frequencies in the range 150-600 kHz. The Doppler sonar provides velocity estimates using bottom reflections typically down to 200 m depth. Beyond this depth, transmitted acoustic pulses are returned as reflections from water layers rather than the seabed. In such a case, the estimated velocity and distance are relative to the water mass, and the efficiency of the Doppler sonar becomes equivalent to that of an electromagnetic log.

Reverberation echoes (scattering) from layers of water 20 to 50 m below the ship can be used to estimate velocities. If these layers are not affected by surface currents, the effect of roll and pitch is minimized as compared to the use of the deeper sea bottom.

9.5.2 Acoustic correlation sonar

Acoustic correlation sonars are used for speed determination. The vessel can be a surface ship or an underwater vehicle. A pair of transducers is mounted on the vessel's hull along the main axis (fore and aft line), placed a known distance s apart from each other. Each transducer transmits identical signals perpendicular to the seabed. The received echo at each transducer reflects the shape of sea bottom and is identical for both transducers but shifted with respect to each other by Δt, see Figure 9.32.

The time delay Δt between the returns of the two transducers is a function of the speed of the vessel v

$$\Delta t = \frac{1}{2}\frac{s}{v} \tag{9.28}$$

The time delay Δt is obtained by a precise correlation of the echoes received by the two transducers. The vessel's speed can therefore be estimated as

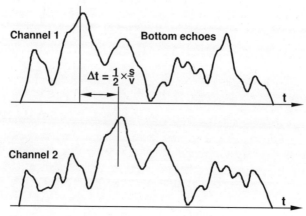

Figure 9.32: Principle of correlation sonar.

$$v = \frac{1}{2}\frac{s}{\Delta t} \qquad\qquad (9.29)$$

Commonly used acoustic correlation sonars operate in the 100-200 kHz frequency range. The ocean floor is used for reflections down to depths of about 200 m. At greater depth, a water mass (using reverberation) located a few tens of metres below the vessel is utilized. Accuracies of such systems are typically 0.1 knots.

A wide lobe angle (beamwidth) signal is used to minimize the dimensions of the transducer as well as to ensure that the vessel will not "run away" from the returned echo. A second set of transducers can be mounted on the vessel's hull perpendicularly to the main axis to measure the vessel's transverse speed.

Acoustic transmission can also take place at an inclined angle from the flat seabed, as shown in (Mio and Rigaud, 1999). Low frequency (less than 20 kHz) high-accuracy correlation sonar, which operates in waters depths up to 5000 m, has also been developed. Accuracies have been reported to be one order of magnitude better than commercial systems.

9.5.3 Electromagnetic speed logs

Electromagnetic (EM) speed logs are designed for underwater use, e.g., in a vessel's hull or in underwater vehicles. The EM speed log is based on Faraday's principle, i.e., the measurement of the flow of a fluid past a sensor by means of electromagnetic induction. Any conductor that moves across a magnetic field will have an electromotive force (emf) induced. The amplitude of the induced emf will be proportional to the speed of the movement. In an EM speed log, the sea water flowing past the sensor becomes a conductor in which an emf is induced.

The design of a rodmeter is shown in Figure 9.33. A magnetic field is produced by a coil in the sensing unit. The outer surface of the sensing unit is made of an insulating layer except for two conducting buttons mounted on each side of the rodmeter. The

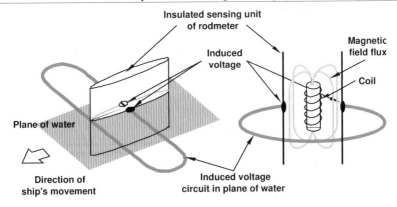

Figure 9.33: Rodmeter used for EM speed log.

axis of the coil, as well as its magnetic flux lines, are perpendicular to the horizontal plane of the vessel's motion.

When the assembly moves together with the vessel in the direction shown, the flux lines cut the water in the horizontal plane and induce a voltage in the conductor (sea water). The voltage (electromotive force, emf) induced in the water is detected by two small electrodes (buttons) set into the outer surface of the sensors, and can be measured. The relationship between the vessel's speed and the output of the buttons (emf in mV) is linear, as shown in Figure 9.34. Accuracies of EM speed logs are approximately 1-2% of the distance travelled.

9.5.4 Radio direction finding (RDF)

Radio Direction Finding (RDF) was the earliest of all radio navigation aids, and has been applied since the very beginning of the 20th century. Direction finding remains unique as the only navigation system with the capability of determining relative bearings of other vessels from their radio transmissions. The RDF receiver has

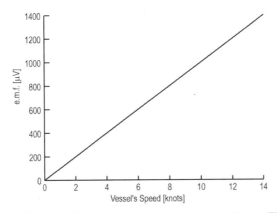

Figure 9.34: Relationship between emf output and speed for an EM speed log.

played an important role in distress situations.

RF signals are transmitted from a network of shore-based (marine) radiobeacons with known positions. The relative direction of incoming RF signals is determined using a shipborne antenna and receiver assembly. On the vessel, the direction to the beacon transmitting the RF signals is referred to another known direction using, e.g., a gyrocompass or a magnetic compass.

Reception from one radiobeacon allows the mariner to determine a single line of position. The use of a second radiobeacon allows the determination of a second line of position. The intersection of the two lines of position provides the horizontal position of the vessel. The position solution is ambiguous since, for each beacon, there are two possible relative bearings 180° apart from each other; in most cases, the ambiguity is trivial because one of the two possible lines of position runs over land. RDF is also used as navigational aid by aircraft (aeronautical radiobeacons).

Hundreds of radiobeacons are available worldwide for direction finding. The majority of marine radiobeacons are specially set up and maintained for maritime service by national administrations, e.g., the Canadian Coast Guard in Canada. Some of the radiobeacons are aircraft beacons conveniently located near the coast. The aircraft beacons, and some of the maritime beacons, transmit cyclically in a group. The transmission frequencies of beacon groups are chosen such that adjacent groups have different frequencies. Groups with the same frequency are separated by sufficiently large distances to avoid interference. In Canada, radiobeacons operate in the following frequency ranges:

- 283.5-315 kHz: marine radiobeacons.
- 315-335 kHz: marine and aeronautical radiobeacons.
- 335-405 kHz: aeronautical radiobeacons.

Single loop antenna

The AC current generated at the radiobeacon creates lines of magnetic force. When a varying magnetic field passes through the windings of a coil, a voltage (electromotive force) is induced in the windings. The ship antenna, in order to be capable of direction finding, must exhibit directional characteristics. The simple loop-type antenna is commonly used for low frequency marine direction finding. The loop aerial can rotate on its vertical axis. Wire windings are installed in the circular tube to make the aerial a large coil as shown in Figure 9.35.

As the aerial rotates, the number of magnetic lines passing through it varies and a voltage is induced. This voltage is measured by the receiver. The maximum voltage occurs when the aerial is aligned with the direction of the transmitting radiobeacon (position DE in Figure 9.36).

In any position of the receiving antenna, $\cos\alpha$ is proportional to the voltage

$$\cos\alpha = \frac{FG}{DE} = \frac{FO}{DO} = \frac{FO}{BO} \qquad (9.30)$$

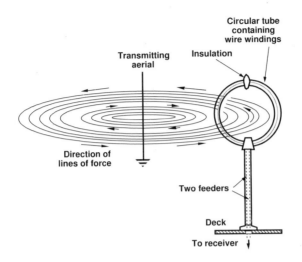

Figure 9.35: Principle of single loop rotating antenna used for RDF.

where α is the angle between the loop aerial (direction of the antenna) and the direction of the transmitting radiobeacon aerial. When the ship aerial is turned 180°, the magnitude of the voltage remains the same but $\cos\alpha$ changes sign ($\cos\alpha$ is negative between 90° and 270°) and the phase of the alternating voltage differs by 180°. In the above system, the rotating aerial is usually installed over the chart room to transmit directly the line of position onto the chart.

Bellini-Tosi (B-T) system

The simple rotating loop direction finding (DF) receiver requires a mechanical coupling between the loop antenna and the bearing pointer, which restricts the location of the loop. This problem is eliminated when using the Bellini-Tosi system, in which the antenna is based on two fixed loops mounted at right angles to each other, as shown in Figure 9.37. In the case of a marine installation, the antenna is positioned such that one loop lies along the vessel's centre line (alongship), and the other one athwartship. A received signal on a relative bearing θ will produce a loop terminal voltage $E\cos\theta$ in the fore-aft loop, and $E\sin\theta$ in the port-starboard loop, where E is the electrical field strength.

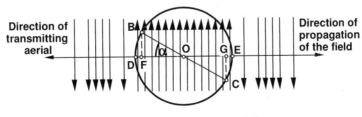

Top view of a loop aerial

Figure 9.36: Magnetic lines in rotating RDF antenna.

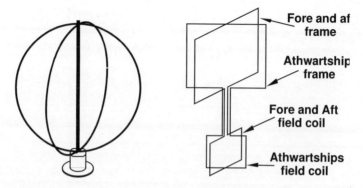

Figure 9.37: Two-fixed loop Bellini-Tosi RDF antenna.

Assume that there is a transmitting station on the starboard side at a bearing 45° to the vessel's head, see Figure 9.38. The alternating voltages set up in the two identical frames are then equal in magnitude and phase. An alternating current in a coil produces an alternating magnetic field proportional to the current. The vector representing such a magnetic field has direction and magnitude. Within the field coils, two such fields are therefore produced perpendicular to each other and, in the case under consideration, these fields are equal in strength. These fields combine into one resultant field, which is aligned along the transmitter's lines of force, independent of the direction of the transmitter.

The direction of the resultant field is measured by using a rotating search coil installed under the aerial assembly. The search coil will measure the field strength produced by the two loops as a result of an incoming field, as shown in Figure 9.39. The search coil can be turned to a position where the lines of force of the resultant field are perpendicular to the plane of the coil. This corresponds to a maximum

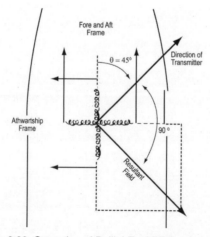

Figure 9.38: Operation of Bellini-Tosi RDF antenna.

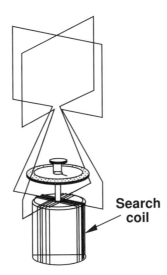

Search coil

Figure 9.39: Rotating search coil with Bellini-Tosi RDF antenna.

alternating voltage being measured. If the search coil is rotated by 90°, no lines of force will pass through it and no voltage will be induced. A Bellini-Tosi aerial with a rotating search coil is called a radiogoniometer.

The overall accuracy of an RDF system under good conditions is at the level of a few degrees. There are, however, several sources of error for RDF:

1) *Night effect*. Normally the RDF bearings are estimated from signals that have propagated as stable, vertically polarized groundwaves. At night, and for longer distances from the transmitter, skywaves (that are instable due to ionospheric D-layer variations) dominate. This results in signal fading and causes bearing errors that are particularly large during sunrise and sunset. At the 90% confidence level, the error of bearings taken at night at long distances does not exceed 10°.

2) *Coast effect*. When a radio wave crosses a coastline, its velocity of propagation changes and refraction occurs. This results in the bending of incoming waves. In the worst cases, when the bearing line is nearly parallel to the coastline, the maximum errors in measured bearings can reach 4° to 5°.

3) *Vessel effects*. A site for installation of a shipborne DF system must be carefully chosen, but the conditions are never ideal. There are numerous conductors in the vessel's structure which create electromagnetic interference. Related error sources can be removed while others can be mitigated within the DF receiver.

9.5.5 *Marine radar*

Radar was initially developed during World War II for military applications, and was first used for civilian navigation in the late 1940's. The acronym RADAR stands for RAdio Detection And Ranging. It is an electro-mechanical navigation aid that measures the range ρ, and direction θ to objects, and frequently indicates the nature of these objects. Marine civilian radar operates in the SHF range (3-30 GHz). It

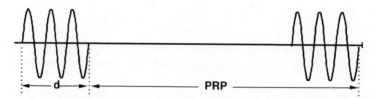

Figure 9.40: Radar pulse waves and pulse repetition period (PRP).

utilizes unmodulated RF pulsed waves which may be horizontally, vertically, or circularly polarized. The radiated pulses have a very short time duration d, typically between 0.05 and 1.0 μs.

The period between two consecutive pulses (the resting period of the transmitter) is usually thousands of times longer than the pulse duration. The number of pulses per second is called the *pulse repetition frequency*. The time between identical phases of two consecutive pulses is called the *pulse repetition period* (PRP), as shown in Figure 9.40.

Example 9.2: Pulse duration.

A pulse duration of $d = 0.5$ μs corresponds to 150 m in distance. If PRP = 1000 μs, then the resting period is computed as

PRP - d = 999.5 μs

The range R between the transmitting antenna and the target is

$$R = \frac{c\Delta t}{2} \ [m] \tag{9.31}$$

where c is the velocity of RF propagation and Δt the travel time of the radar pulse from the transmitter to the target and back. The principle of radar measurement is illustrated in Figure 9.41.

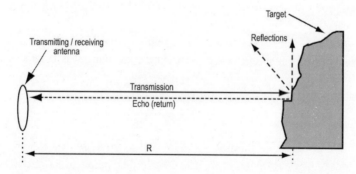

Figure 9.41: Principle of radar – range measurement.

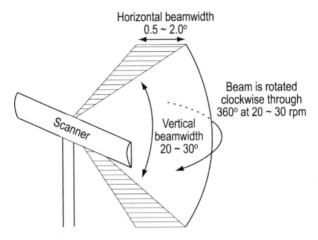

Figure 9.42: Principle of radar – direction measurement.

The time interval Δt between the transmission of the pulse and its subsequent detection is measured electronically. In addition to measuring the range to a target, a direction to the target (in relation to a fixed reference point) can be measured. Directional information relating to the target is obtained by radiating the pulses from a highly directional antenna which rotates in the horizontal plane at a rate of up to a few tens of rotations per minute (rpm), as shown in Figure 9.42.

The antenna beam characteristics are given as follows:

- A very narrow beam (0.5°-2.0°) in the horizontal plane.
- A very wide beam (20°-30°) in the vertical plane (to allow for variations in ship's attitude).

Both the *horizontal beamwidth* (HBW) and the *vertical beamwidth* (VBW) are angles subtended by the half-power points of the antenna polar diagram, i.e., -3 dB points. The narrow beamwidth in the horizontal plane is used to measure directions, while the wide beam in the vertical plane accounts for the vessel's attitude variations. The pulses of energy are directed over a very narrow arc. Only targets which lie within this arc will return energy to the antenna as an echo of the transmitted pulse. As long as the direction of the antenna is known, the relative bearing of the target can be determined. The received echoes are transferred to a cathode ray tube (CRT) for display. The scan origin (the site of the radar antenna) is shown at the center of the display.

The continuous rotation of the radar at a constant speed allows measurement of ranges and bearings to all targets lying within 360° of azimuth. The scanner should rotate sufficiently rapidly to update the display at the rate required. The previous image should not fade completely before the new image appears. On the other hand, the rotation should be sufficiently slow such that all targets remain in the horizontal beam long enough to return several successive echo returns.

To construct an antenna with such directional properties and, simultaneously, to keep its dimensions within practical limitations, the transmission frequency of the radar must be very high. Civil marine radar operating frequencies are

- S band: from 2 GHz to 4 GHz (wavelength $\lambda = 0.075$ to 0.15 m), and
- X band: from 8 GHz to 12.5 GHz ($\lambda = 0.024$ to 0.0375 m)

Using the S band and a scanner length of 3.9 m, an HBW of 1.7° is obtained. Using the X band and a scanner length of 1.8 m, an HBW of 1.3° is obtained. As the scanner length is increased, the HBW is decreased.

Antenna gain G_a

For an *isotropic* antenna (omni-directional in the horizontal plane in the example shown in Figure 9.43), the power transmitted is P_t. At range R, the power density is the same in all directions, namely W_1 (in Watts/m²).

For a *directional* antenna, see Figure 9.44, with the same transmitted power, P_t, the power density at range R (point Q) is denoted by W_2.

The antenna power gain G_a is defined as

$$\text{Antenna gain} = \frac{\text{Energy striking target using directional antenna}}{\text{Energy striking target using omnidirectional antenna}} \qquad (9.32)$$

which can be expressed as

$$G_a = \frac{W_2}{W_1} \qquad (9.33)$$

or, in dB, as

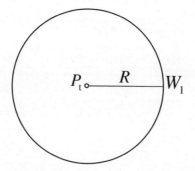

Figure 9.43: Power pattern of an isotropic antenna.

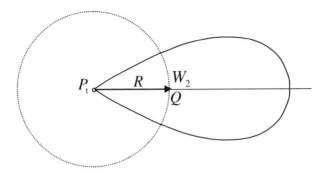

Figure 9.44: Power gain pattern of directional antenna.

$$G_a = 10\log\frac{W_2}{W_1} \qquad\qquad (9.34)$$

The amount of echo energy measured by the antenna depends on the receiving antenna aperture (or effective area) A_e. The aperture of an antenna is a function of the dimensions of the antenna area perpendicular to the direction of radiation (or reception), and the wavelength (or frequency of transmission).

For a given wavelength λ, increasing the effective area A_e increases the power gain G_a and decreases the horizontal beamwidth. The relationship between G_a, A_e, and λ is

$$G_a = \frac{4\pi A_e}{\lambda^2} \qquad\qquad (9.35)$$

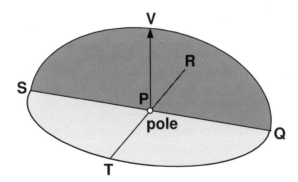

Figure 9.45: Antenna horizontal and vertical planes.

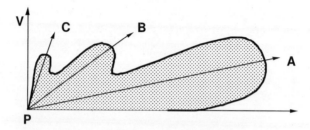

Figure 9.46: Example of a vertical polar diagram.

Radiation patterns

In the case of a directional antenna, the radiation pattern of the antenna varies as a function of azimuth and vertical angle. Assume that (S, R, Q, T) is a horizontal plane through the pole P, and (S, V, Q) is a vertical plane, as illustrated in Figure 9.45.

As an example, the polar diagram of radiation in the vertical plane (S, V, Q) is shown in Figure 9.46; the radiation pattern reveals lobing effects due to surface reflection. The polar diagram of radiation in the horizontal plane (S, R, Q, T), for the same antenna, is shown in Figure 9.47, where A is the major lobe axis, and B and C are minor lobes.

Radar equation

If the target is located at a range of R metres, the total energy will be equally distributed over the surface of a sphere of radius R for an isotropic antenna. Since the surface area of a sphere is $4\pi R^2$, the energy density on the surface (power density at range R) is

$$\text{Power density } (R) = \frac{P_0}{4\pi R^2} \text{ [W/m}^2\text{]} \tag{9.36}$$

where P_0 is the transmitted energy. If the area of the target facing the antenna

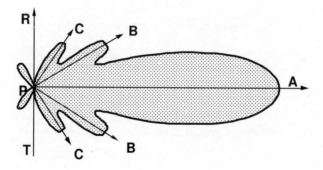

Figure 9.47: Example of a horizontal polar diagram.

(effective echo area) is A_t (in m^2), then the total energy striking the target (power at the target) is

$$\text{Power } (R, A_t) = \frac{P_0 A_t}{4\pi R^2} \text{ [W]} \tag{9.37}$$

With the gain G_a of the radar antenna, the energy striking the target becomes

$$\text{Power } (R, A_t, G_a) = \frac{P_0 A_t G_a}{4\pi R^2} \text{ [W]} \tag{9.38}$$

Assume that the target re-radiates all the incident energy omni-directionally. Then a second sphere is established (centred on the target) which will have radius R at the transmitter location. The power density on the surface of the second sphere at the transmitter - which is the echo power density reaching the antenna - will be

$$\text{Echo power density } (R, A_t, G_a) = \frac{P_0 A_t G_a}{4\pi R^2 \, 4\pi R^2} \text{ [W/m}^2\text{]} \tag{9.39}$$

The amount of echo energy received by the antenna depends on the receiving antenna aperture (effective area) A_e. The received echo power P_r is therefore

$$P_r = \frac{P_0 A_t G_a A_e}{4\pi R^2 \, 4\pi R^2} \text{ [W]} \tag{9.40}$$

The strength of an echo is directly proportional to all factors except for the range. The strength of an echo P_r decreases rapidly as the range R increases. If the range is doubled, the strength of an echo is decreased by a factor of one sixteenth ($1/2^4$). From a minimum returning echo with strength $P_{r_{min}}$, the maximum detectable range can be calculated from

$$P_{r_{min}} = \frac{P_0 A_t G_a A_e}{(4\pi)^2 R_{max}^4} \text{ [W]} \tag{9.41}$$

as

$$R_{max} = \left[\frac{P_0 A_t G_a A_e}{(4\pi)^2 P_{r_{min}}} \right]^{1/4} \text{ [m]} \tag{9.42}$$

The above equation is a simplified form of the *radar equation* for free-space conditions (maximum range equation), in which the following factors are neglected:

• the curvature of the Earth

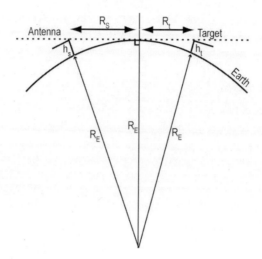

Figure 9.48: Radio horizon SHF radar range.

- the reflection coefficient (at the target)
- the atmospheric conditions

The radar equation should also depend on proximity to the Earth's surface.

SHF radar range between antenna and target

The maximum range from which the echoes can be returned determines the limit of the highest pulse repetition frequency that can be used. The pulse repetition frequency must be low enough to allow all echoes to have been returned to the antenna before the next pulse is transmitted. The maximum range is determined by taking into consideration

- the curvature of the Earth with radius R_E
- the height of the scanner h_s
- the height of the target h_t

From the geometry in Figure 9.48, it can be written

$$R_s^2 = (R_E + h_s)^2 - R_E^2 = 2R_E h_s + h_s^2 \qquad (9.43)$$

where the second term on the right-hand side of the above equation is negligibly small since $h_s \ll R_E$. The range R_s can be approximated by

$$R_s = \sqrt{2R_E h_s} \qquad (9.44)$$

Similarly,

$$R_t = \sqrt{2R_E h_t} \qquad (9.45)$$

and the range is thus

$$R_s + R_t = \sqrt{2R_E}(\sqrt{h_s} + \sqrt{h_t})$$ (9.46)

Due to diffraction at the Earth's surface and refraction in the atmosphere ($n>1$), the line-of-sight path is extended by the Earth radius factor of 4/3 and the radio horizon antenna-target range becomes

$$\frac{4}{3}\sqrt{2R_E}(\sqrt{h_s} + \sqrt{h_t})$$ (9.47)

9.6 Major references

Appleyard, S.F., R.S. Linford: *Marine Electronic Navigation*. 2nd edition, Routledge, 1988.

Bowditch, N.: *American practical navigator*. NIMA, 1995, available from http://pollux.nss.nima.mil/pubs or http://www.irbs.com/bowditch.

FAA: *FAA-E-2892B, Change 1: Wide Area Augmentation System (WAAS) Specification*. Federal Aviation Administration, Washington D.C., 1999.

Fisheries and Oceans Canada: *Radio Aids to Marine Navigation (Atlantic, St. Lawrence, Great Lakes, Lake Winnipeg and Eastern Arctic)*. Canadian Coast Guard, Marine Communications and Traffic Services, DFO 5470, Ottawa, Canada, 2001a.

Fisheries and Oceans Canada: *Radio Aids to Marine Navigation (Pacific and Western Arctic)*. Canadian Coast Guard, Marine Communications and Traffic Services, DFO 5471, Ottawa, Canada, 2001b.

Krakiwsky, E.J., G. Lachapelle, K.P. Schwarz: *Assessment of Emerging Technologies for Future Navigation Systems in the Canadian Transportation Sector, Publication 60007*. Department of Geomatics Engineering, University of Calgary, 1990.

Lachapelle, G., C. Liu, G. Lu, Q. Weigan, R. Hare: *Water-borne Leveling with GPS*. Marine Geodesy, Vol. 17, No. 4, pp. 271-278, 1994.

Lownsborough, R., D. Calcutt: *Electronic Aids to Navigation: Radar and ARPA*. Edward Arnold, 1993.

Mio, K., V. Rigaud: *Underwater vehicle positioning with correlation sonar*. Sea Technology, March 1999, pp. 25-29.

Morley, T., G. Lachapelle: *GPS Augmentation with Pseudolites for Navigation in Constricted Waterways*. Navigation: Journal of the Institute of Navigation, Vol. 44, No. 3, pp. 359-372, 1997.

Morley, T., G. Lachapelle: *Pseudolite Augmentation for OTF Ambiguity Resolution in Shipborne Mode*. Journal of Surveying Engineering, American Society of Civil Engineers, Vol. 124, No. 1, pp. 26-39, 1998.

NAPA: *The Global Positioning System – Charting the Future*. National Academy of Public Administration, Washington, D.C., 1995.

Offermans, G.W.A., A.W.S. Helwig, D. van Willigen: *The Eurofix datalink concept: reliable data transmission using Loran-C*. Proceedings of the 25th Annual Technical Meeting of the International Loran Association, San Diego, CA, USA, 1996.

Offermans, G.W.A., A.W.S. Helwig, D. van Willigen: *Eurofix DGPS service through the Sylt Loran-C transmitter*. Proceedings 26th Annual Technical Meeting of the International Loran Association, Ottawa, Canada, 1997.

Ryan, S., M. Petovello, G. Lachapelle: *Augmentation of GPS for Ship Navigation in Constricted Waterways*. Proceedings of National Technical Meeting, The Institute of Navigation, pp. 459-467, 1998.

Shaw, M., K. Sandhoo, D. Turner: *Modernization of the Global Positioning System*. GPS World, September, pp. 36-44, 2000.

Sonnenberg, G.J.: *Radar and Electronic Navigation*. 6th edition, Butterworths, London, 1988.

Tetley, L., D. Calcutt: *Electronic Aids to Navigation*. Edward Arnold Publishers, London, 1986.

10 Underwater acoustic positioning

10.1 Introduction

Radio waves do not penetrate waters to any significant depth and cannot be used underwater for positioning. The use of underwater acoustic waves constitutes one alternative. Underwater positioning includes the positioning of a surface platform from the seabed and the positioning of underwater vehicles required for detailed soundings, inspection of pipelines and structures, etc. The first category consists largely in the dynamic positioning (DP) of floating platforms used for ocean exploration and exploitation such as drilling rigs. Nowadays, these platforms operate in waters with depth in excess of 2500 m for months to years at the time. Several independent positioning systems are used simultaneously for this purpose, including DGPS and underwater acoustics, in order to achieve a high level of redundancy and reliability.

Numerous underwater position fixing techniques with various degrees of accuracy, have been developed for the offshore industry. They can be classified into two categories, dead reckoning positioning systems and acoustic positioning systems. Examples of the first category are:

- Distance line
- Trailing wheel
- Current meter/gyrocompass
- Doppler log/gyrocompass
- Inertial Navigation System (INS)

Acoustic positioning systems comprise:

- Short baseline (SBL) systems
- Super-short baseline (SSBL), also known as ultra-short baseline (USBL) systems
- Long baseline (LBL) systems
- Combinations of the above

- Integration of one or several of the above with other measurement devices (e.g., gyrocompasses, attitude motion sensors) or systems (e.g., DGPS for acoustic system calibration).

In practice, systems used are integrated systems of the latter category.

Underwater acoustic navigation and position fixing systems use various types of underwater markers: transmitters, receivers or both. They are of the following types:

Transducer - a transmitter/receiver, frequently mounted on a ship's hull or on an underwater platform. It sends out an interrogation signal on one frequency to get a reply on a second frequency.

Transponder - most versatile type of underwater marker, mounted on the sea bottom or on a submersible. It is a receiver/transmitter working in conjunction with a transducer. On receipt of an interrogation signal (command) on one frequency, the transponder sends out a reply signal on a second frequency, and then it becomes passive until the next interrogation (to save power).

Beacon/pinger - most simple active underwater marker, mounted on the sea bottom or on a submersible. It is a transmitter that sends a pulse on a particular frequency on a regular basis; no interrogation is required.

Hydrophone - an omni-directional or directional receiver installed on a hull, which receives signals from a transponder or a beacon/pinger.

Responder - a transmitter attached to submersible or seabed which can be activated by a hard wired external control signal to transmit an interrogation signal for receipt by a transducer or hydrophone.

In all of the above cases, the antenna gain patterns (polar diagram) are either omni-directional or hemispherical. The sound energy being propagated underwater is attenuated by various ambient and self-noise. The majority of ambient or self-noise (background sea noise) in the ocean which affects an acoustic telemetry system, is below the level of 5 kHz. Therefore, to avoid spurious signals and commands, the lowest frequency used for underwater acoustic positioning is 7-12 kHz. The final choice of frequency for an acoustic system is a function of application (range), accuracy, size and cost. It is a result of compromises between different frequency dependent characteristics. In general, the higher the frequency, the shorter the range (due to higher absorption coefficient), and the higher the accuracy. Frequency versus range is shown in Table 10.1. The accuracy of underwater acoustic systems depends on frequency, propagation loss, ambient and machinery noise, refraction, reflection, etc, see also Chapter 6.

Typically, accuracies of a few metres are achievable in deep water. With the use of underwater platforms, the accuracy can be improved to a few decimetres, because the salinity and temperature are more stable once a certain depth has been reached.

Table 10.1: Typical ranges of acoustic systems versus frequency.

Frequency [kHz]	Range [m]
10 - 20	10,000
300	400

10.2 Short baseline systems

A *short baseline* (SBL) acoustic system is an underwater positioning system which is used to position a transponder or pinger installed on the seabed or mounted on an underwater vehicle using a hull-mounted array of co-planar hydrophones spaced typically by 5-20 m. The vessel can either be static or moving. Due to the short distances between the hydrophones relative to the water depth, the positioning geometry is weak and the distance between the hydrophone array and the underwater transponder or pinger must be kept relatively short.

Alternatively, if the transponder or pinger is located at a known position on the seabed, the position of the vessel can be determined, provided additional sensors (e.g., heading sensors) are used on the vessel, since the ship's coordinate frame, defined by the array of hydrophones, should be aligned to the reference frame in which the transponder or pinger location is given.

Due to the above geometry consideration, the method is restricted to confined environments such as dynamic positioning of a stationary platform. A short baseline acoustic system is applied to

- Positioning of a ship within a small radius (from a seabed mounted beacon or transponder) equal to the water depth.
- Positioning/tracking of a submersible or towed fish.
- Dynamic Positioning (keep the ship at rest over a specific point), e.g., drilling.

The methods of operating a short baseline acoustic system are distinguished in terms of the instruments used, i.e., the underwater acoustic markers mounted on the seabed: beacons/pingers, or transponders/responders.

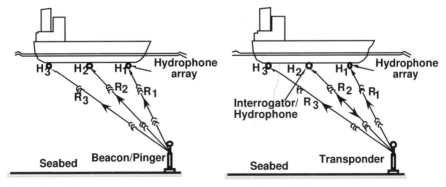

Figure 10.1: Short baseline concept, using a beacon/pinger (left) or a transponder/responder, mounted on the seabed.

In the first method using beacons/pingers, the range differences or bearings are derived from the measured time differences at the hydrophones. Depth of water below surface ship is required to obtain a position fix, see next subsection. In the second method using transponders/responders, the position fix is calculated from absolute ranges, which are derived from the measured absolute travel times. The concept of both methods is shown in Figure 10.1. The hydrophones mounted under the ship's hull must be co-planar. Relative distances and directions between the hydrophones are known.

Three cases of short baseline acoustic system configurations can be considered, namely

- Vessel fixed, and transponder mobile (if transponder is mounted on mobile underwater vehicle and ship is fixed, vehicle positions can be continuously determined).
- Vessel mobile, and transponder fixed (if transponder is fixed on seabed with known coordinates, the coordinates of vessel (surface ship or underwater vehicle) can be determined (with the presence of additional sensors).
- Vessel and transponder are both mobile, but the vessel's coordinates are known.

10.2.1 Beacon/pinger on seabed

Consider a simple case of three hydrophones mounted along two axes, x and y, perpendicular to each other, as shown in Figure 10.2. The x-axis is aligned towards the bow of the vessel, the y-axis to starboard. The z-axis is perpendicular to the plane

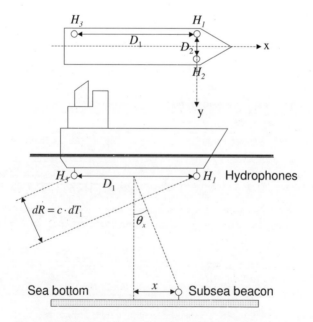

Figure 10.2: Hydrophone/subsea beacon geometry.

of the hydrophones and points downwards. The differences between the times of arrival of a beacon signal at the hydrophones dT_1 and dT_2 along both coordinate axes are measured. The distances D_1 (along the x-axis) between hydrophones H_1 and H_3, D_2 (along the y-axis) between hydrophones H_1 and H_2 and the water depth z are known.

Unknown parameters are the coordinates x, y of the subsea beacon in the coordinate system of the ship's hull hydrophone array, which has its origin coinciding with the geometrical centre of the array. Along the x-axis, the range difference is

$$dR = R_3 - R_1 = c \cdot dT_1 = c \cdot (T_3 - T_1) \tag{10.1}$$

where c is sound velocity. The angle of inclination of the hydrophone array above the beacon along the x-axis is θ_x, as shown in Figure 10.2. This angle can be obtained as

$$\theta_x = \sin^{-1}(\frac{c \cdot dT_1}{D_1}) \tag{10.2}$$

The unknown parameter x then follows from this angle of inclination and the known depth z as

$$x = z \cdot \tan \theta_x \tag{10.3}$$

Similarly, along the y-axis, the range difference is

$$dR = R_2 - R_1 = c \cdot dT_2 = c \cdot (T_2 - T_1) \tag{10.4}$$

The angle of inclination of the hydrophone array above the beacon along the y-axis is θ_y and we can write

$$\theta_y = \sin^{-1}(\frac{c \cdot dT_2}{D_2}) \tag{10.5}$$

and

$$y = z \cdot \tan \theta_y \tag{10.6}$$

10.2.2 Transponder on seabed

Absolute travel times from a transponder to each hydrophone are measured. The water depth need not be known (if known, it serves as a constraint). The coordinate axes of the hydrophone array are defined by the geometry of the hydrophones.

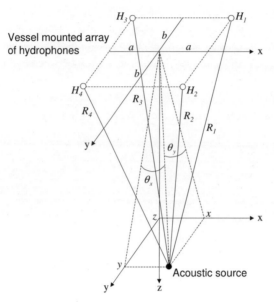

Figure 10.3: Hydrophone/transponder geometry.

Consider the case of a symmetrical array of four hydrophones (one redundant), mounted on the ship's hull, in a horizontal plane, forming a $2a$ by $2b$ rectangle, as shown in Figure 10.3. Measurements consists of the four ranges R_1, R_2, R_3 and R_4, which can be expressed in the unknown coordinates x, y and z and the known parameters a and b

$$
\begin{aligned}
R_1 &= \sqrt{(x-a)^2 + (y+b)^2 + z^2} \\
R_2 &= \sqrt{(x-a)^2 + (y-b)^2 + z^2} \\
R_3 &= \sqrt{(x+a)^2 + (y+b)^2 + z^2} \\
R_4 &= \sqrt{(x+a)^2 + (y-b)^2 + z^2}
\end{aligned}
\tag{10.7}
$$

These are non-linear functions of the unknown coordinates x, y and z. When solving for the unknown coordinates, the observation equations normally have to be linearised about some approximate position. A good approximate position may not be easy to find, due to the geometry of the problem. However, use can be made of the symmetry of the array to get a good initial position. This position is then used in a linearised least-squares system to solve for the final position and to assess the quality of the solution by means of an overall model test, and other associated quality control parameters, such as covariance matrix of the estimated coordinates, internal and external reliability, see Chapter 3. To compute the initial positions, the observation equations are written alternatively as

$$R_1^2 = (x-a)^2 + (y+b)^2 + z^2$$
$$R_2^2 = (x-a)^2 + (y-b)^2 + z^2$$
$$R_3^2 = (x+a)^2 + (y+b)^2 + z^2 \tag{10.8}$$
$$R_4^2 = (x+a)^2 + (y-b)^2 + z^2$$

The solution for x, y and z (with four hydrophones) is obtained from the following combinations of observation equations

$$R_3^2 - R_1^2 = 4ax$$
$$R_4^2 - R_2^2 = 4ax$$
$$R_1^2 - R_2^2 = 4by \tag{10.9}$$
$$R_3^2 - R_4^2 = 4by$$

The x and y coordinates of the transponder are given by

$$x = \frac{R_3^2 - R_1^2 + R_4^2 - R_2^2}{8a}$$
$$y = \frac{R_1^2 - R_2^2 + R_3^2 - R_4^2}{8b} \tag{10.10}$$

Once x and y are known, the z coordinate follows as

$$z = \frac{1}{4}(\sqrt{R_1^2 - (x-a)^2 - (y+b)^2} + \sqrt{R_2^2 - (x-a)^2 - (y-b)^2}$$
$$+ \sqrt{R_3^2 - (x+a)^2 - (y+b)^2} + \sqrt{R_4^2 - (x+a)^2 - (y+b)^2}) \tag{10.11}$$

Note that actually only three observations are required to obtain a solution for the unknown parameters. The above solution is used as initial position for the least squares solution based on the linearised measurement model for the observed ranges R_1, R_2, R_3 and R_4, including their appropriate weights in (the inverse of) the observation covariance matrix.

10.3 Supershort baseline systems

The concept of the *super short baseline* (SSBL), also known as ultra-short baseline (USBL), acoustic systems was developed to simplify underwater position fixing. The *phase difference* of an acoustic signal (carrier frequency f) received by two sensors separated by a distance b is precisely measured. The distance b is very short (less than 30 cm) and one hydrophone array mounted on the ship's hull consists of three such sensors mounted at right angle. Similar to an SBL, if the transponder or beacon is located at a known position on the seabed, additional sensors are required to

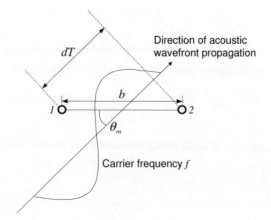

Figure 10.4: Phase delay and angle of incidence.

establish the vessel's position in the same coordinate system as the transponder or beacon.

The relation between the difference in phase of the acoustic signal and the mechanical angle of incidence is shown in Figure 10.4. An acoustic signal of carrier frequency f propagating underwater with the velocity c forms an incidence angle θ_m with the known baseline of length b connecting two sensors 1 and 2. The relationship between the observed electrical phase dT and the mechanical angle of incidence θ_m is given by

$$dT = k \cdot b \cdot \cos\theta_m \qquad (10.12)$$

where $k = 2\pi/\lambda$ with λ the wavelength of the acoustic signal. From (10.12) the mechanical angle of incidence θ_m can be computed. Due to the small size of the hydrophone array, it is assumed that the acoustic signals arriving at hydrophones 1 and 2 are parellel and that the positions of all hydrophones coincide.

The mechanical incidence angle as well as the depth or the slant range to the beacon or transponder are required to determine the apparent position of the beacon or transponder. Three sensors mounted on the hydrophone array allow for the measurement of two incidence angles in the hydrophone array's x- and y-direction, namely θ_{mx} and θ_{my}, as shown in Figure 10.5.

Several modes of SSBL operation exist. In the *beacon mode*, only the two incidence angles θ_{mx} and θ_{my} are observed and depth $z=h$ is assumed known. In that case, the slant distance R, see Figure 10.5, follows from

$$R^2 \sin^2\theta_m = R^2 \cos^2\theta_{mx} + R^2 \cos^2\theta_{my} \qquad \text{and} \qquad R^2 \sin^2\theta_m + h^2 = R^2$$

as

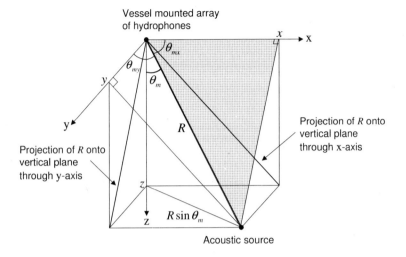

Figure 10.5: SSBL geometry.

$$R = \frac{h}{\sqrt{1 - \cos^2 \theta_{mx} - \cos^2 \theta_{my}}} \qquad (10.13)$$

Then the vessel coordinates x, y and z are given by

$$\begin{aligned}
x &= R \cos \theta_{mx} \\
y &= R \cos \theta_{my} \qquad\qquad\qquad (10.14)\\
z &= h = R \sqrt{1 - \cos^2 \theta_{mx} - \cos^2 \theta_{my}}
\end{aligned}$$

In the *transponder mode*, also the slant range R is observed and the vessel position follows directly from (10.14).

10.4 Long baseline systems

The *long baseline* (LBL) acoustic system consists of at least three seabed mounted transponders, at known locations on the seabed. The line joining two transponders is called a baseline. The baseline length varies with water depth, seabed topography, environmental conditions and the acoustic frequency being used and can range from several tens of metres to more than five kilometres. Aboard the ship or submersible, see Figure 10.6, the time of transponder interrogation is recorded, together with the time of reply. The seabed transponders each reply on a different frequency, in order to distinguish their signals from each other. The basic observation consists of the two-way travel time dT of the acoustic signal between vessel and transponder, from which the distance R can be obtained as $R = c \cdot dT / 2$. The corresponding non-linear observation equation reads

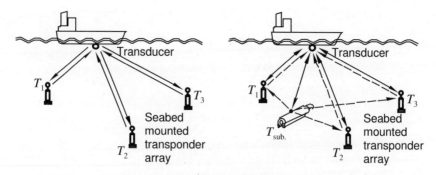

Figure 10.6: LBL positioning of a surface vessel (left) and a submersible.

$$R = \sqrt{(x-u)^2 + (y-v)^2 + (z-w)^2}$$ (10.15).

where u, v and w are the known transponder coordinates and x, y and z are the coordinates to be determined. If an approximate position (x_0, y_0, z_0) is available, this observation equation can be linearised. From observations to at least three transponders, the ship or submersible position can be estimated using a least squares iteration process, as described in Chapter 3. Contrary to SBL and SSBL systems, the estimated coordinates are not vessel oriented, but related to the seabed. This allows for multiple vessels to determine their position with respect to the same transponders without the need for additional sensors.

LBL systems have always been the preferred acoustic positioning systems when

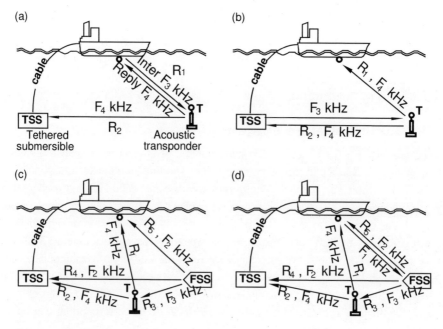

Figure 10.7: LBL system transmission modes.

accuracy was most important. Using a redundant number of transponders allows for quality control in terms of statistical testing, precision and reliability analysis, see again Chapter 3. However, calibration of an LBL system, i.e., the determination of the positions of the seabed transponders relative to each other, is a time consuming procedure, see Section 10.5.

Long baseline acoustic systems can operate in several modes, as shown in Figure 10.7:

- For ship navigation.
- For tethered unmanned submersible navigation.
- For untethered manned submersible navigation.

These different modes make it possible to synchronize the position determination for surface and subsurface vessels. In the *ship mode*, Figure 10.7-a, the transponder array is interrogated with ship mounted transducer using a single frequency F_3. Each transponder replies on its own frequency, collectively called F_4, to measure ranges. A tethered submersible (TSS) can also measure ranges from the transponders using the above F_4 transmission. Positions of both vessel and submersible with respect to the transponder arrays can be obtained from a single transmission.

In the *tethered submersible* (TSS) mode, Figure 10.5-b, the interrogation process is initiated using a transducer on the TSS, instead of the one on the vessel. The TSS interrogates the transponders at the F_3 frequency. Each transponder replies on its own frequency, again collectively called F_4. The ranges between both the TSS, the vessel and the transponder array can be computed in the same way as in the ship mode, and position of the vessel and position of the submersible can be determined.

The range from the Free Swimming Submersible (FSS) to the ship is measured following interrogation either by the FSS or the ship. The procedure for this *FSS mode* consists of two cycles. At the same epoch, the ranges from the FSS to the transducer array can be determined if the interrogation originates from the TSS. The ship can also interrogate the transducers to establish its own position. The additional deployment of a TSS is shown in Fig. 10.5-c.

In the *sync clock* mode, the ship's clock and FSS clock are precisely synchronized in both frequency and phase. The FSS transponder which acts as a master, transmits a signal to the vessel on F_2, followed, after a fixed delay of the order of 30 ms, by an interrogation of the transponders on F_3 which is replied on F_4. On the second cycle, the ship then interrogates directly the transponders on F_3, which are replied on F_4. The second cycle determines the ranges from the vessel to the transponders.

10.5 Calibration and error sources

10.5.1 Short and supershort baseline systems

The apparent position of the transponder refers to a motionless vessel with the hydrophone array in a horizontal plane. The coordinate system of the hydrophone

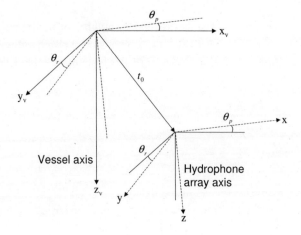

Figure 10.8: Transformation between array and vessel system.

array is generally offset from the coordinate system of the vessel by three translations. The vessel's motion due to pitch θ_p and roll θ_r also has to be taken into account. By choosing the vessel coordinate system aligned through the bow of the vessel, a correction for yaw is avoided. The transformation from the array system to the vessel system is then given by, see also Figure 10.8

$$x_v = R_1(\theta_r)R_2(\theta_p)(x+t_0) \qquad (10.16)$$

where x_v is the position vector in the vessel system, x the position vector in the hydrophone array system, t_0 a translation vector and $R_1(\theta_r)$ and $R_2(\theta_p)$ rotation matrices given by

$$R_1(\theta_r) = \begin{pmatrix} 1 & 0 & 0 \\ 0 & \cos\theta_r & \sin\theta_r \\ 0 & -\sin\theta_r & \cos\theta_r \end{pmatrix} \qquad R_2(\theta_p) = \begin{pmatrix} \cos\theta_p & 0 & -\sin\theta_p \\ 0 & 1 & 0 \\ \sin\theta_p & 0 & \cos\theta_p \end{pmatrix}$$

10.5.2 Long baseline systems

The array of transponders is initially established using a surface vessel or submersible. If a surface vessel is used, the geodetic location (in a known reference system) of the transponder is usually established using a shore-based or satellite-based radio frequency system, such as GPS. Significant errors can occur between the precisely established ship location at the time of launching the transponders and the final positions of the transponders on the seabed. The relative positions of the transponders (their spacing and depth) can be established by direct acoustic measurements on the transponders or between the transponders. Such a procedure leads to a calibration of the transponder array.

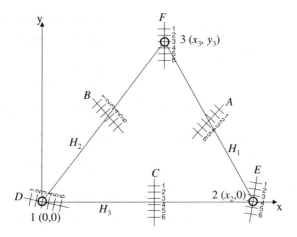

Figure 10.9: Calibration of LBL system from surface vessel measurements.

Mutually intervisible seabed transponders may conduct *inter-transponder* measurements together with measurements of temperature T, salinity S, and pressure p, following specific signals from the surface ship. The local sound velocity can be precisely estimated using the T, S and p measurements, see Chapter 6. This method is rapid and precise, but only certain transponders have the capability of inter-transponder measurements. Transponders are equipped with a weight and a float to keep them at a specified distance above the sea floor. Muddy seafloor must be avoided, otherwise the weight will drag the transponder in the mud and will prevent the acoustic signal from activating the release mechanism. Another rapid calibration procedure requires a combined LBL/SSBL system. Using the SSBL system, the positions of the transponders are determined. Once the positions are known with a sufficiently high accuracy, the LBL system takes over.

A more time-consuming procedure is sketched in Figure 10.9. Several (four to six) passes, e.g., D, E, F, with data collection runs are made by the surface vessel above the individual transponders to determine their depth z. The shortest distance is

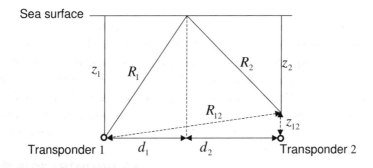

Figure 10.10: Calibration of LBL system. From the observed depths z_1 and z_2 and the observed ranges R_1 and R_2, the distances d_1 and d_2 are computed. Next, the slant distance between the transponders 1 and 2 is computed.

assumed to represent depth. Another set of passes, e.g., A, B, C, is made between each pair of transponders (baseline crossings of H_1, H_2, H_3) to determine the inter-transponder distances. The shortest distances are corrected for the depths and reduced to the direct inter-transponder distances, see Figure 10.10. They are further used to calculate the 3D coordinates of the transponders.

Once the distances between the transponders have been determined, either directly or indirectly, it is possible to compute their relative positions, see again Figure 10.9, and assume for convenience that the sea bottom is horizontal. Select transponder 1 as origin, i.e., $(x_0, y_0) = (0,0)$, then the position of transponder 2 $(x_2, y_2) = (H_3, 0)$. Using the cosine rule in triangle 1-2-3, the angle α between lines 1-2 and 1-3 follows from $H_1^2 = H_2^2 + H_3^2 - 2H_2 H_3 \cos\alpha$ and the position of transponder 3 as $(x_3, y_3) = (H_2 \cos\alpha, H_2 \sin\alpha)$.

It is also possible to determine the transponder positions diretly in a global coordinate system like WGS84 using GPS in combination with an LBL. Simultaneously estimating the ship's position using GPS and measuring the distance to a transponder of the LBL array at a number of different ship locations, results in a set of observations with corresponding covariance matrices

$$(x(t) \quad y(t) \quad z(t))_{GPS} \qquad\qquad Q(t)_{GPS}$$
$$R(t)_{LBL} \qquad\qquad\qquad \sigma^2(t)_{LBL}$$

Parameters to be solved for are both the vessel coordinates $x(t)$, $y(t)$, $z(t)$ and the transponder coordinates u, v, w. The linearised observation model for time t reads

$$E\left\{\begin{pmatrix}\Delta \underline{p}(t) \\ \Delta \underline{R}(t)\end{pmatrix}\right\} = \begin{pmatrix} I_3 & 0_{3\times3} \\ a^T(t) & -a^T(t) \end{pmatrix}\begin{pmatrix}\Delta x(t) \\ \Delta u\end{pmatrix} \qquad (10.17)$$

where

$$\Delta \underline{p}(t) = (\underline{x}(t) - x(t)_0 \quad \underline{y}(t) - y(t)_0 \quad \underline{z}(t) - z(t)_0)^T$$
$$\Delta \underline{R}(t) = \underline{R}(t) - R(t)_0$$
$$a(t) = (\frac{x(t)_0 - u_0}{R(t)_0} \quad \frac{y(t)_0 - v_0}{R(t)_0} \quad \frac{z(t)_0 - w_0}{R(t)_0})^T$$

and the subscript 0 indicates approximate value. For k epochs we get

$$
E\left\{
\begin{pmatrix}
\Delta \underline{p}(t_1) \\
\vdots \\
\Delta \underline{p}(t_k) \\
\Delta \underline{R}(t_1) \\
\vdots \\
\Delta \underline{R}(t_k)
\end{pmatrix}
\right\}
=
\begin{pmatrix}
I_3 & & & & 0_{3\times3} \\
& \ddots & & & \vdots \\
& & I_3 & & 0_{3\times3} \\
a^T(t_1) & & & & -a^T(t_1) \\
& \ddots & & & \vdots \\
& & a^T(t_k) & & -a^T(t_k)
\end{pmatrix}
\begin{pmatrix}
\Delta x(t_1) \\
\vdots \\
\Delta x(t_k) \\
\Delta u
\end{pmatrix}
\tag{10.18}
$$

Note that for the first iteration, the approximate vessel coordinates are taken as the observed values so that $\Delta \underline{p}(t_i) = 0$ for $i = 1,\dots,k$. Note also that the same calibration procedure can be applied to determine the position of SBL and SSBL beacons and transponders. Finally, if the precision of the GPS positions is much better than the precision of the LBL measurements, the former can be assumed known and only the elements of the correction vector Δu appear as parameters to be solved for in model (10.18).

10.6 Major references

Ingham, A.E.: *Hydrography for the surveyor and engineer*. 3rd Edition, BSP, Oxford, 1992.

Kelland, N.C.: *Developments in integrated underwater acoustic positioning*. The Hydrographic Journal, No. 71, 1994, pp. 19-27.

Kelland, N.C., A.J. Wakeling, C.D. Pearce: *Practical applications of an integrated acoustic positioning system*. The Hydrographic Journal, No. 88, 1998, pp. 9-17.

Milne, P.H.: *Underwater acoustic positioning systems*. E. & F.N. Spon, London, 1983.

Figure 1.11: Upwelling caused by cold water.

Figure 1.12: Upwelling caused by leeward winds.

Satellite Altimetry has been used successfully to estimate the sea slope of major ocean currents. This data can then be used to determine the direction and velocity of currents. In case of the Gulf Stream, the sea slope $7 \times 11.2 \pm 0.3 \times 10^{-6}$ rad. This results in a sea surface elevation of 180 cm ± 35 cm, based on SEASAT radar altimetry data collected during the late 1970's.

Upwelling is a vertical movement of cold water from deeper layers to replace warmer surface water. It affects fisheries, weather and current patterns in many areas of the ocean. Shown in Figure 1.11 is cold water that forces its way upward and pushes the warmer water away. On a local scale, leeward winds push the water away from the coast, as shown in Figure 1.12. On a large scale, predominant winds combined with Coriolis forces, push warm surface water away, and cold water rises to replace it, see Figure 1.13.

Measurements, using radioactive tracer techniques have shown that the ocean surface circulation brings its interior water into contact with the atmosphere every 600 years. In this thermohaline circulation, cold, dense water sinks near the poles and is replaced by warmer water flowing poleward from low latitudes. In northern

Figure 1.13: Upwelling caused by predominant winds and Coriolis forces.

11 Sounding methods

11.1 Echo sounder operation

In bathymetry, the object to be positioned is frequently the seabed. Usually, the horizontal position of a surface vessel is obtained first, and then the distance between the vessel and the seabed, i.e., the depth, is determined. In modern hydrographic surveying, depth is determined from *observation of travel time* of acoustic waves. An acoustic pulse transmitted by a transducer travels through the column of water and is then reflected by the target (sea floor) back to the hydrophone. Depth is calculated from the measured travel time ΔT

$$\text{Depth} = c \cdot \frac{\Delta T}{2} \tag{11.1}$$

where c is the speed of sound in water.

A basic echo sounder, used to measure the pulse's two-way travel time through the water column, consists of the following components, as shown in Figure 11.1:

- A *transmitter* which generates pulses.

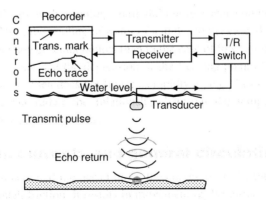

Figure 11.1: Basic echo sounder operation.

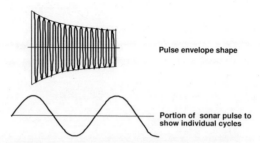

Figure 11.2: Acoustic pulse shape and envelope.

- A *T/R* (*transmitter/receiver*) *switch* which passes the power to the transducer.
- A *transducer*, mounted on the ship's hull, which converts the electrical power into acoustic power, sends the acoustic signal into the water, receives the echo, and converts it into an electrical signal.
- A *receiver* which amplifies the echo signal and sends it to the recording system.
- A *recorder* which controls the signal emission, measures the travel time of the acoustic signal, stores the data, and converts time intervals into ranges.

The *transmitter* is equipped with a quartz clock that oscillates in the range of 1-10 MHz, whose frequency is divided down to obtain the operating frequency of the transducer. The quartz clock is also used to measure time intervals between the transmission and the reception of acoustic signals. Modern echo sounders usually offer a choice of two to three transmitting frequencies, namely:

- *Low frequency* - effective for deep water because the attenuation is lower, but it requires a large transducer.
- *High frequency* - the transducer can be compact but the range is more limited due to a higher attenuation

The *T/R switch* is used to trigger a pulse with a specific length. Normally the pulse length varies from 0.1 to 50 ms. In shallow water, a single short pulse of length of 0.2 ms is transmitted and received before the next pulse is transmitted. In deep water, many pulses of lengths varying from 1 ms to 40 ms are generated and are in the water at any time. The variety of pulse length helps to overcome losses due to attenuation. The pulse shape and its envelope are shown in Figure 11.2.

The *receiver* amplifies the returning echo signal and sends it to the recording system. The receiver is equipped with a time varying gain (TVG), which is used to reduce the gain of the receiver immediately after transmission in order to filter out reverberation. Receiver gain returns as an exponential function of time. The receiver bandwidth must be wide enough to accommodate a Doppler shift if the transducer is not vertical (e.g., case of a speed log).

The *transducer* is mounted on the ship's hull and is in contact with water. Its functions are

- To convert electrical power into acoustic power.
- To send the acoustic signal into the water.
- To receive the echo of the acoustic signal.

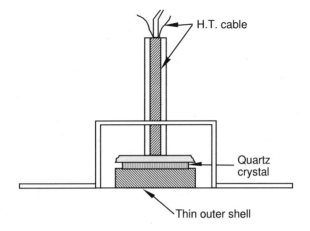

Figure 11.3: Piezoelectric transducer.

- To convert the acoustic signal into an electrical signal.

The electrical pulse from the transmitter causes the diaphragm of the transducer to vibrate. The vibrating diaphragm, in contact with water, generates an acoustic wave. The opposite process occurs when receiving signals, i.e., the vibrating diaphragm generates an electric current which is sent to the receiver. Transducers can be based on different principles. Three types of transducers are briefly presented.

A transducer of *magnetostrictive material* uses the property that the magnetostrictive material (e.g., nickel) changes its length in the presence of a magnetic field. A particular beam shape of the acoustic signal is obtained by configuring an array of elements according to specific patterns.

A *piezoelectric* transducer, see Figure 11.3, uses the property that certain crystals (e.g., ammonium dihydrogen phosphate) change length when a potential difference is applied to electrodes on the opposite faces of the crystal.

An *electrostrictive* transducer, shown in Figure 11.4, uses the property that ceramics change length when placed in an electric field. Ceramics can be molded in any desired shape. Elements are mounted between the face and the tail of a piston to obtain the desired beam width.

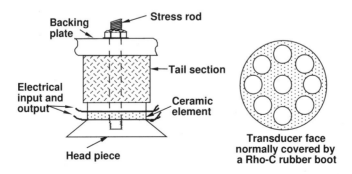

Figure 11.4: Electrostrictive transducer.

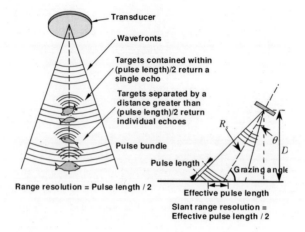

Figure 11.5: Resolution and incidence angle.

The resolution of an echosounder can define either its measuring precision or detection capabilities. It is a function of the following factors:

• Pulse duration.
• Angle of incidence of the acoustic wave front on the target.
• Nature of the target.
• Beamwidth of the transmission.

The minimum distinguishability of an echosounder corresponds to 1/2 pulse length. If two objects less than half a pulse length apart are sensed by an acoustic wave, they will reflect as a single target. Two objects further apart from each other than half a pulse length will be recorded as two separate echoes. The concept is shown in Figure 11.5. For example, consider a pulse with a frequency f of 15 kHz and a duration of 1 ms. Given that the sound velocity c in sea water is approximately 1500 m/s, the wavelength $\lambda = c / f$ is 0.1 m, and the pulse length is 1.5 m. The resolution corresponding to 1/2 pulse length is then 0.75 m.

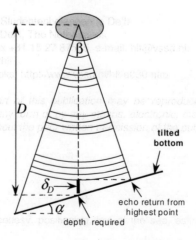

Figure 11.6: Effect of beamwidth due to tilted bottom.

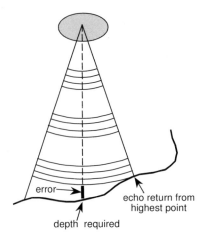

Figure 11.7: Effect of beamwidth due to irregular bottom.

A target will return more power to the transducer from those parts of it at right angle to the ray paths than from parts that will reflect the power away from the transducer.

If the echosounder may be tilted by angle θ due to ship roll, the effects of this tilt are:

a. The resolution of the slant range R_s decreases because the effective pulse length L_{pe} increases.

b. The effect of the tilt angle θ on depth D (flat bottom case) is $D = R_s \cos\theta$ and the depth bias is $R_s(1-\cos\theta)$ if θ is not accounted for. The bias can be removed if θ is known. The effect of an error δR_s in the slant range R_s on D is $\delta D = \delta R_s \cos\theta$.

On the other hand, if the bottom is tilted by an angle α, the effect on D is $\delta D = (D - \delta D)\tan\alpha \tan\beta/2$, see Figure 11.6, which is approximately equal to $D\tan\alpha \tan\beta/2$. For example, for $\alpha = 10°$, $\beta = 20°$ and $D = 100$ m, $\delta D \approx 3.1$ m.

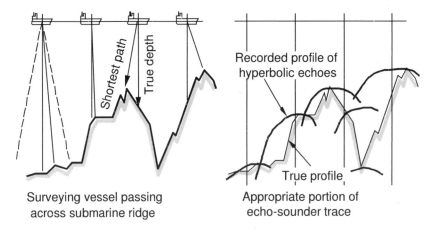

Surveying vessel passing
across submarine ridge

Appropriate portion of
echo-sounder trace

Figure 11.8: Echosounder beamwidth effect.

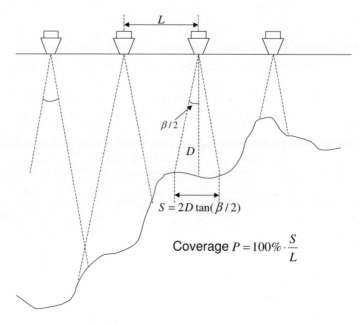

Figure 11.9: Seabed coverage versus beamwidth.

The echosounder has a specified beamwidth. It records the earliest return from its transmission, i.e., the echo having travelled the shortest distance. The effect depends on the actual beamwidth, the water depth and the tilt angle of the seabed, as shown in Figure 11.7. The recorded profile will be distorted and of an hyperbolic shape, as shown in Figure 11.8. The effect of the beamwidth also affects the seabed coverage, as illustrated in Figure 11.9.

11.2 Transducer beam pattern

It is effective to have the echo pulse directed to the target desired in order to increase power and establish the correct range to the target. The pattern of the beam for a transducer should ensure its directional response, i.e., a response as a function of the direction of the transmitted (or incident) sound wave in a specified plane at a specified frequency. Pattern control is important to
- Concentrate energy in a specified direction.
- Reduce noise and interference on receiving transducer.

A single point source radiates energy omni-directionally. In the case of transducers used for hydrography, energy is normally concentrated along the axis that is perpendicular to the radiating surface.

Transducers used in hydrography are designed to produce beams of acoustic power of various shapes. The shape of the beam is determined by the size and shape of the transducer, typically measured in wavelengths at the resonant/transmitting frequency.

The beam pattern of *circular* transducers is of the shape of a cone whose vertex angle varies between 2° and 30°. Most of the energy of the beam is concentrated in the

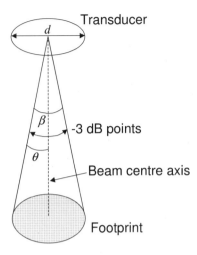

Figure 11.10: Transponder beamwidth for a circular transducer.

main lobe, whose limits are defined as -3 dB points. The angle θ between points at which the acoustic energy intensity has fallen to half (-3 dB point) of that along the main axis is called the *beam angle*, as shown in Figure 11.10. In other words, the intensity of the acoustic energy at the angular limit of the beam, P_2, is defined as half of the intensity P_1 at the centre of the beam

$$P_2 = \frac{1}{2}P_1 \Leftrightarrow 10\log\frac{P_2}{P_1} = 10\log 0.5 = -3 \text{ dB}$$

The *beamwidth* or *total beam angle* is 2θ or β. For a circular transducer, the beamwidth (in degrees) is roughly given as

$$\beta = 65\frac{\lambda}{d} \tag{11.2}$$

where λ is the wavelength corresponding to the frequency of the transmitted signal and d the diameter of the radiating surface of the circular transducer. Both λ and d must be expressed in the same units. An important characteristic of an echosounder is the frequency of the transmission. The higher the frequency the shorter is the wavelength, and the narrower the beamwidth for a given transducer size, as shown in Figure 11.11 for the case of a circular transducer.

A *rectangular* transducer will produce a different beamwidth in each of its two principal axes. Consider a rectangular transducer of dimension L_1 (shorter dimension) by L_2 (longer dimension). The beam footprint will be narrow in the direction parallel to the long direction of the transducer. By contrast, the footprint will be wide in the direction orthogonal to the long direction of the transducer (i.e., parallel to the short dimension of the transducer), as shown in Figure 11.12. The

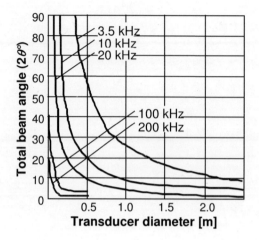

Figure 11.11: Beamwidth versus diameter for a circular transducer.

narrow beamwidth β_1 and the wide beamwidth β_2 of a rectangular transducer, both expressed in degrees, are given respectively by

$$\beta_1 = 2\theta_1 = 50\frac{\lambda}{L_1}$$

$$\beta_2 = 2\theta_2 = 50\frac{\lambda}{L_2}$$

(11.3)

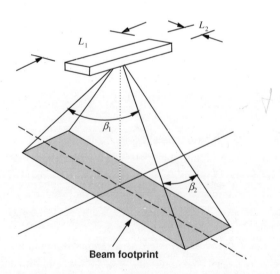

Figure 11.12: Beam shaping characteristics of a rectangular transducer.

11.3 Single beam echosounders

The beamwidth of conventional *single beam echosounders* (SBES) is usually of the order of 30°. However, narrow beam echo sounders with beamwidth of $\beta = 2\theta \le 5°$ have also been available since the mid 1980's. Operation of a narrow beam echosounder requires the transducer to be mechanically or electronically stabilized for roll and pitch motion of the vessel. Narrow beam echosounders are used to:

- Obtain depths directly under the vessel, thus avoiding wide beam biases caused by underwater slopes. This depth is used either for safety of navigation or for sea floor mapping.
- Improve the quality of the data in terms of both resolution and accuracy. For instance, in order to meet the IHO Special and Order 1 requirements, see Section 8.3, a narrow beam or array of narrow beam echosounders can be used.

To produce a narrow beam, larger size transducers are needed than for a wide beam. The equipment becomes bulky and expensive. Narrow beam echosounders do not provide information off the sides of the ship. Sometimes they are used in conjunction with broad beam systems as a complementary source of data.

Two examples of typical circular transducers of narrow beam echosounders:

1) Frequency of 12 KHz, wavelength $\lambda = 0.125$ m, beamwidth $\beta = 2\theta = 2°$. Diameter $d = 65\lambda / \beta = 4.06$ m (note that β is entered in degrees).
2) Frequency of 120 kHz, wavelength $\lambda = 0.0125$ m, beamwidth $\beta = 2\theta = 2°$. Diameter $d = 0.41$ m.

11.4 Multibeam echosounders

Multibeam echosounder (MBES) systems are used to increase bottom coverage and, consequently, productivity. Each of the narrow beams produced yields a resolution of the bottom equivalent to that of a narrow single beam echosounder. The measurement accuracy is not better than that of single beam echosounders, however. In fact, accuracy decreases as the swath angle increases. MBES are divided into two groups, namely *swath* systems and *sweep* systems

A swath system produces multiple acoustic beams from a single transducer system (although dual transducer systems are used and, sometimes, the transmitter and receiver are separate). A sweep system simply consists of an array of single beam echosounders mounted on booms deployed on each side and perpendicular to the surface vessel. Most of this section will deal with swath systems, with an introduction to sweep systems at the end. The operation principle of the latter is much more straightforward than that of the former.

The development of deep water swath systems began in the 1970's. These systems, which permit effective and accurate bathymetric surveys of extensive areas, can also be used for other oceanographic applications such as geological mapping and other scientific investigations, EEZ surveys and surveying for cable laying. Shallow water swath MBES have evolved rapidly during the 1990's and they are being increasingly used for shallow water surveys, such as harbour and constricted waterway surveys

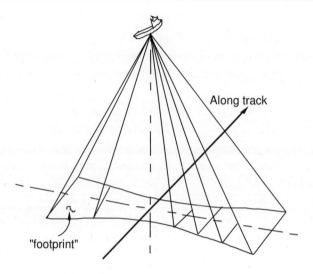

Figure 11.13: MBES footprints.

where 100% coverage and a high accuracy are required. Adoption of the more stringent 1998 IHO Standards for hydrographic surveys is further accelerating the use of MBES systems for shallow water applications.

Certain swath systems have such a wide swath width that they can also be used simultaneously as sidescan sonars (see next section for principles). Swath MBES can be used in a surface vessel where it is mounted under the hull or beside the vessel, or in an under water vehicle such as a remotely operated vehicle (ROV).

A swath MBES transmits an acoustic pulse in a wide fan in one direction (fore-and-aft or athwartships). This results in a wide footprint in that direction. The back scattered signal is received by a transducer which segments the above wide footprint into multiple smaller beams, as shown in Figure 11.13. The width of these beams is of the order of one to a few degrees, depending on the system. In this manner a high number of depth soundings are generated for each pulse transmission. A lane of soundings is obtained from a single vessel's track, rather than a single line of soundings. The advantages over the use of a single beam echosounder are obvious, the major one being that 100% coverage of the bottom can be achieved in a relatively cost effective manner. This is important for harbour and constricted waterway applications.

The advantage of a MBES, as compared to a sweep system (multi-single beam) approach, is that similar or wider coverage is achieved even in shallow waters using a much more compact system. In deeper waters, the coverage is much wider and can be several times the water depth, depending on the MBES system specifications.

For each receive beam, there is a ΔT two-way travel time of the slant range measurement and a swath angle ψ measurement as shown in Figure 11.14. In the absence of errors and vessel's motion, these measurements can be converted into depth (D) and across-track positions (y) of the sounding as

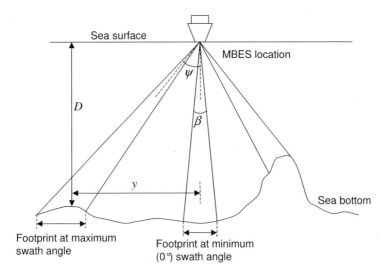

Figure 11.14: MBES footprint size versus swath angle ψ.

$$D = \frac{1}{2} c \Delta T \cos \psi$$

$$y = \frac{1}{2} c \Delta T \sin \psi$$

(11.4)

where c is the acoustic wave propagation in the medium. D and y can also be compensated for the effects of vessel pitching, yawing and rolling by using motion sensors of sufficient accuracy. Acoustic refraction can be compensated for by measuring the sound velocity profile in water, and by modelling the raypath of each beam in the model. The survey line spacing is selected such that neighbouring swaths are overlapping in order to avoid gaps. The ship's speed can also be selected such that there is 100% measurement overlap in order to enhance reliability.

An MBES can be mounted on a vessel permanently or temporarily. Deep water transducers are large (up to 5 m arrays) and mounting is more permanent. The ship's size has to be sufficiently large to support such transducers. Shallow water systems are much smaller (several dm) and can be mounted on survey launches. For portable use, a rig, which can be attached to the bow of a launch, can be used to mount the echosounder and motion sensor. Once the rig is calibrated, it can be moved from one vessel to another without the need for re-calibration.

The footprint of an MBES varies with swath angle. Let the beam width be β, as shown in Figure 11.14. For a vertical sounding, in which case the swath angle ψ is 0°, the footprint r, in the y-axis perpendicular to the ship is

$$r = 2D \tan(\beta / 2)$$

For a swath angle $\psi \neq 0$, the footprint is approximately equal to

$$r \approx D\{\tan(\psi + \beta/2) - \tan(\psi - \beta/2)\}$$

As an example, let us consider the case of a deep water swath MBES system with a beamwidth of $2°\times2°$. The footprint at depth D of 500 m is therefore approximately 17 m. The system has a maximum swath angle of 140° (70° each side of the vertical axis). The maximum footprint for a depth of 500 m is therefore about 136 m. The footprint size increases with increasing depth.

In addition, the measured depth error of a footprint with a large swath angle is also larger than that with a small swath angle due to the effect of roll motion and acoustic refraction errors. In order to limit the footprint size and measured depth errors, many systems automatically reduce the swath angle as the depth increases.

The vessel's roll, pitch and yaw attitude motion parameters and heave (vessel's vertical motion) are required in real-time by the swath MBES. The accuracy requirements are function of the system's performance. For high performance systems, the roll and pitch parameters are usually required with an accuracy of 0.05° or 3 arcmins, while the heave is required with an accuracy of 5-10 cm. A three or four-antenna GPS system can deliver the roll and pitch components with the accuracy required. Difficulties can however arise with the rigidity of the multi-antenna GPS system with respect to the MBES transducer located in the water under or beside the vessel. As a consequence, the preferred solution is to use a motion sensor that contains an inertial measuring unit (IMU) and that can be located near the transducer. A mid-range IMU integrated with a DGPS system (which is nearly always used for positioning) can meet both the attitude and heave requirements. Heave compensators, which are essentially one-axis inertial accelerometers, can also be used to measure heave.

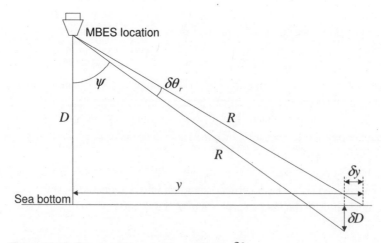

Figure 11.15: Geometry for a residual roll bias $\delta\theta_r$.

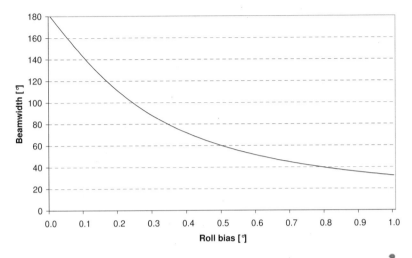

Figure 11.16: Beamwidth and residual roll bias, where the requirement is fulfilled that the resulting depth error is 0.5% of the depth or less.

The effect of a residual roll bias $\delta\theta_r$ is shown in Figure 11.15. While the swath angle is assumed to be ψ, in reality it is $\psi + \delta\theta_r$. Together with the observed slant distance $R = c \cdot dT / 2$, we may write

$$R = \frac{D + \delta D}{\cos\psi} = \frac{D}{\cos(\psi + \delta\theta_r)}$$

$$R = \frac{y - \delta y}{\sin\psi} = \frac{y}{\sin(\psi + \delta\theta_r)} \qquad (11.5)$$

where δD and δy are the depth error and the error in the error in the y-coordinate, respectively, due to the roll bias $\delta\theta_r$. For small $\delta\theta_r$ and neglecting second order terms, it follows from (11.5) that

$$\delta D \approx D\delta\theta_r \tan\psi$$

$$\delta y \approx -D\delta\theta_r \qquad (11.6)$$

Shown in Figure 11.16 is the maximum beamwidth as a function of residual roll bias, corresponding to the requirement that the depth error δD should be less than 0.5% of the depth D.

For a residual pitch bias $\delta\theta_p$ the situation is sketched in Figure 11.17. Its effect follows from

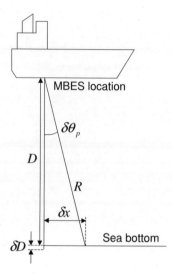

Figure 11.17: Geometry for a residual pitch bias $\delta\theta_p$.

$$R = \frac{D + \delta D}{\cos 0} = \frac{D}{\cos \delta\theta_p}$$

$$\frac{\delta x}{D} = \tan \delta\theta_p$$

(11.7)

where δx is the error in the direction perpendicular to the transmit beam. For small pitch biases, it follows from (11.7) that

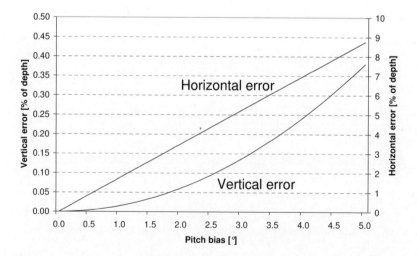

Figure 11.18: Horizontal and vertical positioning errors as a function of residual pitch bias $\delta\theta_p$.

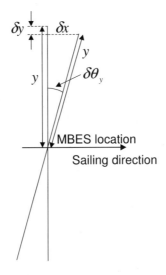

Figure 11.19: Geometry for a residual yaw bias $\delta\theta_y$.

$$\delta D \approx \tfrac{1}{2} D \delta\theta_p^2$$
$$\delta x \approx D \delta\theta_p \tag{11.8}$$

Shown in Figure 11.18 are the errors δD and δx as function of the residual pitch bias $\delta\theta_p$.
A residual yaw error $\delta\theta_y$, finally, results in an error in the x- and y-direction, as shown in Figure 11.19

$$\delta x \approx y \delta\theta_y$$
$$\delta y \approx \tfrac{1}{2} y \delta\theta_y^2 \tag{11.9}$$

These are the effects of residual angular ship motions. The total list of MBES errors and error sources is much longer. The most important are:

- System measurement errors, due to the system's electronics.
- Depth measurement error due to beamwidth (same as for single beam echosounders).
- Effect of beam angle error, due to the system's electronics; the effect of this error increases with the swath angle ψ. This error is therefore more significant than for single beam systems.
- Acoustic propagation errors: these errors increase with the swath angle due to the ray bending effect and are similar in concept to RF propagation in the atmosphere.
- Effect of attitude errors (roll, pitch and yaw); these errors increase with swath angle.

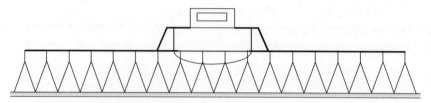

Figure 11.20: Vertical sweep system.

- Beam steering error due to surface sound speed error.
- Transducer misalignment error.
- Heave, dynamic draught and water level errors; same as for single beam echosounders.
- System calibration errors.
- Tides and/or other water level effects.

A vertical acoustic sweep system consists of a linear array of evenly spaced transducers mounted on booms attached perpendicularly to the vessel, as shown in Figure 11.20. These systems are used in critical shallow, calm water areas (harbours, channels, etc.) for 100% coverage. The coverage of the bottom is 100%, depending on transducer spacing and water depth. These systems are very accurate for IHO Special Order and Order 1 surveys where 100% coverage and high accuracy and resolution are required. The mobilization-demobilization logistics are complex due to the deployment of the booms and the use of these systems is usually limited to harbours and constricted waterways. In Canada, vertical acoustic sweep systems are used by the Canadian Coastguard (CCG) in the St. Lawrence navigation channel and the Canadian Hydrographic Service (CHS) for shallow waters in general.

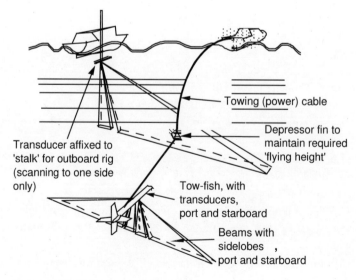

Towing (power) cable

Depressor fin to maintain required 'flying height'

Transducer affixed to 'stalk' for outboard rig (scanning to one side only)

Tow-fish, with transducers, port and starboard

Beams with sidelobes, port and starboard

Figure 11.21: Sidescan sonar concept.

11.5 Sidescan and oblique sonars

A sidescan sonar is basically a transducer mounted obliquely with respect to the major axes of the ship. The sidescan sonar is primarily used for interpretation between sounding lines obtained with single beam echosounders. It can also be used to detect thin obstacles hazardous to navigation even when a multibeam echosounder is used. It is widely used for harbour and navigation channels to ensure obstacle detection between the sounding lines.

A single-sidescan is performed using a hull-mounted transducer to one side of the vessel's track while a dual-sidescan is performed using two transducers mounted obliquely on each side of the ship or on a towed-fish, as shown in Figure 11.21.

Two fish-mounted transducers (one on each side) are typically installed 10° below the horizon for good horizontal coverage, and therefore for good obstruction detection. The beam is rectangular shaped and the beamwidth is of the order of 30° in the vertical plane perpendicular to the vessel's heading, and 1° to 2° in the horizontal plane, as shown in Figure 11.22. Sidescan sonars can therefore cover wide areas and are useful to detect rough topographic irregularities.

The extent of coverage of the seabed by the sidescan sonar beam depends on:
- The beamwidth in the vertical plane.
- The tilt of the beam axis with respect to the horizontal.
- The height of the transducer above the seabed.
- The power of the acoustic transmission, frequency and of the echo.

The "flying" height of the towed fish configuration is selected for optimum results. The measured depth accuracy is affected by the same error sources affecting vertically mounted single beam sonars. However, the effect of the vessel's attitude parameters (roll, pitch and heading) plays a critical role.

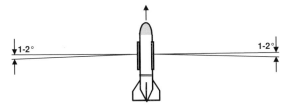

HORIZONTAL SYSTEM BEAMWIDTH (-3 dB POINTS)

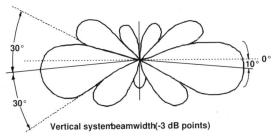

Vertical system beamwidth(-3 dB points)

Figure 11.22: Side scan sonar transducer and beam patterns.

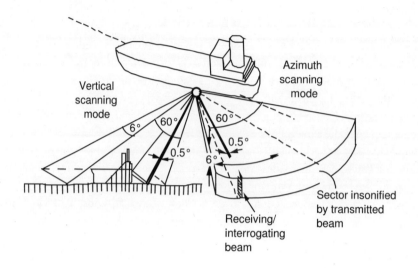

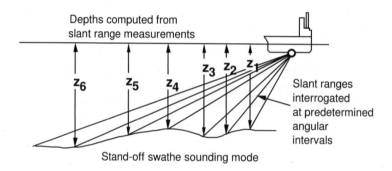

Figure 11.23: Oblique mounted sonar.

Towing a sidescan sonar is often impractical in confined areas such as ports. Another problem is multiple acoustic reflections from ships and other natural or man-made structures, due to their wide acoustic beams. For these reasons, swath MBES are replacing sidescan sonars in such constricted areas.

Oblique mounted sector scan sonars or sounders are used for seabed searches in "dangerous" shallow waters. The idea is that the vessel remains in safe water while mapping the seabed alongside. Both the vertical and azimuth scanning modes are being used in the system.

An example of an oblique system is shown in Figure 11.23. A transmitted beam of $60° \times 6°$ is interrogated at a rate of 10 kHz by a focused array beam of $0.5° \times 6°$. The interrogation beam is steered across the transmitted sector with no physical rotation of the array.

The basic observable of a sidescan sonar is the two-way travel time. No information is available on the direction of the reflected signal. As a result, a sidescan sonar may not produce reliable images of areas that are not flat, see Figure 11.24. As discussed

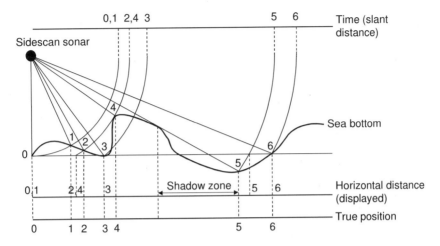

Figure 11.24: Sidescan sonar performance for a non-flat sea bottom. Due to the bottom relief, the image of the seafloor is distorted.

in the previous section, a multibeam system is based on the computation of slant ranges for a number of predefined directions. An *interferometric* sidescan sonar, on the other hand, determines the direction of a signal from an observed difference in travel time. Such a system consists of a limited number of transducers (or transducer arrays, in order to get a narrow beam for each array), mounted at short distances from each other. To explain the principle of operation of an interferometric system, we will consider the simplified set-up of Figure 11.25. Two transducers, at distance Δx from each other receive a signal with an unknown angle of incidence θ. The signal at transducer i can be written as

$$p_e(r_i, t) = \frac{\hat{p}_e}{r_i} \cos(\omega t - kr_i) \tag{11.10}$$

If the distance to the reflecting body is large enough to assume planar wavefronts, the

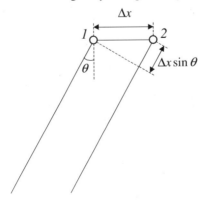

Figure 11.25: Range difference observed by interferometric sidescan sonar.

range differenc between transducer *1* and *2* is equal to (see again Figure 11.25)

$$r_2 - r_1 = \Delta x \sin \theta \qquad (11.11)$$

and the phase difference between them

$$\frac{2\pi}{\lambda}(r_2 - r_1) = \frac{2\pi}{\lambda} \Delta x \sin \theta \qquad (11.12)$$

from which the angle θ can be determined. The phase difference is unambiguous when $\Delta x < \lambda/2$. However, for such short distances between transducers, it is not possible to precisely measure the phase difference. Resolution can be increased by increasing the distance Δx. Using more than two transducers at different distances, the ambiguities can be resolved. The exact configuration is usually not disclosed by manufacturers of interferometric sidescan sonar equipment.

11.6 Echosounding measurement corrections

All depths must refer to a *common datum*. Numerous corrections must be applied to the results of soundings in order to get chartered depths which refer to the defined datum. *Chart depth* is obtained as the sum of

- Observed depth (raw uncorrected sounding).
- Instrumental corrections.
- Sound velocity correction (discrepancy between actual and constant velocity used by the sounder to derive depth).
- Dynamic draft correction, which is the sum of
  - Static draft (depth of transducer when the vessel is at rest).

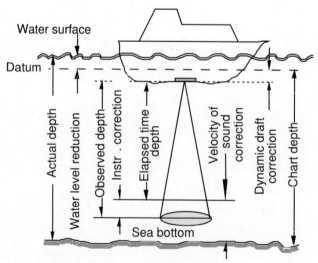

Figure 11.26: Depth measurement corrections.

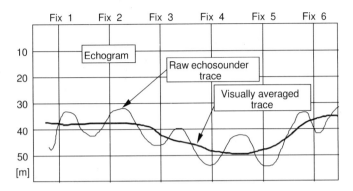

Figure 11.27: Heave compensation by averaging raw sounding data.

- Settlement (difference between rest and underway positions).
- Squat (change in trim when underway).
• Water level (tidal correction).

The corrections are visualized in Figure 11.26.

The heave correction compensates for the vertical displacement of the sounding vessel from the mean water surface. It becomes very significant in shallow waters. The heave correction reflects the periodic features of waves, i.e., it has a period of 1 to 20 s and the wave amplitude is less than 20 m. When the sea bottom is regular, the sounding record can be scaled, averaged and heave corrections can be calculated. Irregular bottom causes problems in calculating heave corrections. With rough sea and irregular bottom, the heave is impossible to correct. In such conditions the sounding operations must be stopped. There are numerous ways to compensate or correct for heave:

1. Heave compensation by averaging the raw sounding data, shown in Figure 11.27.
2. Shore-based electro-optical method to correct for heave (for near-shore surveys), see Figure 11.28.
3. Use of a heave compensator. This is a vertically mounted accelerometer on a stabilized platform.
4. Use of precise DGPS. Carrier phase data observed at a high sampling rate (1 Hz or more) is used to average the height variations caused by heave motion.

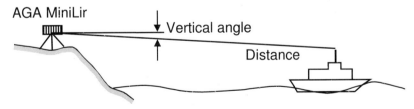

Figure 11.28: Heave compensation by shore-based electro-optical methods.

11.7 Airborne laser methods

In the mid 1960's the use of laser technology for measuring distances led to the experimental use of *airborne laser radar* (lidar) for determining topography. It was noticed that when the aircraft overflew a lake, the receiver showed a double return, which indicated that such a system could sense the surface and bottom and infer the water depth. A laser is the electromagnetic signal in the frequency band of the optical window of the electromagnetic (EM) spectrum.

Propagation of light in seawater, similarly to propagation of acoustic waves, depends on three basic state variables, namely temperature T, pressure p and salinity S. Seawater is somewhat transparent to EM radiation in the infrared and optical windows of the EM spectrum. *Transparency* is a function of the amount of material suspended in water. When no suspended material is present, attenuation is expressed as a function of absorption and scattering, with the absorption quantified by the *absorption coefficient k*. When suspended material is present then the absorption coefficient is replaced by the *extinction coefficient*. Due to absorption or extinction, the intensity of radiation I will decrease with the increasing path of the laser ray. The change dI in the intensity of radiation along the distance dz is proportional to intensity and thickness, and it is expressed by the following first order linear differential equation

$$dI = -kIdz \qquad\qquad (11.13)$$

where k is either the absorption or the extinction coefficient. The coefficient k is assumed constant and has the dimension of the inverse of length (m^{-1}). The solution of the above differential equation is

$$I_z = I_0 e^{-kz} \qquad\qquad (11.14)$$

where I_z is the intensity at distance z and I_0 is the intensity at the initial distance z_0. For example, if $k = 1$ m^{-1}, the radiation intensity would drop to $1/e$ (37% of its initial value) after a travel distance of 1 m through the medium.

A distance equal to $1/k$, at which the intensity is reduced by $1/e$, is called the *attenuation length*. The fractional intensity remaining after 1 m is called the *transmission factor t*, and is expressed as

$$t = \frac{I_1}{I_0} = e^{-k} \qquad\qquad (11.15)$$

The extinction coefficient k is characterized by the following properties:
- No significant variation with T, S, p.
- Nearly the same for filtered seawater and pure fresh water.
- It is a function of wavelength λ as shown in Figure 11.29.

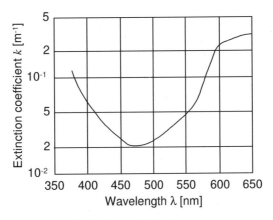

Figure 11.29: Extinction coefficient of pure water.

Dissolved material in water causes an increase of absorption. Suspended solid material increases scattering. Scattering also increases with decreasing wavelength λ.

The maximum transparency is

- In pure water, at the wavelength $\lambda = 475$ nm (nanometre) corresponding to $k = 0.02 \text{ m}^{-1}$, the mimimum value in Figure 11.29.
- In coastal water, at $\lambda = 550$ nm.

If $k = 0.02 \text{ m}^{-1}$, then the fractional intensity after 1 m $t = e^{-k} = 0.98$. In the "clearest" water which occurs in sub-tropical regions, the extinction coefficient is twice as good as that of pure water. Coastal water may sometimes be practically opaque due to muddy bottom and biological activities.

The refractive index n_i for light propagating through a medium is defined as

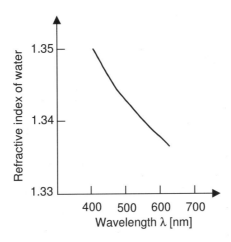

Figure 11.30: Refractive index of water as a function of wavelength for sodium light.

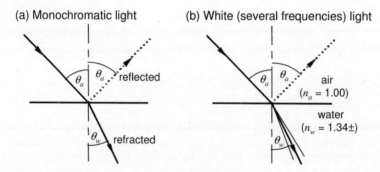

Figure 11.31: Snell's law at the air-water interface.

$$n_i = \frac{c_0}{c_i} \tag{11.16}$$

where c_0 is the speed of light in vacuo and c_i the speed of light in the medium. The refractive index n_w for the light propagating through water increases with S, T, p and decreases with increasing wavelength λ, as shown in Figure 11.30.

Snell's law states that the passage through a boundary between two media with refractive indices n_1 and n_2 is governed by the equation

$$n_1 \sin \theta_1 = n_2 \sin \theta_2 \tag{11.17}$$

where θ_1 is the angle of incidence and θ_2 is the angle of refraction. For the passage through a boundary between air and water, the refractive indices are n_a and n_w and Snell's law is expressed as

$$n_a \sin \theta_a = n_w \sin \theta_w \tag{11.18}$$

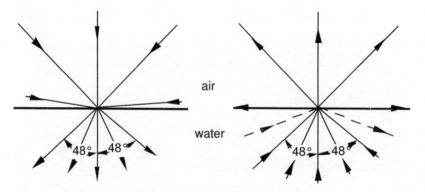

Figure 11.32: Critical angle of refraction for air-water interface.

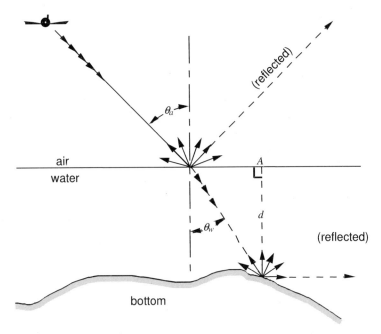

Figure 11.33: Airborne LIDAR bathymetry system concept.

as shown in Figure 11.31. The larger the angle of incidence, the larger the angle of refraction. With n_a/n_w being approximately $1/1.34$, the critical refraction angle will occur when $\theta_a = 90°$ and $\sin\theta_a = 1$. In that case $\theta_w = \sin^{-1}(1/1.34) = 48°$. Thus, the light entering water through a horizontal surface will be refracted within a cone with edges of $48°$, as shown in Figure 11.32.

Many countries have developed operational light detection and ranging (LIDAR) systems for airborne bathymetry in shallow waters. Using a laser airborne bathymetry system, the water depth in shallow waters (depth less than 50 m) is determined by measuring the arrival time difference between laser light pulses reflected from the surface and bottom. For mapping purposes, the horizontal position of the aircraft must be accurately determined throughout the operation. The use of GPS in

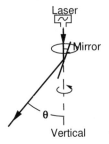

Deflection of light path for rotary sweep scanning

Figure 11.34: Canadian Larsen system concept.

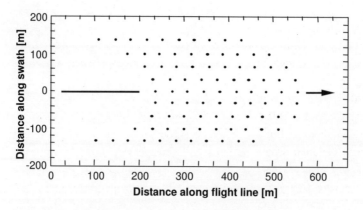

Figure 11.35: Grid produced by Canadian Larsen system.

differential mode has been a key factor in recent success. The laser airborne bathymetry system consists thus of a pulsed laser, and a positioning system, as shown in Figure 11.33. The height of the aircraft above water is measured separately.

The output of a pulsed laser creates a grid whose spacing determines the resolution of the survey. Two principles of scanning are used:

- Zero scanning angle - the laser is fired vertically (downward) at a high rate (much higher than 1 Hz). At 20 Hz, it would provide data every 2 m if the aircraft's horizontal velocity $v = 40$ m/s (144 km/h).
- Sweep scan - the optical axis of laser is fixed to the aircraft; the beam is deflected by a moving mirror.

The Canadian Larsen system uses a rotary sweep scanning method, see Figure 11.34, which results in the grid pattern shown in Figure 11.35.

11.8 Major references

Casey, M.J., J. Vosburgh: *Chartmaking with Larsen.* The Canadian Surveyor, 40, 3, 1986, pp. 251-260.

FIG Commission 4: *Report on the detection of depth anomalies.* 2nd edition, 1984.

Geng, X., A. Zielinski: *Precise multibeam acoustic bathymetry.* Marine Geodesy, 22, 1999, pp. 157-167.

Godin, A., M. Crutchlow: *Swath sounding initiatives in Canada.* International Hydrographic Review, LXXV, 1, 1998, pp. 65-80.

Hare, R.: *Calibrating Larsen-500 LIDAR bathymettry in Dolphin and Union strait using dense acoustric ground-truth.* International Hydrographic Review, LXXI, 1, 1994, pp. 91-108.

Hare, R.: *Depth and position error budgets for multibeam echosounding.* International Hydrographic Review, LXXII, 2, 1995, pp. 37-69.

Hare, R. et al.: *Accuracy estimation of Canadian swath (multibeam) and sweep (mutli-transducer) sounding systems.* CHS/UNB Working Report, 1995.

Ingham, A.E.: *Hydrography for the surveyor and engineer*. 3rd edition, BSP, Oxford, 1992.

Kielland, P., J. Hagglund: *Using DGPS to measure the heave motion of hydrographic survey vessels*. International Hydrographic Review, LXXII, 2, 1995, pp. 83-100.

Lachapelle, G., G. Lu, B. Loncarevic: *Precise shipborne attitude determination using wide antenna spacing*. Proceedings International Symposium on Kinematic Systems in Geodesy, Geomatics and Navigation - KIS94, Dept. of Geomatics Engineering, University of Calgary, 1994, pp. 323-330.

EMR: *Surveying Offshore Canada Lands for Mineral Resource Development*. 3rd edition, EMR Surveying and Mapping Branch Report No. M52-43/1983E, 1982.

Renouf, J.K.: *Heave compensation for hydrographic survey*. UNB Survey Eng. Grad. Seminar, 1987.

Sinclair, M.: *Australians get on board with new laser airborne depth sounder*. Sea Technology, June 1998, pp. 19-25.

Thomson, D.B., D.E. Wells, W.H. Falkenberg: *Hydrographic surveying*. Surveying Engineering Report No. 10002, University of Calgary, 1986.

UNB Ocean Mapping Group: *Multibeam sonar surveying training course*. Ocean Mapping Group, University of New Brunswick, 2001.

Whitman, E.C.: *Laser airborne bathymetry - lifting the littoral*. Sea Technology, August 1996, pp. 95-98.

Index

A

absolute humidity, 109
absorption, 97, 189
absorption coefficient, 340
accuracy, predictable, 245
accuracy, relative, 245
accuracy, repeatable, 245
acoustic correlation sonar, 287
acoustic impedance, 175
acoustic pressure, 163
adaptation, 51
Additional Secondary Factor, 135
airborne laser radar, 340
Allan variance, 146
alternating current, 91
alternative hypothesis, 51
AM, 151
Ambient Noise, 187
ambiguity, 94
amphidrome, 36
amplitude modulation, 151
angular velocity, 92
antenna gain, 296
archipelagic baseline, 203
archipelagic waters, 208
Area, the, 209
array of transmitters, 177
ASF, 135

astronomical time scales, 141
atmosphere, 106
atmospheric attenuation, 131
atomic time scale, 143
attenuation, 97, 189
attenuation length, 340
attenuation loss, 188
aurora, 99
autocorrelation function, 153

B

barycentre, 22
baseline, 201
basepoints, 201
basepoints, precision of, 203
bathythermograph, 194
beacon, 304
beam angle, 325
beam steering, 181
beamwidth, 179, 325
beat frequency, 157
Beaufort Scale, 18
bel, 96
Bellini-Tosi system, 291
Bias to Noise Ratio, 54
bi-phase modulation, 152
BNR, 54
boundaries, 209
boundaries, precision of, 214

bulk modulus, 163

C

cavitation, 182
cavitation threshold, 182
CD, 265
central plasma sheet, 121
CEP, 50
cesium beam, 145
Chart Datum, 86
chart depth, 338
Chayka, 260
chinook, 114
Circular Error Probable, 50
circular mode, 232
circular polarization, 90
CLCS, 207
coarse measurement, 263
coast effect, 293
coding delay, 223
Coding Delay, 265
column space, 41
Commission on the Limits of the Continental
    Shelf, 207
compressibility, 163
condition equations, 46
conductance, 100
conductivity, 100
confidence region, 49
conformal mapping, 80
contiguous zone, 205
continental shelf, 205
continuous wave, 150
control segment, 271
coordinate surface, 71
co-phase lines, 36
co-range lines, 36
Coriolis force, 7
covariance matrix, 43
covariance update, 57
critical frequency, 124
critical rays, 197

CW, 150
cycle matching, 263
Cytac, 260

D

datum for elevations, 87
datum transformation, 74
decibel, 96
deep isothermal layer, 196
deep sound channel, 198
design matrix, 41
detection, 51
Detection Threshold, 186
DGPS, 274
DI, 184
Differential GPS, 274
differential UERE, 275
diffraction, 98
Dilution of Precision, 48
direct problem, 77
direct waves, 134
directional factor, 178
directivity, 104
Directivity Index, 184
dispersion, 43
Distance Root Mean Squared, 50
disturbance vector, 62
diurnal effects, 267
diurnal tide, 31
DOP, 48
Doppler effect, 155
Doppler equation, 156, 281
Doppler shift, 155, 281
Doppler sonar, 280
DRMS, 50
DT, 141, 186
DUERE, 275
dynamic time, 141

E

echo level, 193
ED, 265

EEZ, 207

eikonal equation, 169

elastic properties, 164

electromagnetic spectrum, 93

electromagnetic speed log, 288

electrostrictive transducer, 321

Emission Delay, 265

enclaving islands, 212

energy spectrum, 14

ephemeris time, 141

equation of continuity, 164

equations of force, 164

equatorial currents, 5

equidistance line, 210

equilibrium theory, 21

error ellipse, 49

ET, 141

Eurofix, 269

excess pressure, 163

excitation factor, 257

Exclusive Economic Zone, 207

expectation, 43

external reliability, 51

extinction coefficient, 340

F

fading, 97

fetch, 17

first eccentricity, 72

fishery zone, 208

flattening, 72

FM, 152

fog, 134

free-space transmission loss, 102

frequency and time standards, 145

frequency conversion, 152

frequency diversity, 98

frequency mixing, 152

frequency modulation, 152

FSS mode, 313

FTS, 145

full enclaving, 212

G

gain, 104

geodetic datum, 71

geopotential surface, 8

geostrophic equation, 9

Global Positioning System, 272

GLONASS, 278

GPS, 272

GPS time, 144

grating lobes, 179

GRI, 266

ground waves, 134

Group Repetition Interval, 266

group velocity, 125

guided wave, 98

H

hail, 134

half effect, 211

halocline, 195

HBW, 295

HHWLT, 85

HHWMT, 85

high sea, 208

high tide, 27

Hooke's law, 163

horizontal beamwidth, 295

humidity, 109

hydrogen maser, 146

hydrophone, 182, 304

hyperbolic mode, correlation, 228

hyperbolic mode, no correlation, 227

hyperbolic positioning, 222

I

ice crystals, 134

ICJ, 216

IDC, 157

identification, 51

IL, 176

index of refraction, 101, 169

integrated Doppler count, 157

intensity, 175

intensity level, 176

internal reliability, 51

internal waters, 204

internal waves, 19

International Court of Justice, 216

International Seabed Authority, 209

International Tribunal for the Law of the Sea,
   215

inverse problem, 77

ionosphere, 120

ionospheric propagation, 122

ionospheric waves, 134

ISBA, 209

isobaric surface, 8

isothermal layer, 196

ITLOS, 215

J

Janus configuration, 282

Janus system, two-axis, 286

joint development arrangement, 214

K

Kalman filter, 63

L

lagging the tides, 30

lane, 223

lane expansion factor, 225

lanewidth, 223

laser system, 255

LAT, 85

LBL system, 311

LBL system, calibration, 314

leakage, 189

least squares, 42

least squares residuals, 43

lidar, 340

limiting rays, 197

lines of position, 219

LLWLT, 85

LLWMT, 85

LNT, 85

Local Overall Model (test), 66

Local Slippage (test), 66

LOM, 66

long baseline system, 311

long period tide, 32

looming, 115

LOP, 219

Loran-A, 260

Loran-C, 260

Loran-C Grid Distortions, 269

low tide, 27

loxodrome, 80

LS, 66

M

magnetosphere, 121

magnetostrictive transducer, 321

main thermocline, 196

marine radar, 293

maritime zones, 204

Maximum Usable Frequency, 124

MBES, 327

MDB, 53

MDE, 54

Mean Radial Square Error, 50

Mean Sea Level, 84

Mean Squared Position Error, 50

measurement model, 41

measurement update, 57

median line, 209

Mercator projection, 80

meridian convergence, 82

Minimal Detectable Bias, 53

Minimal Detectable Effect, 54

mirages, 115

mixed layer, 196

mixing ratio, 109

MLLWS, 85

MRSE, 50

MSL, 84, 85
MSPE, 50
MUF, 124
multibeam echosounder, 327
MWL, 85

N

Navy Navigation Satellite System, 271
neap tide, 30
NELS, 260
night effect, 293
NL, 186, 187
NNSS, 271
noise masking background level, 193
noise-limited, 193
non-centrality parameter, 52
normal baseline, 201
Nortwest European Loran-C System, 260
null hypothesis, 51

O

oblique sonar, 335
observation equations, 41
Omega, 255
optical sytem, 255
Order 1 hydrographic surveys, 250
Order 2 hydrographic surveys, 250
Order 3 hydrographic surveys, 251
orthometric height, 84
overall model test, 52

P

partial effect, 211
partial enclaving, 212
PCA, 217
period, 91
Permanent Court of Arbitration, 217
permeability, 99
permittivity, 99
PF, 135
phase angle, 91
phase modulation, 152

phase speed, 15
phase velocity, 125
phase velocity diurnal variations, 257
piezoelectric transducer, 321
pinger, 304
plasma, 120
plasmasphere, 121
PM, 152
polar motion, 142
polarization, 89
positioning solutions, 227
power, 175
PPS, 273
Precise Positioning Service, 273
predicted residuals, 57
Primary Factor, 100, 135
primary phase lag, 100
primary standards, 145
priming the tides, 30
PRN, 153
projector, 182
PRP, 294
pseudolites, 279
pseudo-random noise, 153
pseudoranging mode, 229
pulse repetition frequency, 294
pulse repetition period, 294
PW, 150

Q

quartz clock, 146

R

radar, 293
radar equation, 298
radial error, 50
radiation patterns, 298
radio direction finding, 289
Radio Frequency, 97
random noise, 153
range curves, 37
range space, 41

range-range mode, 233

ranging mode, 234

ray theory, 169

RDF, 289

receiver, 320

reference intensity, 176

refractive index, 101

refractivity, 101, 113

relative humidity, 109

responder, 304

reverberation, 190

reverberation-limited, 193

rho-rho mode, 233

rho-theta mode, 234

rhumbline, 80

rip currents, 11

Root Sum Squared, 50

RSS, 50

rubidium clock, 146

S

saturation water vapour pressure, 111

SBES, 327

SBL system, 305

SBL system, calibration, 313

scale factor, 81

scattering, 98, 189

scintillation, 98, 130

seasonal effects, 268

seasonal thermocline, 196

second eccentricity, 74

Secondary Factor, 135

Self-Noise, 186

SELS, 260

semi-diurnal tide, 31

semi-major axis, 72

semi-minor axis, 72

SEP, 51

SF, 135

shadow zone, 197

ship mode, 313

short baseline system, 305

sidereal time, 141

sidescan sonar, 335

sidescan sonar, interferometric, 337

significant wave height, 15, 18

single beam echosounder, 327

single loop antenna, 290

single point positioning, 274

sky waves, 134

SL, 184

slippage test, 52

Snell's law, 101, 170

SOFAR, 198

sonar equations, 191

sonar parameters, 183

sound in water, 193

sounding datum, 87

Source Level, 184

South European Loran-C System, 260

space segment, 270

space waves, 134

Special Order hydrographic surveys, 246

specific attenuation, 132

Spherical Error Probable, 51

Spreading loss, 188

spring tide, 30

SPS, 273

SSBL system, 309

SSBL system, calibration, 313

Standard Positioning Service, 273

state vector, 41

straight baseline, 202

sublunar point, 24

Sub-tropical gyres, 4

super short baseline system, 309

surface circulations, 4

surface currents, 4

surface waves, 134

swath systems, 327

sweep systems, 327

swell, 17

sync clock mode, 313

T

T/R switch, 320
TAI, 144
Target Strength, 191
TEC, 102, 127
Temps Atomique International, 144
territorial sea, 205
tethered submersible mode, 313
thermocline, 195
thermohaline circulation, 4
thermohaline currents, 4
tidal current, 21
time curves, 37
time update, 60
TL, 188
TM mode, 256
total attenuation, 257
total beam angle, 325
Total Electron Content, 102, 127
tractive forces, 27
transducer, 304, 320
transducer, circular, 325
transducer, rectangular, 325
Transit, 271
transition matrix, 59
transition model, 59
transmission factor, 340
Transmission Loss, 97, 188
transparency, 340
transponder, 304
transverse magnetic mode, 256
troposphere, 107
tropospheric delay, 116
tropospheric refractivity, 113
TS, 191
Tsikada, 271
TSS mode, 313
turning points, 210

U

UERE, 273

ultra-short baseline system, 309
UNCLOS, 199
United Nations Convention on Law of the Sea, 199
universal time, 141
Universal Time Coordinated, 144
Universal Transverse Mercator system, 84
unmodulated pulsed wave, 150
upwelling, 10
USBL system, 309
user equivalent range error, 273
user segment, 271
UT0, 141
UT1, 141
UT2, 141
UTC, 144
UTM system, 84

V

VBW, 295
velocimeter, 194
vertex velocity, 172
vertical beamwidth, 295
vertical datum, 84
vessel effects, 293
volume elasticity, 163

W

WAAS, 277
WADGPS, 277
wave equation, 165
wave theory, 166
wavefronts, 169
weighted least squares, 43
wet snow, 134
white noise, 153
Wide Area Augmentation System, 277
Wide Area Differential GPS, 277